Passage to Abstract Mathematics
Second Edition

Mark E. Watkins
and
Jeffrey L. Meyer

Syracuse University

Bassim Hamadeh, CEO and Publisher
John Remington, Acquisitions Editor
Gem Rabanera, Project Editor
Christian Berk, Production Editor
Emely Villavicencio, Graphic Designer
Trey Soto, Licensing
Natalie Piccotti, Director of Marketing
Kassie Graves, Vice President of Editorial
Jamie Giganti, Director of Academic Publishing

cognella® | ACADEMIC PUBLISHING
3970 Sorrento Valley Blvd., Ste. 500, San Diego, CA 92121

Contents

Preface for the Instructor

THIS BOOK has evolved from our notes for a one-semester course, Introduction to Abstract Mathematics, at Syracuse University. Ideally, this course is taken right after our required calculus sequence and after one semester of linear algebra. At Syracuse, this course is required for all mathematics majors and all mathematics-education majors and is a prerequisite for all upper-division courses in algebra, analysis, combinatorics, number theory, and topology.

Lower-division undergraduate mathematics courses (such as single-variable and multiple-variable calculus, basic linear algebra, and ordinary differential equations) are usually taken within the first three or four semesters. To varying degrees, these courses emphasize computation and procedures and de-emphasize theory. They tend to form the mathematical common ground for majors in mathematics, the physical sciences, and engineering, as well as for many mathematically interested liberal arts students. Upper-division mathematics courses emphasize theory, definitions, and theorems together with their proofs. This course and this book, *Passage to Abstract Mathematics*, stand just beyond the fork in the road, greeting the students who believe that they want to study mathematics and enabling them to confirm whether they are choosing the direction that is right for them. For these students, we hope to illuminate and facilitate the mathematical passage from the computational to the abstract.

Too often in an undergraduate mathematics curriculum, each course or sequence is taught as a discrete entity, as though the intersection of its content with the content of any other course or sequence were empty. This book belies that premise. Here students learn a body of fundamental mathematical material shared by many upper-level courses, material which instructors of upper-level courses often presume their students to have already learned (somehow)—or wish they had learned—by the time their students arrive in their classrooms.

We have very deliberately titled our book *Passage to Abstract Mathematics*. Just as a (nonmetaphorical) passage joins two places divided by some physical obstruction, so this book is intended to prepare the mathematics student passing from a more computational and procedural image of the subject to what mathematics *really* is. The transition involves acquiring knowledge and understanding of a number of definitions, theorems, methods of proof, and also that elusive property called "mathematical sophistication," which cannot be taught explicitly but which we hope can be learned.

Unlike various texts written for the same purpose, this is a *thin* book. We intend it to be portable. We want our students to bring it to every class in order to have the definitions, the examples, and the statements of the exercises right under their noses (if not already in their heads) during the class. Therefore, we have refrained from including many attractive optional topics, each of which will likely be covered more appropriately and fully in some course for which this course is a prerequisite.

We want our students to learn to *read* mathematics the way that mathematicians do. Mathematics is not a spectator sport; it must be read actively, a sentence or phrase at a time, with pencil and scrap paper handy to verify everything. To facilitate understanding proofs, we often insert explanatory comments and provocative questions within brackets [like this]. The student must learn to proceed as though the authors' work is chock-full of errors and that he/she is the sleuth who will be the first to detect their carelessness and ignorance!

Learning to *write* mathematics is as important as learning to read it. There is the story about a mathematician who is reputed to be a terrible joke teller. After finally persuading his nonmathematical friends to listen to his latest joke, he begins by saying, "Before we can start my joke, we will need a few definitions." While perhaps not so with jokes, it is unquestionably true in mathematics that one cannot proceed without a precise vocabulary. We place much emphasis on complete and correct definitions and even more emphasis on *using* definitions. As a language, mathematics also has a grammar and a syntax. Therefore, much emphasis is also placed on expressing mathematics in a syntactically correct fashion. It is at the level of this course that these abilities are acquired and practiced. A language is not merely a mode of expression but must have some content to express, and there is much mathematical content in these pages.

Serving this end, the unique placement of the exercises sets this text apart from others. It is conventional in mathematics texts to accumulate all the exercises pertinent to a chapter or section at the end of that chapter or section in order of increasing difficulty. That is only partially the style of this text. Basically, there are three kinds of exercises.

- There are many exercises **embedded in the text material** immediately following a definition or example or theorem. They are straightforward and are intended to reinforce the understanding of that definition or to expose the properties of that example or to provide some very routine steps in the proof of that theorem. These exercises thus become part of the text material. They should be fully worked immediately on encounter and before one proceeds, thus reinforcing our earlier assertion that *mathematics is not a spectator sport.*

- Intermediate-level exercises appear at the **ends of the sections**. They are highly dependent on the material in the current or previous sections. They may involve such activities as proving further identities or executing procedures similar to those of the closely foregoing text material.

- The **final section of each chapter** is named "Further Exercises." It is a repository of exercises of varying difficulty based on material that may span more than one earlier chapter. Some provide an opportunity for new terms or notions to be introduced that may make a reappearance in the Further Exercises of subsequent chapters. These Further Exercises are not arranged in order of increasing difficulty; their listing is in the order in which the relevant explanatory text comes up in the chapter. A number of these exercises, as well as some in the intermediate category, begin with the words "Prove or disprove ..." or "Find the flaw in the following. ..." Some of these exercises have a recreational flair, a chance perhaps to have a little fun with this stuff.

With regard to exercises, we issue the following caveat: we do not believe in "answers at the back of the book." Even the best student can yield to impatience, check "the" answer in the back, and then figure out a way to arrive at it. We believe this to be contrary to the spirit of the present material and not in the student's interest. Nonetheless, in many instances, hints are offered within the exercise itself. Such hints are enclosed within brackets [like this]. More importantly, many of the exercises have more than just one correct answer. Often, there are several very different proofs or methods that work, and so to provide "the" answer is stifling to creativity at exactly the point educationally when creativity should blossom. We do, however, provide an *Instructor's Solution Manual* with solutions, especially for most of the less routine exercises.

Since there are many allusions to single-variable calculus, much will be missed by the student who has not yet completed a single-variable calculus sequence. There are many occasions, especially in Chapters 4, 6, and 8, where students may need either to refer back to their old Calculus I–II texts or be reminded by their instructor, as this book is not self-contained. On the other hand, the occasional allusions to multivariable calculus and to linear algebra are not at all essential to the understanding of *Passage*, but the student who has already studied these subjects will have the opportunity to gain deeper insights from our book than the student who has not.

There are four more caveats.

- There is no entire chapter explicitly titled "Proofs," although Section 1.5 lays out the general strategies and underlying logic of direct proof, contrapositive proof, and proof by contradiction. Proof by mathematical induction awaits Chapter 5, so that the student will be acquainted with more mathematical material to which inductive proofs can be applied. Proofs will be learned by *proving*. One cannot be taught how to invent a proof any more than one can be taught how to compose a symphony. One *can* be taught the correct notation and the correct mathematical idiom for expressing a mathematical idea (just as the student of musical composition can be taught the rules of harmony and characteristics of various orchestral instruments), but one must first actually have a mathematical idea. The ability to formulate that idea is one of the powers that we aid the student to develop.

- It has not been our intention to present a self-contained, axiomatic introduction to logic (which may be best left to a philosophy department or deferred to an advanced course in Foundations of Mathematics). The purpose of Chapter 1 is rather to equip prospective mathematics majors with the tools and language that they will need in higher-level mathematics courses.

- The symbolic logic notation presented in Chapter 1 is fully integrated into the rest of this book. Many of the definitions, propositions, and theorems are stated (though not always exclusively) in this language. Having emphasized the importance of precise expression, we believe that there is no more precise way to express these notions than in this way. The intellectual process of "unpacking" a sterile presentation and grasping an intuitive "gut feeling" for its underlying idea is what learning to *read* mathematics is all about. The purpose of the embedded exercises is to facilitate this process.

- Functions are first defined in Chapter 4 as they were in calculus, in terms of a "rule" and a domain. Students have an intuitive feel for this familiar definition and can work with it. The rigorous definition, as a set of ordered pairs, is held off until Section 6.6 after a general presentation of binary relations.

A course that meets three hours per week should be able to cover almost this entire book in one 14-week semester. The chapters were written with the intention that they be covered in the order in which they are placed here, especially the first four chapters. Thus changing their order of presentation could present difficulties.

If time runs short, one could omit the latter sections of Chapter 6 (on order relations) or Chapter 7. One could also omit some of the sections from Chapter 8 (Algebraic Systems). Nonetheless, we recommend winding up the course with Section 8.1, because it pulls together notions from most of the earlier chapters.

In preparing the second edition of this book, we have made a few non-radical changes from the first edition. Most notably, Chapters 4 and 5 have swapped locations; we now cover functions before induction. We have slightly shortened our book by removing two topics that are really more appropriate for a course on number theory; namely, we deleted a section from Chapter 2 on Euclid's Algorithm and we've expunged the Chinese Remainder Theorem from Chapter 8. These two topics had generally been safely omitted by our instructors anyhow. Beyond these items, the preparation of this edition has consisted of clarifying minor points of ambiguity, sometimes at the risk of redundancy, and of correcting typos, some trivial, some embarrassing. We believe we got 'em all now. But if not, then please contact us with regard to any errors. Your suggestions are also welcome. Mark Watkins can be reached at ⟨mewatkin@syr.edu⟩ and Jeff Meyer can be reached at ⟨jlmeye01@syr.edu⟩.

Syracuse, NY   Summer 2020

Preface for the Student

YOU LIKE mathematics, and if you weren't already good at it, then you probably wouldn't be taking this course.

You probably excelled in algebra and geometry in high school, and you've been successful thus far in your calculus courses. But beyond these courses lies a whole new world, a higher level of mathematics. This course offers you a passage to that world. It is in *this* course where you first learn what it really means to study and communicate mathematics the way that mathematicians do.

Advanced mathematics is much more than, for example, being able to evaluate an integral like

$$\int \frac{x^3}{\sqrt{9 + x^2}} \, dx,$$

or being able to compute the derivative of a more complicated function like

$$f(x) = \tan\left(\frac{e^{3x}}{\sqrt{\sin(x^4)}}\right),$$

or being able to factor $108x^4 - 489x^3 - 1022x^2$. Don't get us wrong; we expect that you can do these things. It's just that beyond this point, there is so much more to mathematics than finding more difficult functions to differentiate and integrate or more challenging equations to solve. The mathematics courses for which this course is a prerequisite are theoretical and abstract. Furthermore, there is joy and beauty to mathematics that lies beyond computation.

There are two parallel goals of this text. One goal is to impart to you a body of mathematics that you will have to use in your present and future mathematical studies. Secondly, you will learn how to communicate this mathematics through proofs—both reading proofs and writing proofs. When learning higher mathematics, one starts by learning *definitions*. Precise, unambiguous definitions are the basic building blocks for every area of higher mathematics. Definitions are not mere formalities or space-fillers but the tools in the mathematician's toolbox. Look for defined terms in **boldface!** Some definitions may be too bulky to be easily memorized, and so if and when you don't fully memorize a given definition, at least keep the text of it handy. Also, try to have a good intuitive notion of what that definition is describing. Success in this and all subsequent mathematics courses depends on your diligence in learning definitions *as soon as* they are introduced.

In the world of mathematics, one speaks, writes, and reads in the language of mathematics. With practice, you will soon find yourself speaking this language precisely and correctly. Correct notation is the language with which mathematicians communicate with users of mathematics and with each other. Here is where you will learn to talk the language of mathematics.

Almost all the theorems in this book come with complete proofs. Occasionally, you will be asked to supply some or all of a proof, and to do so, you will need those definitions.

In subsequent mathematics courses, you may learn more by reading printed text than by listening to an instructor. For that reason, we have inserted exercises appropriate to a concept very soon after a definition or theorem. Within many of the proofs in this text, we have inserted remarks about why we are writing the way that we do. These remarks are not actually part of the proofs themselves, which is why we have placed them within brackets [like this]. We want (in fact, we *expect*) you to do these exercises as you proceed. Have a pencil and paper handy. This is precisely how we mathematicians learn mathematics from a book. We read a little, write out notes and examples, and try to solve exercises that help us understand what was just presented. Then we read a little more and repeat. Speed readers have no advantage when it comes to reading mathematics. On the contrary, we mathematicians proceed cautiously as though the author has made an error and we will be the first to uncover the author's carelessness or ignorance.

Proof writing is a very different skill from the computational skills you perfected in previous mathematics courses. To succeed in future mathematics courses, you must be able to understand a mathematics text that includes proofs. You also need to be good at writing proofs, not just proofs that are solutions to homework problems and quiz questions, but also proofs of facts that *you* will discover. A proof is the means to convince others (and yourself) of the eternal truth of your discovery.

The last section of each chapter consists of still more exercises. They are not ordered by difficulty. They occasionally draw on previous chapters.

This book will come in handy after this course ends when you need to remind yourself about one topic or another. If you graduate as a mathematics major, you will look back at this book and find some of it shockingly simple. But you will also remember when it was new to you. Many notions that you learn in this course are usually not taught elsewhere in a mathematics curriculum, but your future instructors may, nonetheless, assume that you are familiar with them.

At first, we considered calling this book *Bridge to Abstract Mathematics*. The metaphor is apt. This text is a means for the reader to move from an understanding of computational areas (like calculus and high school algebra) to an understanding of abstract areas like set theory, analysis, topology, and modern algebra. But the fact is that a bridge is usually the easier and safer way to get from one place to another (across a river or gorge or railroad track). The move from computational to abstract mathematics is a process that isn't short or easy (we suppose that it is relatively safe). The passage is harder for some people than for others. If you are cut out for mathematics, you will be reassured by this course. If mathematics doesn't suit you, you may find that out too. (And that knowledge is just as important.)

Higher mathematics is not just our occupation; for us, it is both useful and beautiful. This text is our way to pass along what works for us as we show you the way toward your goal of a major in mathematics.

Syracuse, NY   Summer 2020

Chapter 1

Logic and Proof

THINK OF AN ODD integer.[1] Square that integer. Subtract 1 from that result. Now divide by 8. Is your final number an integer? As long as you did the arithmetic correctly, we know that the answer is yes. The answer always is yes. In mathematics, it is never sufficient simply to compute this for a few (or for many) odd integers and observe the divisibility by 8 and then conclude that this procedure *always* delivers an integer. We need to see proof that this process works no matter with which odd integer one starts. Proofs in this book (and in most mathematical writing) begin with *Proof* and conclude with a little square like this: □. Here is how to state this number property formally, together with its proof.

Proposition 1.0.1 *For every odd integer n, the integer $n^2 - 1$ is divisible by 8.*

Proof. Every odd integer n can be expressed as $2k + 1$ for some integer k. Then

$$
\begin{aligned}
n^2 - 1 &= (2k+1)^2 - 1 \\
&= 4k^2 + 4k \\
&= 4k(k+1).
\end{aligned}
$$

---

[1]An odd integer is an integer with remainder 1 when divided by 2.

Since k and $k + 1$ are consecutive integers, one of them must be even, and thus k times $k + 1$ must be even. It is also the case that 4 times an even number is divisible by 8. Thus $n^2 - 1$ is divisible by 8.   □

1.1   Proofs: What and Why?

A proof in mathematics is a logically sound argument or explanation that takes into account all generalities of the situation and reaches the desired conclusion. By no means is this a formal definition of a proof; rather, it is a description of how the word "proof" is used in a mathematical context.

In the earlier proof of divisibility by 8, we left no doubt that the argument would work for all odd integers and that each step followed from the definition of an odd integer, from the assumption that n is an odd integer (the *hypothesis*), or from a previous step. The algebraic manipulation

$$\begin{aligned} n^2 - 1 &= (2k + 1)^2 - 1 \\ &= 4k^2 + 4k \\ &= 4k(k + 1) \end{aligned}$$

alone does not constitute a proof. While proofs frequently do contain such manipulations, they are *only part* of the proof. In this proof, it is absolutely essential to declare in words what the symbol n stands for, to explain how k is related to n, and to interpret in complete sentences the expression $4k(k + 1)$. Unlike a definite integral problem in calculus, for example, where a sequence of operations leads to an expression called "the answer," in the case of a proof, the entire proof is "the answer." It is the answer to whether the statement of the theorem is a true statement. Be on the lookout for this kind of completeness in the proofs in this text as well as in the many proofs that you will write.

Here is an elegant theorem from geometry, together with its proof.

Theorem 1.1.1 (Midpoint-Quadrilateral Theorem) *In any quadrilateral, the quadrilateral formed by joining midpoints of adjacent sides is a parallelogram.*

Proof. Consider the following figure in which $M, N, O,$ and P are the midpoints of $\overline{AB}, \overline{BC}, \overline{CD},$ and $\overline{DA}$, respectively.

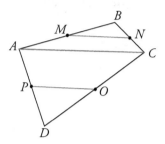

Since $\triangle ABC$ and $\triangle MBN$ are similar triangles, we have $\overline{MN} \parallel \overline{AC}$. Since $\triangle ADC$ and $\triangle PDO$ are similar triangles, it holds that $\overline{PO} \parallel \overline{AC}$. Thus $\overline{MN} \parallel \overline{PO}$ since both are parallel to $\overline{AC}$. We next deduce that $\overline{MP} \parallel \overline{NO}$ by drawing diagonal $\overline{BD}$ and examining $\triangle ABD$ and $\triangle BCD$. Since quadrilateral $MNOP$ has two pairs of parallel opposite sides, it is a parallelogram (by the definition of a parallelogram). $\qquad \square$

The proof requires a property of similar triangles. We are reluctant to rely on it unless we know that it is true. Therefore, we ask you to prove this property in the next exercise.

Exercise 1.1.2 Use facts from coordinate geometry to prove the fact mentioned in the proof of the Midpoint-Quadrilateral Theorem. Use the fact that the segment joining the midpoints of two sides of a triangle is parallel to the third side of the triangle. Start your proof with Figure 1.1.1.

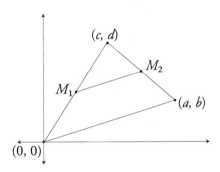

Figure 1.1.1: Exercise 1.1.2.

While there are many intriguing facts in many areas of mathematics, mathematicians do not regard them as "facts" until they have been proved. Let us examine another proof from plane geometry.

Theorem 1.1.3 *The sum of the distances from any given interior point of an equilateral triangle to each of the three sides of the triangle is the same for every interior point of the triangle.*

Proof. Consider an arbitrary equilateral triangle $\triangle ABC$, the length of whose sides are each equal to a number ℓ. Also consider an arbitrary interior point P of the triangle. Let d_1, d_2, and d_3 denote the respective distances from P to the three sides of the triangle. We will prove that the number $d_1 + d_2 + d_3$ depends only on ℓ and is therefore independent of our choice of the point P.

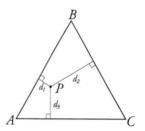

We calculate the area of $\triangle ABC$ in two different ways. The height of $\triangle ABC$ is $\dfrac{\sqrt{3}}{2}\,\ell$ and the base has length ℓ, and so the area of $\triangle ABC$ is $\dfrac{\sqrt{3}}{4}\,\ell^2$.

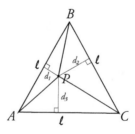

It is also the case that

$$\text{area } \triangle ABC = \text{area } \triangle APB + \text{area } \triangle BPC + \text{area } \triangle CPA.$$

The areas of $\triangle APB, \triangle BPC,$ and $\triangle CPA,$ are $\dfrac{\ell\, d_1}{2}, \dfrac{\ell\, d_2}{2},$ and $\dfrac{\ell\, d_3}{2},$ respectively. Thus we have

$$\frac{\sqrt{3}}{4}\,\ell^2 = \frac{\ell\, d_1}{2} + \frac{\ell\, d_2}{2} + \frac{\ell\, d_3}{2}.$$

After some simplification, we see that

$$d_1 + d_2 + d_3 = \frac{\sqrt{3}}{2}\,\ell. \tag{1.1.1}$$

[The proof is complete since the number on the right side of equation (1.1.1) depends only on the size of the triangle, not on where the point P is located.]

$\square$

Notice a few things about how this proof started. (Getting started is often the hardest part of writing a proof.) The first thing we did was to declare some symbols: A, B, and C for the vertices of an arbitrary equilateral triangle and ℓ for the length of each side. (The letter ℓ is a good choice, because it reminds us that it represents the length of something.) We then let P denote an arbitrary interior point of $\triangle ABC$ and made no assumption about the location of P other than that it lies in the interior of the triangle, which is all that is required in the hypothesis. Finally, we needed to talk about the distance of P from each of the three sides, and we denoted these distances by $d_1, d_2,$ and d_3. We needed three different symbols because, quite possibly, the distances in question are three different numbers.

Once chosen, all of these symbols retain their assigned meanings for the entirety of the proof. After the proof is finished, they all lose their assigned meanings (unless we state otherwise) and are free to mean something else the next time that we want an A or an ℓ or a d for another proof. There are a few letters in mathematics that do have a kind of universal meaning. For example, π is the Greek lowercase pi; the letter e has a fixed meaning in the context of natural logarithms; the symbol Σ is the Greek capital sigma used in summations. These are the few main ones that we mathematicians use frequently, but sometimes each of these may be used to mean something else.

The next theorem has a proof with a very different format, one that will be discussed in Section 1.5.

Theorem 1.1.4 *In any group of two or more people who meet and some of whom shake hands with each other, at least two people shake hands with the same number of other people.*

Proof. Suppose that there are n people in the group, where $n \geq 2$. The possible values for the number of hands that any one person could have shaken are the n integers in the following list:

$$0, \ 1, \ldots, \ n-1. \tag{1.1.2}$$

If it were the case that no two people had shaken hands with the same number of people, then each of the integers in this list would have to be represented exactly once. However, this leads to an impossibility, because then one member would have shaken nobody's hand and another person would have shaken hands with all of the $n-1$ other people, including the one who had shaken no hands. Therefore some two people must have shaken hands the same number of times. $\qquad\square$

Very often a variety of proofs can be devised that prove the same result. For example, in the handshake problem (Theorem 1.1.4), one may argue that the list (1.1.2) cannot include both the number 0 and the number $n-1$, leaving only $n-1$ numbers to be matched with n people. Therefore, at least two people must be matched with the same number of handshakes. This is an example of an argument that uses the **pigeonhole principle:**[2] if there are more pigeons than pigeonholes, at least two pigeons must share a roost.

A **prime number** is a positive integer with exactly two positive divisors,[3] and a **composite number** is an integer ≥ 2 that is not a prime number. There are many interesting facts associated with prime numbers, including the next result.

Theorem 1.1.5 *There are arbitrarily large gaps between consecutive prime numbers. In other words, given any positive integer k, there exists a sequence of k consecutive composite numbers.*

---

[2]The German mathematician P.G. Lejeune Dirichlet (1805–1859) is credited with the first statement of what he named with the German word *Schubfachprinzip*, or "drawer principle." Dirichlet made significant contributions to number theory and in particular wrote the first papers on analytic number theory.

[3]Some mathematics relating to prime numbers will be covered in detail in Section 2.4.

Proof. Let k be an arbitrary positive integer. [The style of this proof is called "constructive." We will construct a list of k consecutive composite numbers.] To prove this theorem, we need the **factorial function**, which will be defined more rigorously in Section 5.2. For now we define $n!$ (say, "n factorial") as $n! = n(n-1)(n-2)\cdots 2 \cdot 1$ whenever n is a positive integer. Here is a sequence of k consecutive composite numbers:

$$(k+1)! + 2, \; (k+1)! + 3, \ldots, (k+1)! + k, \; (k+1)! + (k+1).$$

Note that for each $j = 2, 3, \ldots, k+1$, we have that j is a factor of $(k+1)! + j$. □

When $k = 7$, the proof produces the numbers

$$40322, 40323, 40324, 40325, 40326, 40327, 40328.$$

This is indeed a sequence of seven consecutive composite numbers, but it turns out that these seven numbers are actually part of a sequence of 53 consecutive composite numbers!

Exercise 1.1.6 Find the *first* occurrence of seven consecutive composite numbers. [Hint: Two-digit numbers will suffice.]

At this point, it may be helpful to give an example of what a proof is *not*.

False Theorem. *For every positive integer n, the number $A_n = n^2 + n + 41$ is a prime number.*

Flawed proof. We verify this assertion for some values of n, starting with $n = 1$. We find that $A_1 = 43$ and $A_2 = 47$, both of which are prime numbers. We next find more prime numbers $A_3 = 53$, $A_4 = 61$, and $A_5 = 71$. As we compute a few more values of A_n, we keep getting more and more prime numbers. □

May we conclude that the claim is true? Have we chanced upon a "prime number generating machine"? It so happens that, in 1752, Christian Goldbach proved that no nonconstant polynomial function $p(x)$ with integer coefficients has the property that $p(n)$ is prime for all positive integers n. Had we known of Goldbach's result, we may have been more skeptical of the claim and might have sought an example to disprove it. Such an example obviously occurs when $n = 41$, since clearly, A_{41} is divisible by 41. We also have the composite number $A_{40} = 40^2 + 40 + 41 = 40^2 + 2 \cdot 40 + 1 = (40 + 1)^2 = 41^2$. Even though it happens that $n^2 + n + 41$ is prime for all positive integers $n \leq 39$, the given statement is still false. The "flawed proof" illustrates the point that in mathematics, unlike in natural sciences, experimental results do not yield certainty. *Mathematical certainty is attained only by means of a proof.*

That said, we hasten to add that experimental results are not necessarily useless. Quite the contrary is true. Many conjectures are made and many theorems are discovered by experimentation. Suppose that we don't know whether some given mathematical statement is true or false, and we want to establish it one way or the other. In that case, some experiments may give us a clue as to which course of action is more likely to lead to success. Some of the exercises in this book begin with the words, "Prove or disprove." You will have to select which path to take.

One of the goals of this chapter is to develop some vocabulary and notation that provide the means to communicate the logic about which you already have strong and solid intuition. In mathematics, we need to be very precise about what we are saying. For example, in a calculus course, you may have learned the definition of "the limit of f as x approaches c equals L."[4]

$\lim\limits_{x \to c} f(x) = L$ *means that, for every number $\epsilon > 0$, there exists a number $\delta > 0$ such that, for any real number x in the domain of f, if $0 < |x - c| < \delta$, then $|f(x) - L| < \epsilon$.*

The definition lays the precise foundation for the meaning of *limit* and later the meaning of *derivative*. Of course, some calculus students also learn how to find limits without ever writing ϵ or δ. No calculus course would ever progress past computing the derivative of even the simplest functions if we had to

---

[4]We make the usual assumption that f is defined in some open interval containing c, except possibly at c.

resort to the definition each time instead of using the formulas developed to expedite the computations. Nonetheless, mathematicians need to be able to understand the definition precisely, because there are times when one must communicate what it means for a function f to have *no* limit as x approaches c or to say what it means precisely that a number L is *not* the limit of f as x approaches c. In the remaining sections of this chapter, you will acquire the necessary logical tools to answer such a challenge.

1.2 Statements

The term **statement** refers to any sentence that has exactly one **truth value**. By a truth value, we mean either *true* or *false*, denoted **T** and **F**, respectively. A statement can never have both truth values. Here are some examples of statements.

1. $3^2 + 4^2 = 5^2$.

2. $\left|7 - 13\right| > 9$.

3. The official Lake Minnetonka ice-out date in 1976 was April 3.

4. There are infinitely many prime numbers of the form $n^2 + 1$.

The first and third statements have the truth value **T**. The second statement has truth value **F**. The last sentence *has* a truth value. However, whether that value is **T** or **F** is still an unsolved problem. The important point is that the last statement either *really is* true or *really is* false—the truth value may be unknown, but it is not ambiguous.

Here are some examples of nonstatements.

1. $0 < \left|x - 3\right| < \dfrac{1}{1000}$.

2. $t^2 + 4t - 12 = 0$.

3. n is an odd number.

4. Why are you reading this book?

5. Go to the dentist every six months!

6. $\dfrac{-b \pm \sqrt{b^2 - 4ac}}{2a}$.

7. The truth value of this sentence is **F**.

These fail to be statements for a variety of reasons. We are mostly concerned with the first three, but we address them all. The first three are not statements because the variables x, t, and n are not specified or quantified in any way. For example, sentence (1) is true if x is replaced by 2.999999999 but false if $x = 3$. This means that, as written, (1) is a sentence but not a statement, because it has no single truth value. When you first looked at sentence (2), you might have assumed that $t = 2$ or $t = -6$. But sentence (2) is not asking you to solve anything. In general, an equation is not a command to solve. This equation is just a sentence about the variable t. When $t = -6$, the sentence is certainly true. But if $t = 7$, then (2) is false. Again, there is no truth value without first specifying t. The same goes for sentence (3).

Sentences (4) and (5) are interrogative and imperative English sentences, respectively. They have no interpretation that allows assignment of a truth value. Statements must, in the proper grammar in whatever language they are written, have a subject and a predicate. Sentence (6) has no predicate, even though it is loaded with mathematical symbols.

Sentence (7) is an example of a **paradox**—a sentence with the proper grammatical structure, yet one that cannot have a truth value. Remember that a statement can have only one truth value. If (7) is false, then since it is declaring itself false, it is thus true, and if (7) is true, then it is false.

Statements are usually labeled with uppercase letters such as P, Q, R, etc. Sometimes a letter is chosen to make the label suggestive of the meaning of the statement. For example, we might let C stand for the statement "Squares are convex polygons." Statements are also called *logical variables*. In algebra or calculus, a variable such as x or y, can usually take on infinitely many values. By contrast, a logical variable assumes exactly two values: **T** and **F**. Computer scientists often denote these values by binary digits 1 and 0, respectively.

Recall that the sentence "$t^2 + 4t - 12 = 0$" is not a statement because, until t is specified, the sentence has no truth value. A sentence like this is an example of a **propositional function**. We designate this by[5]

$$P(t) : t^2 + 4t - 12 = 0.$$

The sentence behaves like a function whose output is either **T** or **F** depending on the input value of t. For example, $P(8)$ is false, $P(-6)$ is true, and $P(\text{My friend Steve})$ is false. If we collect all the possible values of t that make $P(t)$ true, we would have the set

$$\{-6, 2\}.$$

Remark. The only notions of set theory necessary for the present discussion are that a *set* is a collection of objects and that each of the objects in a set is an *element* of the set. The notation $x \in X$ means "x is an element of X." These ideas are covered more thoroughly in Section 2.1.

The set of objects for which a propositional function has the truth value **T** is called the **truth set** of the propositional function. For the propositional function $P(t)$, it makes mathematical sense to restrict the values t for which we are willing to consider $P(t)$. We could declare that we are going to entertain values of t only from the set of integers or, perhaps, values of t only from the set of real numbers. The set of all input values for a propositional function is called the **universal set**.

Example 1.2.1 Here is an example of a propositional function with two variables. Let

$$P(\ell, m) : line\ \ell\ is\ parallel\ to\ line\ m,$$

---

[5] Note the colon following $P(t)$. Do not replace the colon with an "equals" sign ($=$). Other notation will be introduced in the next section to indicate equivalence of statements, but the equals sign is not such notation.

where the universal set is the set of all lines in the xy-plane. Consider the following lines:

k_1 denotes the graph of $y = 3x - 4$;

k_2 denotes the graph of $x - y = 5$;

k_3 denotes the graph of $y = x + 7$.

Then $P(k_1, k_2)$ is false and $P(k_2, k_3)$ is true. Also $P(k_3, k_2)$ is true.

Exercise 1.2.2 Let $A(x, y, z) : x^2 + y^2 = z^2$. Determine the truth value of the following.

(a) $A(5, 12, 13)$.

(b) $A(3, 6, 9)$.

(c) $A(24, 7, 25)$.

(d) $A(24, 25, 7)$.

1.3   Logical Operations and Logical Equivalence

Suppose we offer you the following challenge.

> *We bet that our friend Leslie can solve the equation $x^2 - 7x - 18 = 0$* **and** *that he can run 50 meters in under 7.3 seconds.*

If you were to take this bet with us, how might we resolve it? We would have Leslie sit down and work on the equation. Then we would have Leslie run 50 meters and record the time. Under what circumstances would we win the bet? Because the deal was based on the word *and* in the bet, we would win the bet only in the case that Leslie *both* solved the equation *and* ran 50 meters in less than 7.3 seconds. We lose the bet in each of the following cases:

1. Leslie fails both tasks.

2. Leslie solves the equation but takes longer than 7.3 seconds to run 50 meters.

3. Leslie fails to solve the equation but runs fast enough.

Definition 1.3.1 *Let P and Q be statements. Then the statement "P and Q" is the* **conjunction** *of P with Q, written $P \wedge Q$. The truth value of the conjunction is given by the following table:*

P	Q	$P \wedge Q$
T	T	T
T	F	F
F	T	F
F	F	F

Such a table is called a **truth table**. In this case, it gives the value of $P \wedge Q$ for each of the four possible combinations of the truth value of P and the truth value of Q.

Let us offer instead a different challenge.

> *We bet that Leslie can solve the equation $x^2 - 7x - 18 = 0$* **or** *that he can run 50 meters in under 7.3 seconds.*

This time, we win the bet as long as Leslie accomplishes at least one of the required tasks. We lose precisely when Leslie both fails to solve the equation *and* fails to run fast enough. We have formed a new statement by connecting two existing statements with the word *or*.

Definition 1.3.2 *Let P and Q be statements. Then the statement "P or Q" is the* **disjunction** *of P with Q, written $P \vee Q$. The truth value of the disjunction is given by the following truth table:*

P	Q	$P \vee Q$
T	T	T
T	F	T
F	T	T
F	F	F

Do you think that we should win the bet if Leslie accomplishes both tasks? We do. In mathematical usage, the disjunction of two true statements is true (as defined earlier). However, there are other circumstances in ordinary English usage of the word *or* that would consider the truth value of such a statement to be false. For example, consider the statement, "The complete dinner includes soup or salad." If you tell the waiter, "Yes, I'll have both," you would surely be charged extra. Yet we all understand the use of the word *or* in the original statement. The use of the word *or* in the restaurant context is called the *exclusive or*. This operation appears in Exercise 1.3.13.

Exercise 1.3.3 Consider the following pair of statements. (An equation with no variables in it is always a statement; it is true or it is false.)

$$3^2 + 4^2 = 5^2.$$
$$7^2 + 12^2 = 15^2.$$

(a) Write the conjunction of these two statements, and give the truth value of the conjunction.
(b) Write the disjunction of these two statements, and give the truth value of the disjunction.

The statement "$2^{223857457} - 1$ is a prime number" is indeed a statement, because it has a truth value, even though we don't know presently whether that value is **T** or **F**. (It is a question waiting to be resolved.[6]) For the same reason, we do not know the truth value of the statement "$2^{223857457} - 1$ is *not* a prime number," but we *do* know that whatever the truth value of "$2^{223857457} - 1$ is a prime number" may be, the truth value of "$2^{223857457} - 1$ is not a prime number" is the opposite value.

Definition 1.3.4 *Let P be a statement. The statement "not P" is the* **negation** *of P, written ¬P. Its truth value is* **F** *whenever P is true and* **T** *whenever P is false, as seen in the following truth table:*

P	$\neg P$
T	F
F	T

Consider the statement $\sin \frac{\pi}{4} + \cos \frac{\pi}{4} \leq \sin \frac{\pi}{2}$. (This statement happens to be

---

[6]As of April, 2020, the largest known prime number is the 24,862,048-digit number $2^{82589933} - 1$. To view the current record and to learn more about the search for large prime numbers, go to the website http://primes.utm.edu/largest.html.

false, but that doesn't matter for the point that we are about to make.) Some of the ways to state the negation of this statement include the following:

1. It is not the case that $\sin \frac{\pi}{4} + \cos \frac{\pi}{4} \leq \sin \frac{\pi}{2}$;

2. $\sin \frac{\pi}{4} + \cos \frac{\pi}{4}$ is not $\leq \sin \frac{\pi}{2}$;

3. $\sin \frac{\pi}{4} + \cos \frac{\pi}{4} > \sin \frac{\pi}{2}$.

It usually doesn't matter which one of these you write. However, when there is notation available to make the wording more efficient, we tend to opt for the most efficient wording. In this case, statement 3 is our choice. Certainly statement 3 most directly conveys what the negation of the original statement means.

Exercise 1.3.5 Express the negation of each of the following statements. Do not write, "It is not the case that ...."

(a) $7^2 + 24^2 = 25^2$.

(b) $\dfrac{1}{2} + \dfrac{2}{3} + \dfrac{3}{4} \geq \dfrac{1+2+3}{2+3+4}$.

(c) In 1983, the ice went out of Lake Minnetonka before April 18.

(d) Leslie can solve the equation $x^2 - 7x - 18 = 0$.

(e) Ambrose did not score at least 90 on the last exam.

Example 1.3.6 We construct a truth table for the logical expression

$$(P \wedge \neg Q) \vee \neg P.$$

Notice the parentheses around the expression $P \wedge \neg Q$ to indicate that we first must find the truth value of this expression and use the result to proceed. As you will see in Exercise 1.3.7, the placement of the parentheses can make a difference in just the same way that $3 \cdot (5 + 4) \neq (3 \cdot 5) + 4$. To make a truth table, we need to plan ahead for the appropriate number of columns, and we need to label them. We begin by inserting truth values for P and Q.

P	Q	$\neg P$	$\neg Q$	$P \wedge \neg Q$	$(P \wedge \neg Q) \vee \neg P$
T	T				
T	F				
F	T				
F	F				

We always follow this order for the truth values of P and Q. Now we fill in the rest of the truth table with truth values based on the definitions.

P	Q	$\neg P$	$\neg Q$	$P \wedge \neg Q$	$(P \wedge \neg Q) \vee \neg P$
T	T	F	F	F	F
T	F	F	T	T	T
F	T	T	F	F	T
F	F	T	T	F	T

Even though the table includes intermediate expressions that are helpful in determining the truth value of the expression in the last column, when we speak of the *truth table for* $(P \wedge \neg Q) \vee \neg P$, we really mean only the columns for the simple, original statements P and Q and for the final expression.

P	Q	$(P \wedge \neg Q) \vee \neg P$
T	T	F
T	F	T
F	T	T
F	F	T

Exercise 1.3.7   Make a truth table for each of the following statements.

(a) $P \wedge (\neg Q \vee \neg P)$. (Compare with Example 1.3.6.)
(b) $(P \vee Q) \vee (\neg P \wedge \neg Q)$.
(c) $(P \vee \neg Q) \wedge (\neg P \vee Q)$.
(d) $\big(P \vee (\neg Q \wedge \neg P)\big) \vee Q$.
(e) $P \vee \big((\neg Q \wedge \neg P) \vee Q\big)$.

Consider the truth table for the expression $\neg(P \wedge Q)$.

P	Q	$P \wedge Q$	$\neg(P \wedge Q)$
T	T	T	F
T	F	F	T
F	T	F	T
F	F	F	T

Compare this to the truth table in Example 1.3.6. When the same truth values for P and Q are given, the expressions $\neg(P \wedge Q)$ and $(P \wedge \neg Q) \vee \neg P$ have the same truth value.

Definition 1.3.8 *When two logical expressions E_1 and E_2 have the same truth value as each other for every possible combination of truth values of the logical variables $P, Q, \ldots$ that appear in them, then we say that E_1 is* **logically equivalent** *(or, more briefly,* **equivalent***) to E_2, and we write $E_1 \iff E_2$. Of course, then $E_2 \iff E_1$.*

Proposition 1.3.9 *Let P, Q, and R be statements. Then*

(i) $\neg(\neg P) \iff P$;
(ii) $\neg(P \vee Q) \iff \neg P \wedge \neg Q$;
(iii) $\neg(P \wedge Q) \iff \neg P \vee \neg Q$;
(iv) $P \wedge (Q \vee R) \iff (P \wedge Q) \vee (P \wedge R)$;
(v) $P \vee (Q \wedge R) \iff (P \vee Q) \wedge (P \vee R)$.

Proof. By definition, two statements are logically equivalent provided they have the same truth tables. We show the tables for (ii) and (v). The others are left as Exercise 1.2.10.

P	Q	$\neg P$	$\neg Q$	$P \vee Q$	$\neg(P \vee Q)$	$\neg P \wedge \neg Q$
T	T	F	F	T	F	F
T	F	F	T	T	F	F
F	T	T	F	T	F	F
F	F	T	T	F	T	T

Since the truth values of the last two columns are identical, we conclude that $\neg(P \vee Q)$ is logically equivalent to $\neg P \wedge \neg Q$.

For part (v), we have the truth table in Table 1.1. Note carefully the order of the $8 = 2^3$ cases when we have three logical variables. This standard order is always used because it makes it easier to compare truth tables of different statements.

P	Q	R	$Q \wedge R$	$P \vee (Q \wedge R)$	$P \vee Q$	$P \vee R$	$(P \vee Q) \wedge (P \vee R)$
T	T	T	T	T	T	T	T
T	T	F	F	T	T	T	T
T	F	T	F	T	T	T	T
T	F	F	F	T	T	T	T
F	T	T	T	T	T	T	T
F	T	F	F	F	T	F	F
F	F	T	F	F	F	T	F
F	F	F	F	F	F	F	F

Table 1.1: Proof of part (v)

We compare the fifth column with the eighth column to reach the desired conclusion. □

Parts (ii) and (iii) of Proposition 1.3.9, called **De Morgan's Laws**,[7] provide the rules for negating conjunctions and disjunctions. For example, according to part (ii), the negation of the statement "2 is an even prime number and $5 + 9 \leq 11$" is "2 is not an even prime number or $5 + 9 > 11$."

Parts (iv) and (v) are the **distributive laws**. They are analogous to the distributive property of multiplication over addition in the real numbers that you learned in middle school algebra. Note that each of the logical operations $\wedge$ and $\vee$ distributes over the other, although addition of numbers does not distribute over multiplication.

Exercise 1.3.10   (a) Prove Proposition 1.3.9 part (i).
(b) Prove Proposition 1.3.9 part (iii).
(c) Prove Proposition 1.3.9 part (iv).

The two logical operations $\wedge$ and $\vee$ satisfy the **commutative law**. That is,

---

[7]Augustus De Morgan (1806–1871) was an English mathematician who developed rules and symbols of logic that made it possible to solve problems that had confounded ancient logicians. He is also credited with developing mathematical induction, the main topic of Chapter 5.

for all statements P and Q,

$$P \wedge Q \Longleftrightarrow Q \wedge P \quad \text{and} \quad P \vee Q \Longleftrightarrow Q \vee P.$$

They also satisfy the **associative law**. That is, for all statements P, Q, and R,

$$(P \wedge Q) \wedge R \Longleftrightarrow P \wedge (Q \wedge R) \quad \text{and} \quad (P \vee Q) \vee R \Longleftrightarrow P \vee (Q \vee R).$$

We say more simply that $\vee$ and $\wedge$ are commutative and associative.

One needs to be careful that the symbols that one writes create meaningful expressions. Just because $\neg, P, Q,$ and $\vee$ are each legitimate and meaningful symbols doesn't mean that the "expression" $\neg PQ\vee$ means something. Each of the symbols in an expression is part of a structure that works in grammatically correct English. A random string of symbols is very likely to be meaningless.

Exercise 1.3.11 Write as complete sentences the negations of each the following sentences.
(a) The function f is decreasing on $(-\infty, 0]$ and increasing on $[0, \infty)$.
(b) Either the number 0 is not in the domain of f or $\lim_{x \to 0} f(x) \neq f(0)$.

Exercise 1.3.12 Let the propositional function $C(f, a)$ mean, "The function f is continuous at the point a," and let the propositional function $D(f, a)$ mean, "The function f is differentiable at the point a." Using these symbols together with logical symbols, express the following statements.
(a) Neither the tangent function nor the secant function is continuous at $\pi/2$.
(b) Either $a > 0$ or the natural logarithm function is not differentiable at a .
(c) The absolute value function is continuous at 0 but not differentiable at 0.

Exercise 1.3.13 Let P and Q be statements and define $P \oplus Q$ by the following truth table.

P	Q	$P \oplus Q$
T	T	F
T	F	T
F	T	T
F	F	F

Note that $\oplus$ is the **exclusive or** operation that we mentioned following Definition 1.3.2. Prove that $P \oplus Q \iff (P \vee Q) \wedge \neg(P \wedge Q)$.

Exercise 1.3.14 The operation $\oplus$, as defined in Exercise 1.3.13, is clearly commutative, but is it also associative?

1.4 Conditionals, Tautologies, and Contradictions

Many mathematical statements are expressed in what is called conditional form, namely "*If P, then Q.*" For example,

If $\triangle ABC$ is a right triangle with right angle C, then $AC^2 + BC^2 = AB^2$.

Or,

If a function f is differentiable at a point c, then f is continuous at c.

We examine the truth value of the sentence "If P, then Q" through the following example.

Suppose that a particular college advertises with the claim,

If you earn a college degree, then you will get a great job.

How do we evaluate the truth of this statement? Think of such a statement as a promise. Its truth value is **F** if the promise is broken and **T** if the promise is not broken. Each of the simple statements "you earn a college degree" and "you will get a great job" is either true or false. Here are the four possibilities.

1. You earn a college degree; you get a great job.

2. You earn a college degree; you do not get a great job.

3. You do not earn a college degree; you get a great job.

4. You do not earn a college degree; you do not get a great job.

In the first case, the promise is clearly kept, and so the truth value of the statement is **T**. In the second, the promise is clearly broken, and hence its truth value is **F**. The analysis is less obvious in the other two cases. In the fourth case, the promise does not come into play, and therefore the promise is not broken; thus its truth value is **T**. In the third case, the college does not break its promise. In the original statement, there are no stipulations on the side of the college about when people get great jobs, except that you *will* get a great job *if* you earn a college degree. So in the third case, the truth value of the statement is **T**. In summary, the *only* case where the statement "If P, then Q" is false is when P is true and Q is false.

Definition 1.4.1 *Let P and Q be statements. The **conditional** "If P, then Q," written $P \Rightarrow Q$, has truth value according to the following truth table:*

P	Q	$P \Rightarrow Q$
T	T	T
T	F	F
F	T	T
F	F	T

*The statement $P \Rightarrow Q$ is also read "P implies Q." In a statement of the form $P \Rightarrow Q$, P is the **hypothesis** and Q is the **conclusion**.*

When we say P implies Q, we in no way suggest that P *causes* Q. Raininess implies cloudiness, but rain does not cause clouds; rather, clouds cause rain— usually. Implication and causality really have little to do with each other in the context of logic.

There are several ways to express $P \Rightarrow Q$ in spoken English. Besides "P implies Q," the conditional "If P, then Q" can be expressed in any of the following ways.

Q, if *P*.

P, only if *Q*.

P is **sufficient** for *Q*.

Q is **necessary** for *P*.

Q whenever *P*.

All of these forms can and do appear in mathematical writing.

Proposition 1.3.9 (ii, iii) give negations of conjunctions and disjunctions. The next result shows how to negate a conditional.

Theorem 1.4.2   *Let P and Q be any two statements. Then*

$$\neg(P \Rightarrow Q) \Longleftrightarrow P \wedge \neg Q.$$

Exercise 1.4.3   Prove Theorem 1.4.2 by comparing truth tables.

You saw in Section 1.3 that $\vee$ and $\wedge$ are commutative, but is the same true for $\Rightarrow$? Consider the following truth table.

P	Q	$P \Rightarrow Q$	$Q \Rightarrow P$
T	T	T	T
T	F	F	T
F	T	T	F
F	F	T	T

The two expressions $P \Rightarrow Q$ and $Q \Rightarrow P$ are *not* logically equivalent; thus $\Rightarrow$ is *not* commutative. The statement "If one lives in Onondaga County, then one lives in New York State" is true, but the statement "If one lives in New York State, then one lives in Onondaga County" is not true. However, the statement "If one doesn't live in New York State, then one doesn't live in Onondaga County" is true.

Definition 1.4.4   *For the conditional P $\Rightarrow$ Q, the statement Q $\Rightarrow$ P is its* **converse**, *and the statement $\neg Q \Rightarrow \neg P$ is its* **contrapositive**.

The next theorem establishes the logical equivalence of the conditional and its contrapositive.

Theorem 1.4.5 *Let P and Q be any two statements. Then*

$$P \Rightarrow Q \iff \neg Q \Rightarrow \neg P.$$

Proof. We simply construct the truth tables of each statement.

P	Q	$\neg P$	$\neg Q$	$P \Rightarrow Q$	$\neg Q \Rightarrow \neg P$
T	T	F	F	T	T
T	F	F	T	F	F
F	T	T	F	T	T
F	F	T	T	T	T

$\square$

Note that, while a conditional is logically equivalent to its contrapositive, the converse of a conditional is equivalent neither to the statement nor to its negation.

Exercise 1.4.6 Form the converse and contrapositive for each of the following conditionals.

(a) If you live in Minneapolis, then you live in Minnesota.
(b) If n is an even integer, then n^2 is an even integer.
(c) If f is differentiable at $x = a$, then f is continuous at $x = a$.
(d) If p is not prime, then $x^p + 1$ is not factorable.
(e) If you live in Minnesota, then you do not live in Syracuse.

We have seen that the converse is not logically equivalent to the conditional from which it is formed. However, consider the statement in Exercise 1.4.6(b),

If n is an even integer, then n^2 is an even integer.

Certainly, this is true and is proved in Section 2.3. And while the statement

If n^2 is an even integer, then n is an even integer

is *not* logically equivalent to the previous statement, nonetheless, it is just as true. Therefore we know that the compound statement "If n is an even integer, then n^2 is an even integer *and* if n^2 is an even integer, then n is an even integer" is true. Mathematicians combine a conditional with its converse in the following way.

$$n \text{ is an even integer if and only if } n^2 \text{ is an even integer.}$$

The statement "P if and only if Q" is a shorter way of saying, "If P then Q, and if Q then P." In formal notation, this is $(P \Rightarrow Q) \wedge (Q \Rightarrow P)$. The words "if and only if" are sometimes further abbreviated as "iff."

Definition 1.4.7 *Let P and Q be statements. The statement "P if and only if Q" is the* **biconditional** *of P with Q, written $P \Leftrightarrow Q$. The truth value of the biconditional is given by the following truth table.*

P	Q	$P \Leftrightarrow Q$
T	T	T
T	F	F
F	T	F
F	F	T

We see in this truth table that the truth value of $P \Leftrightarrow Q$ is **T** whenever the truth values of P and Q agree and **F** when they disagree.

Exercise 1.4.8   Make a truth table for the statement $(P \Rightarrow Q) \wedge (Q \Rightarrow P)$ and observe that it is equivalent to $P \Leftrightarrow Q$.

Exercise 1.4.9   Determine whether the operation $\Rightarrow$ is associative; that means, if $S : P \Rightarrow (Q \Rightarrow R)$ and $T : (P \Rightarrow Q) \Rightarrow R$, then does $S \Longleftrightarrow T$ hold? If not, is either $S \Rightarrow T$ or $T \Rightarrow S$ always true? Which one?

Exercise 1.4.10   Prove that $\Leftrightarrow$ is both associative and commutative.

Exercise 1.4.11   Prove that the following are true for any conditional.
(a) The contrapositive of the contrapositive is logically equivalent to the original statement.
(b) The converse of the converse is logically equivalent to the original statement.
(c) The contrapositive of the converse is logically equivalent to the converse of the contrapositive.
(d) If a conditional is false, then its converse is true.

Certain types of logical expressions have special significance because of their particular truth tables. Consider the expression

$$(P \Rightarrow Q) \Leftrightarrow (\neg P \vee Q)$$

and its truth table.

P	Q	$\neg P$	$P \Rightarrow Q$	$\neg P \vee Q$	$(P \Rightarrow Q) \Leftrightarrow (\neg P \vee Q)$
T	T	F	T	T	T
T	F	F	F	F	T
F	T	T	T	T	T
F	F	T	T	T	T

The expression is true independently of the individual truth values of P and Q. This is an example of an expression that is called a *tautology*.

Definition 1.4.12 *A **tautology** is an expression whose truth value is **T** for all combinations of truth values of the variables that appear in it.*
*A **contradiction** is an expression whose truth value is **F** for all combinations of truth values of the variables that appear in it.*

The simplest possible tautology is a statement of the form $P \vee \neg P$, and the simplest possible contradiction has the form[8] $P \wedge \neg P$. Here are their truth tables.

P	$\neg P$	$P \vee \neg P$	$P \wedge \neg P$
T	F	T	F
F	T	T	F

An expression X is a tautology if and only if $\neg X$ is a contradiction. Note that, by the first of De Morgan's Laws (Proposition 1.3.9(ii)) and part (i) of the same proposition,

$$\neg(P \vee \neg P) \Longleftrightarrow P \wedge \neg P.$$

---

[8]In Aristotelian logic, this is called "the principle of the excluded middle."

Suppose that two expressions, call them X and Y, are logically equivalent. (Recall Definition 1.3.8.) To say $X \Longleftrightarrow Y$ is *exactly* the same thing as saying that the expression $X \Leftrightarrow Y$ is a tautology.

Exercise 1.4.13   Show that the following statements are tautologies.
(a) $(P \Leftrightarrow Q) \Rightarrow \big((R \wedge P) \Leftrightarrow (R \wedge Q)\big)$.
(b) $(P \Leftrightarrow Q) \Rightarrow \big((R \vee P) \Leftrightarrow (R \vee Q)\big)$.

Exercise 1.4.14   Determine whether each of the following expressions is a tautology, a contradiction, or neither.
(a) $\big((P \Rightarrow Q) \Rightarrow P\big) \Rightarrow Q$.
(b) $P \Leftrightarrow \big(P \wedge (P \vee Q)\big)$.
(c) $(P \Rightarrow Q) \Leftrightarrow (P \wedge \neg Q)$.
(d) $P \Rightarrow \big(Q \Rightarrow (P \Rightarrow Q)\big)$.
(e) $\big(Q \wedge (P \vee \neg P)\big) \Leftrightarrow Q$.
(f) $\big(P \Rightarrow (Q \wedge R)\big) \Rightarrow \big((P \Rightarrow Q) \wedge (P \Rightarrow R)\big)$.
(g) $\big(P \Rightarrow (Q \vee R)\big) \Rightarrow \big((P \Rightarrow Q) \vee (P \Rightarrow R)\big)$.
(h) $\big((P \vee Q) \Rightarrow Q\big) \Rightarrow P$.

The following tautology will be used a few thousand times in your mathematical career.

Exercise 1.4.15   Prove that the expression $\big((P \Rightarrow Q) \wedge P\big) \Rightarrow Q$ is a tautology.[9]

1.5   Methods of Proof

In this section, we consider three basic formats for proving conditionals. While many mathematical statements are not in the standard conditional form of $P \Rightarrow Q$, it is usually possible to reword the statement so that it is in this form.

For example, consider the statement, *"The diagonals of a parallelogram bisect each other."* This statement clearly does not have the usual form of a

---

[9]This tautology is called *Modus ponens* in propositional logic.

conditional. However, we can write an equivalent statement that does have this form: *"If the quadrilateral $ABCD$ is a parallelogram, then the segments $\overline{AC}$ and $\overline{BD}$ bisect each other."* In this case, we introduced some symbols—namely, the labels of the vertices of an arbitrary parallelogram—but at the same time, we now have some handy notation to use in the proof.

One isn't always compelled to use symbols just to make a mathematical statement have the familiar "If ..., then ..." appearance. The statement *"It is impossible to trisect an angle using only a compass and straightedge"* can be restated as *"If one has only a straightedge and compass, then one cannot trisect an angle."*

Turn back to Definition 1.4.1, and note that $P \Rightarrow Q$ is true in lines 1, 3, and 4 but false in line 2 of the truth table. The goal of all three proof formats is to demonstrate that the situation at hand places us on one of the three "true" lines—that is, *not* on line 2.

The first of the three proof formats considered here is called **direct proof**. It is without question the format that mathematicians most frequently use and is the simplest one conceptually. There are many, many examples of direct proofs in the subsequent chapters of this book.

In the course of a direct proof of $P \Rightarrow Q$, we always assume P to be true. Often, but not always, we assert this assumption at the outset. If P is false, then $P \Rightarrow Q$ is true anyway, so there is no point even considering the option of P being false. Assuming P to be true limits us to the first two lines of the truth table of $P \Rightarrow Q$. If we now deduce (using P) that Q must be true, then we know that we are in line 1 of the truth table and not in line 2. In line 1, the truth value of $P \Rightarrow Q$ is **T**, which is exactly what we were aiming for. Mission accomplished! Here is an application of the format of a direct proof.

Example 1.5.1 Prove the following.

$$\text{If } x < -6, \text{ then } x^2 + 4x - 12 > 0.$$

Proof. We assume that $x < -6$. [This time the assumption of P is the first step in our argument.] It follows that $x + 6 < 0$ and $x - 2 < -8$.

We multiply the latter inequality by the negative quantity $x + 6$ to obtain $(x + 6)(x - 2) > (x + 6)(-8) > 0$. By elementary algebra, we deduce $x^2 + 4x - 12 > 0$. We have proved that if $x < -6$, then $x^2 + 4x - 12 > 0$. □

As you study this simple proof, you may wonder where we got the idea to subtract 2 from our initial assumption to come up with $x - 2 < -8$. That's where a little forward thinking comes in. We looked ahead at the desired conclusion, saw a quadratic polynomial, and tried factoring it. It worked! There are other arguments that also work. See if you can devise one of your own.

The next definition is familiar. We review it here in order to state and prove the important *Triangle Inequality*.

Definition 1.5.2 *Let x be any real number. The* **absolute value of** x, *written $|x|$, is defined by*

$$|x| = \begin{cases} x & \text{if } x \geq 0; \\ -x & \text{if } x < 0. \end{cases}$$

The Triangle Inequality is a simple, yet fundamental and important statement about real numbers. (A justification for its geometric name will come in Section 8.4, where we extend it to include complex numbers as well.)

Theorem 1.5.3 (The Triangle Inequality) *For any real numbers a and b, we have*

$$|a + b| \leq |a| + |b|.$$

Proof. We prove the Triangle Inequality by examining four cases. [Sometimes it is more practical to consider separately several cases of the hypothesis of a theorem. Here the hypothesis is that a and b are real numbers. Each of these cases becomes its own little direct proof.] There are four cases that cover all possibilities for a and b—namely,

Case 1: $a, b \geq 0$;   Case 2: $a, b < 0$;

Case 3: $a \geq 0, b < 0$;   Case 4: $a < 0, b \geq 0$.

Case 1. Suppose $a, b \geq 0$. Then $a + b \geq 0$ and, by Definition 1.5.2, $|a + b| = a + b$, $|a| = a$, and $|b| = b$. So we have

$$|a + b| = a + b = |a| + |b|.$$

[To prove $x \leq y$, it is sufficient to prove $x = y$, since the expression $x = y \Rightarrow x \leq y$ is a tautology.]

Case 2. Suppose that $a, b < 0$. Then $a + b < 0$, and we have $|a+b| = -(a+b)$, $|a| = -a$, and $|b| = -b$. Then

$$|a + b| = -(a + b) = -a + (-b) = |a| + |b|.$$

Case 3. Suppose that $a \geq 0$ and $b < 0$. Then either $a + b \geq 0$ or $a + b < 0$. [There are two subcases of case 3.] If $a + b \geq 0$, then $|a + b| = a + b$, $|a| = a$, and $|b| = -b > 0$. Thus $|b| > b$ and so

$$|a + b| = a + b = |a| + b < |a| + |b|.$$

If $a + b < 0$, then $|a + b| = -(a + b)$, $|a| = a$, and $|b| = -b$. Since $a \geq 0$, $-a \leq |a|$. Thus

$$|a + b| = -(a + b) = -a + (-b) = -a + |b| \leq |a| + |b|.$$

To prove Case 4, simply swap a and b in the proof of Case 3. □

Exercise 1.5.4 Let $b \geq 0$. Prove that $|a| \leq b$ if and only if $-b \leq a \leq b$. [Hint: This is a biconditional statement. Therefore, it is necessary to prove, under the assumption $b \geq 0$, that each of the two statements $|a| \leq b$ and $-b \leq a \leq b$ implies the other.]

In each of the direct proofs that you've seen in this section, the full hypothesis has been brought to bear almost at the outset. Sometimes it works better instead to invoke the hypothesis piecemeal at convenient steps in the course of the proof. A direct proof of a familiar theorem from first-semester calculus provides a suitable example.

Theorem 1.5.5 *Suppose that a function f is defined in an open interval containing the real number c. If f is differentiable at c, then f is continuous at c.*

Proof. To satisfy the definition of continuity, we must show that $\lim_{x \to c} f(x)$ exists and equals $f(c)$. [Before invoking the hypothesis that f is differentiable at c, we require some algebraic preparation.] Clearly,

$$f(x) = \big(f(x) - f(c)\big) + f(c).$$

When considering a limit as x approaches c, one must assume that $x \neq c$; that is, $x - c \neq 0$. Hence

$$f(x) = \frac{f(x) - f(c)}{x - c} \cdot (x - c) + f(c). \tag{1.5.1}$$

The goal of determining $\lim_{x \to c} f(x)$ will be achieved if we can compute $\lim_{x \to c}$ of the right-hand side of equation 1.5.1.

We are now ready to apply the hypothesis that f is differentiable at c. By the definition of derivative, $\lim_{x \to c} \dfrac{f(x) - f(c)}{x - c}$ exists and equals $f'(c)$. Since the limit of each of the two factors in the product $\dfrac{f(x) - f(c)}{x - c} \cdot (x - c)$ exists, the limit of this product equals the product of the limits of its factors. Thus

$$\begin{aligned}
\lim_{x \to c} f(x) &= \lim_{x \to c} \frac{f(x) - f(c)}{x - c} \cdot \lim_{x \to c}(x - c) + f(c) \\
&= f'(c) \cdot 0 + f(c) \\
&= f(c).
\end{aligned}$$

We have proved that $\lim_{x \to c} f(x) = f(c)$, which means that f is continuous at c. $\qquad\square$

Because the contrapositive of a conditional is logically equivalent to the original statement, we can approach the proof of a conditional by way of its contrapositive. Sometimes this approach is easier. Thus the second proof format presented here is called **proof by the contrapositive**, or more briefly, **contrapositive proof**.[10] It is simply a direct proof of the statement $\neg Q \Rightarrow \neg P$.

---

[10]This is called *Modus tollens* in propositional logic.

Example 1.5.6 Suppose we want to prove the following claim.

If at least 19 balls are distributed into six baskets,

then some basket contains at least four balls.

We think of the conditional that we are trying to prove as $P \Rightarrow Q$, where

P : *at least 19 balls are distributed into 6 baskets*, and

Q : *some basket contains at least 4 balls.*

Then the contrapositive, $\neg Q \Rightarrow \neg P$ would read

If every basket contains at most three balls,

then at most 18 balls are distributed into six baskets.

Let us now embark upon a direct proof of the contrapositive.

Proof. We assume $\neg Q$: Each basket contains at most 3 balls. Then the total number of balls in all 6 baskets is at most $6 \cdot 3 = 18$. [This is the statement $\neg P$.] Thus we have proved the contrapositive of the claim. Since the contrapositive is equivalent to the given conditional, we have proved the claim. $\qquad\square$

Exercise 1.5.7 Let x and y denote positive real numbers. Give a contrapositive proof that if $x \neq y$, then $x + y > \dfrac{4xy}{x+y}$.

The foundation of a **proof by contradiction** is presented next. There will be many examples of proof by contradiction throughout this book and throughout your mathematical career.

Theorem 1.5.8 *For statements E and R, the expression*

$$\big(\neg E \Rightarrow (R \wedge \neg R)\big) \Rightarrow E$$

is a tautology.[11]

---

[11]This is called *Reductio ad absurdam* in propositional logic.

Exercise 1.5.9   Use a truth table to prove Theorem 1.5.8.

The meaning of this tautology is that the following line of argument is valid. We assume that E is *not* true; that is, we assume $\neg E$. If the assumption of $\neg E$ implies a contradiction, such as $R \wedge \neg R$, then $\neg E$ must be false, in which case, E is true.

Example 1.5.10   Prove that $\log_2 19$ is not a positive integer.

Proof. Suppose that $\log_2 19$ is a positive integer, say $\log_2 19 = n$, where n is some positive integer. [Here we have $E : \log_2 19$ is not a positive integer, and so $\neg E : \log_2 19$ is a positive integer.] Then, by the definition of logarithm, we have that $2^n = 19$. [This is R.] We also know that, for every positive integer n, 2^n is even. So, since 19 is odd, we have $2^n \neq 19$. [This is $\neg R$.]

So we have shown that

$$(\log_2 19 \text{ equals a positive integer } n) \;\Rightarrow\; \left[(2^n = 19) \wedge (2^n \neq 19) \right].$$

Because we reached the contradiction $R \wedge \neg R$, we conclude that our original assumption, that $\log_2 19$ is a positive integer, is false. Thus $\log_2 19$ is not a positive integer.   □

Exercise 1.5.11   Let m be a positive integer that has an odd divisor greater than 1. Prove that $\log_2 m$ is not an integer.

Very often, the statement E that we wish to prove by contradiction is itself a conditional $P \Rightarrow Q$. When we assume $\neg E$—that is, when we assume $\neg(P \Rightarrow Q)$—we in fact must assume $P \wedge \neg Q$, and we seek a contradiction $R \wedge \neg R$, where R is something other than P or Q. (If R turns out to be P, then what we really did was to prove the contrapositive $\neg Q \Rightarrow \neg P$. Do you see why?) In order to illustrate this method with the example that we want to use, we need the following lemma,[12] which we prove by a direct proof.

Lemma 1.5.12   *If a perfect square is divided by 4, then the remainder is either 0 or 1.*

---

[12] A **lemma** is a theorem of perhaps not much interest in its own right but which is used in the proof of a theorem of greater interest.

Proof. Assume that n is a perfect square. That means that $n = m^2$ for some integer m. Now m is either even or odd.

Case 1: m is even. That means $m = 2k$ for some integer k. So

$$n = m^2 = (2k)^2 = 4k^2,$$

which means that when n is divided by 4, then the remainder is 0.

Case 2: m is odd. That means $m = 2k + 1$ for some integer k. So

$$n = m^2 = (2k + 1)^2 = 4(k^2 + k) + 1,$$

which means that when n is divided by 4, then the remainder is 1. $\qquad\square$

Example 1.5.13 Suppose that a, b, and c are integers. We prove the following.

$$\text{If } a^2 + b^2 = c^2, \text{ then } a \text{ or } b \text{ is even.}$$

Proof. For $P : a^2 + b^2 = c^2$ and $Q : a$ *or* b *is even*, we assume $\neg(P \Rightarrow Q)$. Equivalently, we assume $P \wedge \neg Q$, namely: $a^2 + b^2 = c^2$ *and* a *is odd and* b *is odd*. Thus there exists some integer k such that $a = 2k + 1$, and there exists some integer ℓ such that $b = 2\ell + 1$. Also,

$$\begin{aligned}
c^2 &= a^2 + b^2 \\
&= (2k + 1)^2 + (2\ell + 1)^2 \\
&= 4(k^2 + k + \ell^2 + \ell) + 2.
\end{aligned}$$

This implies the statement

$$R : \text{the remainder is 2 when } c^2 \text{ is divided by 4,}$$

which is to be "half" of our contradiction. But by Lemma 1.5.12, we know that

$$\neg R : \text{the remainder cannot be 2 when } c^2 \text{ is divided by 4.}$$

And therein lies a contradiction! $\qquad\square$

The proof of Theorem 1.1.4 is an example of a proof by contradiction. Have another look at it! Let us reformulate the statement as a conditional.

> *If two or more people meet and some shake hands with each other, then some two of the people shake the same number of hands.*

In the proof, we assumed the negation of this statement—namely that $n \geq 2$ and that no two of the n people shake the same number of hands. We deduced the contradiction that the person who shook no hands shook the hand of the one who shook everybody's hand.

We summarize these three proof formats of $P \Rightarrow Q$ with the following table.

Proof format	Assume	Deduce
direct proof	P	Q
contrapositive proof	$\neg Q$	$\neg P$
proof by contradiction	$P \wedge \neg Q$	$R \wedge \neg R$

In this section, we have discussed three basic proof formats. We have indicated *how* to execute each format, but we've given no clue as to *when* to select one format over another. The "when" question, however, has no definite answer. An analogy to calculus is the situation where you are given a continuous function and are asked to find its antiderivatives. At this point, you know many techniques for finding antiderivatives, but how do you know which one—or which ones—to apply? Often, several different techniques will work, while for some continuous functions, none of the techniques that you learned will work.[13]

And so it is with proofs. For some proofs, more than one of these three formats will work. For some, you will need a method called "mathematical induction," which will be covered in Chapter 5.

Often, it is a good idea to start out by trying a direct proof, if only because it is the most simple. However, if the hypothesis seems very lean, with modest

---

[13]For example, e^{-x^2} and $\frac{\sin x}{x}$ are such functions.

conditions, while the conclusion looks easy to negate, then you might try one of the other formats. A more complicated proof frequently uses more than one format in the same proof, just as an antiderivative problem may require both integration by parts and a trigonometric substitution in the same problem. If you don't know at the outset whether the statement $P \Rightarrow Q$ is true, and if you are not successful in coming up with a proof, it may be that the statement is actually false, and so no proof can exist. In that case, you may try to prove the negation of the statement by looking for a *counterexample*. We discuss counterexamples in the next section.

1.6 Quantifiers

Consider the propositional function

$$I(x) : x^2 + 1 > 0,$$

where the universal set is the set of real numbers. What is the truth set of $I(x)$? Are there any real numbers for which $I(x)$ is false? The truth set of $I(x)$ is the entire set of real numbers. In other words, the truth set *is* the universal set.

Consider the sentence

For all real numbers x, $x^2 + 1 > 0$.

While this sentence includes the variable x, it is *not* a propositional function; its truth value does not depend on any actual value of x. This sentence is rather the *statement* that the truth set of $I(x)$ is the set of all real numbers. By the way, the truth value of this statement is **T**.

Definition 1.6.1 *Let $P(x)$ be a propositional function with universal set X. The sentence*

For all $x \in X$, $P(x)$

is a **universally quantified statement** *whose truth value is* **T** *if the truth set of* $P(x)$ *is the universal set* X *and* **F** *otherwise. We write*

$$(\forall\, x \in X)[P(x)],$$

or simply

$$(\forall x)[P(x)]$$

when the universal set is clear from the context. The symbol $\forall$ *is the* **universal quantifier**.

Thus the statement, with the set $\mathbb{Z}$ of integers as the universal set,

For all integers t, $t^2 + 4t - 12 = 0$

or

$$(\forall t \in \mathbb{Z})\left[t^2 + 4t - 12 = 0\right]$$

is a false statement since its truth set, $\{-6, 2\}$, is not the set of all integers.

The truth value of a universally quantified statement depends on the answer to the question, "Is the truth set the entire universal set?"

A different question to ask about a propositional function $P(x)$ is, "Are there *any* values at all in the truth set of $P(x)$?" Consider the sentence

There exists an integer t *such that* $t^2 + 4t - 12 = 0$.

Since there is at least one integer in the truth set of this propositional function, it is a true statement.

Definition 1.6.2 *Let* $P(x)$ *be a propositional function with universal set* X. *The sentence*

There exists $x \in X$ *such that* $P(x)$

is an **existentially quantified statement** *whose truth value is* **F** *if the truth set of* $P(x)$ *has no elements and* **T** *otherwise. We write*

$$(\exists\, x \in X)[P(x)]$$

or simply

$$(\exists x)[P(x)],$$

when the universal set is clear from the context. The symbol $\exists$ *is the* **existential quantifier**.

Notice in Definition 1.6.2 that $(\exists x)[P(x)]$ is true as long as there is *at least one* element x in its truth set. Sometimes it is useful to distinguish propositional functions where there is *exactly one* element in its truth set (or *not* exactly one element in the truth set).

Definition 1.6.3 *Let $P(x)$ be a propositional function with universal set X. The sentence*

There exists a unique $x \in X$ such that $P(x)$

is a **uniquely existentially quantified statement** *whose truth value is* **T** *if the truth set of $P(x)$ has exactly one element and* **F** *otherwise. We write*

$$(\exists! \, x \in X)[P(x)]$$

or

$$(\exists! \, x)[P(x)],$$

when the universal set is clear from the context. The symbol $\exists!$ is the **unique existential quantifier**.

Example 1.6.4 Suppose the universal set is the set of real numbers. The statement $(\exists! x)[2x - 3 = 7]$ is true since the only solution to the equation $2x - 3 = 7$ is $x = 5$. The statements $(\exists! t)[t^2 + 4t - 12 = 0]$ and $(\exists! y)[y^2 + 1 < 0]$ are both false. The statement $(\forall x)(\exists! \, y)[x + y = 4]$ is true.

We can express the unique existential quantifier in terms of logical symbols already defined:

$$(\exists! x)[P(x)] \iff (\exists x)\big[P(x) \wedge (\forall y)\,(P(y) \Rightarrow \; x = y)\big].$$

If $P(x)$ is a propositional function with universal set X, then each of the following is a statement.

1. $(\forall x \in X)[P(x)]$;

2. $(\exists x \in X)[P(x)]$;

3. $(\exists! \, x \in X)[P(x)]$.

Since these are statements, so are their negations.

Consider the statement "There exists a car that is red," where the universe is the set of cars in a particular parking lot. We can express this statement symbolically as

$$(\exists x \in L)[R(x)],$$

where L is the set of cars in the parking lot and $R(x) : x$ *is red*. What does it mean for this statement to be true? It means that there is at least one car in the lot that is red. What does it mean if this statement is false? That is, when is the statement $\neg\big((\exists x \in L)[R(x)]\big)$ true? The original statement $(\exists x \in L)[R(x)]$ is false *only* if there are no red cars at all in the lot. In other words, *all* cars in the lot are *not* red. With the symbols we have already adopted for this example, this statement is expressed as

$$(\forall x \in L)\,[\neg R(x)]\,.$$

We see here that $\neg\big((\exists x \in L)[R(x)]\big)$ and $(\forall x \in L)[\neg R(x)]$ have the same truth value. The rules for negating quantified expressions are stated in the following theorem.

Theorem 1.6.5 *Let $P(x)$ be a propositional function with universal set X. Then the following hold.*
(i) $\neg\big((\exists x)[P(x)]\big) \Longleftrightarrow (\forall x)[\neg P(x)]$.
(ii) $\neg\big((\forall x)[P(x)]\big) \Longleftrightarrow (\exists x)[\neg P(x)]$.

Proof. (i) Suppose that $\neg\big((\exists x)[P(x)]\big)$ is true; thus $(\exists x)[P(x)]$ is false. This means that the truth set of $P(x)$ has no elements. In other words, every $x \in X$ has the property that $P(x)$ is false; that is to say that $\neg P(x)$ is true for every $x \in X$. Thus $(\forall x)[\neg P(x)]$ is true.

If $\neg\big((\exists x)[P(x)]\big)$ is false, then $(\exists x)[P(x)]$ is true. By the definition of $\exists$, there is at least one element of X such that $P(x)$ is true. So the statement $(\forall x)[\neg P(x)]$ is false. Since the statements $\neg\big((\exists x)[P(x)]\big)$ and $(\forall x)[\neg P(x)]$ have the same truth values, we conclude that they are equivalent.

To prove part (ii), we have from part (i) that

$$(\forall x)[\neg P(x)] \Longleftrightarrow \neg\big((\exists x)[P(x)]\big).$$

After we negate both sides we get

$$\neg\big((\forall x)[\neg P(x)]\big) \iff \neg\Big(\neg\big((\exists x)[P(x)]\big)\Big).$$

Now substitute $Q(x)$ for $\neg P(x)$ and simplify according to Proposition 1.3.9(i) to obtain

$$\neg\big((\forall x)[Q(x)]\big) \iff (\exists x)[\neg Q(x)].$$

Finally, substitute $P(x)$ for $Q(x)$ to obtain the desired conclusion. $\square$

Example 1.6.6 The negation of the statement about the set $\mathbb{R}$ of real numbers

$$(\forall x \in \mathbb{R})[2\sin(x) = \sin(2x)]$$

is the following.

$$\neg\big((\forall x \in \mathbb{R})[2\sin(x) = \sin(2x)]\big) \iff (\exists x \in \mathbb{R})\neg\,[2\sin(x) = \sin(2x)]$$
$$\iff (\exists x \in \mathbb{R})[2\sin(x) \neq \sin(2x)].$$

Definition 1.6.7 *Let X be the universal set for $P(x)$. An element x_0 of X is a* **counterexample** *to the statement $(\forall x)[P(x)]$ provided that $P(x_0)$ is false.*

Example 1.6.8 The value $\dfrac{\pi}{2}$ is a counterexample to the statement

$$(\forall x)\big[2\sin(x) = \sin(2x)\big]$$

because it shows this statement to be false.

Exercise 1.6.9 Write the symbolic negation of each of the following expressions so that $\neg$ never immediately precedes a parenthesis or bracket.

(a) $(\forall x)\big[P(x) \Rightarrow \big(Q(x) \wedge R(x)\big)\big]$.
(b) $(\exists y)\big[P(y) \vee (\forall x)[Q(x) \Rightarrow \neg R(x)]\big]$.
(c) $(\forall x)(\exists y)(\forall z)\big[P(x,y) \Leftrightarrow Q(y,z)\big]$.

You are now in a position to address the example from the end of Section 1.1. Recall from your calculus courses the following definition.

Definition 1.6.10 *A function f has* **limit** *L as x approaches c provided that the following condition is satisfied: for every $\epsilon > 0$, there exists $\delta > 0$ such that, for any real number x, if $0 < |x - c| < \delta$, then $|f(x) - L| < \epsilon$.*

We can express the given condition with symbols.

$$(\forall \epsilon > 0)(\exists \delta > 0)(\forall x \in \mathbb{R}) \left[0 < \left|x - c\right| < \delta \Rightarrow \left|f(x) - L\right| < \epsilon\right]. \quad (1.6.1)$$

Note that there are several symbols for variables in statement (1.6.1). The variables f, L, and c were introduced prior to the statement and so are not quantified. But statement (1.6.1) introduces three quantified variables: ϵ, δ, and x. The universal set from which ϵ and δ are drawn is the set of positive real numbers, and the universal set for x is the set $\mathbb{R}$ of real numbers. The universal sets for each variable remain unaffected by negation; *they never change.* So a statement that begins with $\neg(\forall \epsilon > 0)$ does not become one that begins with $(\forall \epsilon \leq 0)$; it becomes a statement that begins with $(\exists \epsilon > 0)$.

Let us next consider the negation of statement (1.6.1). That is, precisely what does it mean to say that L is *not* the limit of f as x approaches c? In order to state clearly and correctly the negation of condition (1.6.1), we use the rules of negation from Theorem 1.6.5 and Theorem 1.4.2.

$$\neg\left[(\forall \epsilon > 0)(\exists \delta > 0)(\forall x \in \mathbb{R}) \left[0 < \left|x - c\right| < \delta \Rightarrow \left|f(x) - L\right| < \epsilon\right]\right]$$

$$\Longleftrightarrow (\exists \epsilon > 0)\neg\left[(\exists \delta > 0)(\forall x \in \mathbb{R}) \left[0 < \left|x - c\right| < \delta \Rightarrow \left|f(x) - L\right| < \epsilon\right]\right]$$

$$\Longleftrightarrow (\exists \epsilon > 0)(\forall \delta > 0)\neg\left[(\forall x \in \mathbb{R}) \left[0 < \left|x - c\right| < \delta \Rightarrow \left|f(x) - L\right| < \epsilon\right]\right]$$

$$\Longleftrightarrow (\exists \epsilon > 0)(\forall \delta > 0)(\exists x \in \mathbb{R})\neg \left[0 < \left|x - c\right| < \delta \Rightarrow \left|f(x) - L\right| < \epsilon\right]$$

$$\Longleftrightarrow (\exists \epsilon > 0)(\forall \delta > 0)(\exists x \in \mathbb{R}) \left[0 < \left|x - c\right| < \delta \wedge \neg(\left|f(x) - L\right| < \epsilon)\right]$$

$$\Longleftrightarrow (\exists \epsilon > 0)(\forall \delta > 0)(\exists x \in \mathbb{R}) \left[0 < \left|x - c\right| < \delta \wedge \left|f(x) - L\right| \geq \epsilon\right]$$

Translated back from logical symbols to English, this could read,

There exists $\epsilon > 0$ such that for all $\delta > 0$, there exists a real number x such that we have $0 < |x - c| < \delta$ and $|f(x) - L| \geq \epsilon$.

In this logical derivation, take particular note of the locations of the negation symbol $\neg$; it advances to the right in each successive line until it vanishes in the last line.

If existential and universal quantifiers are both used in an expression, it is entirely possible that the statement formed with the quantifiers in a different order is not equivalent to the original expression. Consider the statement

$$(\forall x)(\exists y)[3x + y = 5].$$

This statement is true; no matter what x we choose, we can set $y = 5 - 3x$, and this value for y satisfies the existential quantifier. However, what happens when the order of the quantifiers is reversed? The statement

$$(\exists y)(\forall x)[3x + y = 5]$$

says that there exists a real number y such that for *every* value of x, we have $3x + y = 5$. This is absurd.

Exercise 1.6.11 Let $P(x, y) : x^2 + y < 0$, where the universal set for each variable is the set of real numbers. Identify the truth value of each of these statements. Pay attention to the scrambling of the quantifiers and the variables.

(a) $(\forall x)(\exists y)[P(x, y)]$.
(b) $(\forall y)(\exists x)[P(x, y)]$.
(c) $(\exists x)(\forall y)[P(x, y)]$.
(d) $(\exists y)(\forall x)[P(x, y)]$.

Most mathematical statements that mathematicians seek to prove or disprove are quantified in some way. Often the quantifiers are hidden. For example, the statement

If n is an even integer, then n^2 is an even integer

looks like a propositional function. But it *really* is the statement

  For every integer n,

             if n is an even integer, then n^2 is an even integer.

Here is another example.

Terminating decimals represent rational numbers.

A correct, complete translation of the statement is

$(\forall x \in \mathbb{R})$ [*x has a terminating decimal expansion* $\Rightarrow$ *x is a rational number*].

Much of the time, even if a conditional is expressed without *written* quantifiers, the variables are quantified in some way before the conditional is written.

Frequently, mathematicians will state theorems or facts with the words *all*, *every*, *each*, or *some*. These are words that indicate the presence of a quantifier. For example,

All differentiable functions are continuous.

Or

Every prime number greater than 2 is odd.

Or

Some quadratic polynomials have complex roots.

If $P(x)$ means that x has condition p and $Q(x)$ means x has condition q, then the statement

$$\text{\textit{All x's with p have q}} \tag{1.6.2}$$

is expressed as

$$(\forall x)[P(x) \Rightarrow Q(x)],$$

and the statement

$$\text{\textit{Some x's with p have q}}$$

is expressed as

$$(\exists x)[P(x) \wedge Q(x)]. \tag{1.6.3}$$

Note that statement (1.6.3) is equivalent to "some x's with q have p," but the statement (1.6.2) is *not* equivalent to "all x's with q have p."

Exercise 1.6.12 Write a sentence in everyday English that properly communicates the negation of each statement.
(a) Every even natural number ≥ 4 can be written as the sum of two prime numbers.[14]
(b) Some differentiable functions are bounded.

Exercise 1.6.13 Let $J(p, \ell)$ mean that line ℓ passes through point p, and let $P(\ell, \ell')$ mean that lines ℓ and ℓ' are parallel. Use logical symbols and this notation to express the following.
(a) No line is parallel to itself.
(b) Two parallel lines never pass through a common point.
(c) Every line passes through (at least) two distinct points.

1.7 Further Exercises

Exercise 1.7.1 Consider the following statements about a given integer n.

P: The integer n is divisible by 2.
Q: The integer n is divisible by 3.
R: The integer n is divisible by 6.

(a) Translate the following logical expressions into good English sentences.

(i) $\neg P \vee \neg Q$ (ii) $[(P \vee Q) \wedge \neg (P \wedge Q)] \Rightarrow \neg R$

(b) What logical expression conveys the meaning of the following English sentence?

An integer n is divisible by 6

if and only if it is divisible by both 2 and 3.

(c) Write the contrapositive (in symbols) of the expression in part (a)(ii) and simplify it so that no $\neg$ immediately precedes a parenthesis or bracket.

---

[14]The truth of this statement, known as the *Goldbach Conjecture*, remains one of the oldest unresolved mathematical questions. In 1742, the Prussian mathematician Christian Goldbach (1690–1764) communicated it by letter to L. Euler, who reformulated the problem in the form that we see here. If you prove this conjecture, then you stand a good chance of passing this course.

Exercise 1.7.2   For each of the following statements, write an equivalent statement that uses neither "or" nor "and."
(a) Two sets are equal or they have nothing in common.
(b) A given number is a perfect square and the number is less than 1000.

Exercise 1.7.3   An important tool for finding limits in calculus is **l'Hôpital's Rule**, one form of which is the following.

> *If functions f and g have continuous derivatives in an open interval containing a and $g'(x) \neq 0$ in this interval, and if $\lim_{x \to a} f(x) = \lim_{x \to a} g(x) = 0$, then $\lim_{x \to a} \dfrac{f(x)}{g(x)} = \lim_{x \to a} \dfrac{f'(x)}{g'(x)}$.*

(a) State this conditional in contrapositive form.
(b) State the converse of this statement.
(c) State the negation of this conditional, but do *not* begin with something of the form, "It is not so that...."

Exercise 1.7.4   Here is another handshake problem, but a little more complicated than the one in Theorem 1.1.4. A couple invites n couples to a party. Upon arriving, some people shake hands with each other and some do not, but nobody shakes hands with one's own spouse or with oneself. After all the guests have arrived, the hostess asks each of her guests as well as her husband how many individuals the person shook hands with. Amazingly, she comes up with $2n + 1$ different numbers. The problem now is this: with how many people did the hostess shake hands, and with how many people did the host shake hands? [Suggestion: Work this out first for $n = 3$ and then $n = 4$, and then find a general pattern that works for an arbitrary positive integer n. You will need to prove that it does indeed work.]

Exercise 1.7.5   Prove the following.
(a) $P \Rightarrow (Q \vee R) \Longleftrightarrow (P \wedge \neg R) \Rightarrow Q$.
(b) $\neg(P \Leftrightarrow Q) \Longleftrightarrow P \oplus Q$. (See Exercise 1.3.13 for the definition of $\oplus$.)
(c) $P \Rightarrow (Q \vee R) \Longleftrightarrow (P \Rightarrow Q) \vee (P \Rightarrow R)$.
(d) $P \Rightarrow (Q \wedge R) \Longleftrightarrow (P \Rightarrow Q) \wedge (P \Rightarrow R)$.
(e) $(P \vee Q) \Rightarrow R \Longleftrightarrow (P \Rightarrow R) \wedge (Q \Rightarrow R)$.
(f) $(P \wedge Q) \Rightarrow R \Longleftrightarrow (P \Rightarrow R) \vee (Q \Rightarrow R)$.

Exercise 1.7.6 Let P and Q be statements, and define $P \Diamond Q$ according to the following truth table.

P	Q	$P \Diamond Q$
T	T	T
T	F	T
F	T	F
F	F	T

(a) Prove that $P \Diamond Q \iff \neg Q \vee (P \wedge Q)$.

(b) Find a different logical expression that uses some or all of the symbols $P, Q, \neg, \vee, \wedge$ that is logically equivalent to $P \Diamond Q$. Prove that your answer is correct.

(c) Is $\Diamond$ commutative? Prove that your answer is correct.

(d) Is $\Diamond$ associative? Prove that your answer is correct.

Exercise 1.7.7 Make a truth table for the logical expression

$$\big((P \Rightarrow Q) \wedge \neg Q\big) \Rightarrow \neg P$$

and say whether it is a tautology, a contradiction, or neither.

Exercise 1.7.8 Prove that each of the following expressions is a tautology.

(a) $[(P \Rightarrow Q) \wedge (Q \Rightarrow R)] \Rightarrow (P \Rightarrow R)$.

(b) $[(P \Leftrightarrow Q) \wedge (Q \Leftrightarrow R)] \Rightarrow (P \Leftrightarrow R)$.

These tautologies illustrate the *transitivity* of $\Rightarrow$ and $\Leftrightarrow$.

Exercise 1.7.9 At an international mathematics conference, Professor X has just demonstrated the proof of his latest theorem, when Professor Y, seated in the back of the lecture hall, interrupts.

"Your result," shouts Professor Y, "follows immediately from a result of mine, which I published many years ago."

"I have no doubt that my result follows from yours," responds Professor X calmly. "I am also confident that your result does not follow from mine."

Explain in terms of logic why the reply of Professor X is damning, and why, if Professor X is correct, then the claim by Professor Y carries no information.

Exercise 1.7.10 Let a and b be real numbers. Then $z = a + bi$, where $i^2 = -1$, is called a **complex number**.[15] A complex number $z = a + bi$ is also a real number if and only if $b = 0$. The **conjugate** of a complex number $z = a + bi$, written $\overline{z}$, is defined by

$$\overline{z} = a - bi.$$

Prove that, for any complex number z, if $z = \overline{z}$, then z is real.

Exercise 1.7.11 Prove that for all real numbers a and b,

$$\big||a| - |b|\big| \leq |a - b|.$$

[Hint: Use Theorem 1.5.3 and Exercise 1.5.4.]

Exercise 1.7.12 Recall that we can express the definition of the unique existential quantifier $\exists!$ by

$$(\exists! x)[P(x)] \iff (\exists x)\big[P(x) \wedge (\forall y)\,[P(y) \Rightarrow x = y]\big].$$

Write an expression that is logically equivalent to $\neg\big((\exists! x)[P(x)]\big)$. Follow the rule that the negation symbol $\neg$ never immediately precedes a parenthesis or bracket.

Exercise 1.7.13 As in Exercise 1.6.13, let $J(p, \ell)$ mean that line ℓ passes through point p, and let $P(\ell, \ell')$ mean that lines ℓ and ℓ' are parallel. Use logical symbols and this notation to express the following.
(a) Every point lies on (at least) two lines.
(b) Every two distinct points lie on a unique line.
(c) For every line and every point not on the given line, there exists a line through that point that is parallel to the given line.[16]
(d) For every line and every point not on the given line, there exists a unique line through that point that is parallel to the given line.[17]
(e) For every line and every point not on the given line, there exists no line through that point that is parallel to the given line.[18]
(f) Distinct lines have at most one point in common.
(g) If a line is parallel to two distinct lines, then those lines are parallel to each other. (Assume that statement (a) of Exercise 1.6.13 holds.)

---

[15] More about complex numbers will be presented in Section 8.4.
[16] This is known as the *Hyperbolic Parallel Postulate*.
[17] This is known as *Euclid's Parallel Postulate*.
[18] This is known as the *Elliptical Parallel Postulate*.

Exercise 1.7.14   Let $E(a)$ mean that a is an even integer, $R(a,b)$ mean that a and b are relatively prime integers, and $D(a,b)$ mean that the integer a divides the integer b. Use this notation and logical symbols to express the following. (Note that not all of these statements are true. And you don't even need to know what any of these terms mean.)
(a) Any two distinct even integers are not relatively prime.
(b) Any two distinct integers that are not even are relatively prime.
(c) An integer is even if and only if it is not relatively prime with 2.
(d) For integers a,b,c, if a divides b and b divides c, then a divides c.
(e) Whenever an integer divides the product of two integers, then it divides one of the factors.
(f) For integers a,b,c, if a and b are relatively prime and a divides bc, then a divides c.
(g) Every integer z with the property that z and 2 are relatively prime has the property that 8 divides $z^2 - 1$.

Exercise 1.7.15   For positive integers n and k, let $L(n,k)$ mean that n can be written as the sum of exactly k squares. For example, since $17 = 4^2 + 1^2 = 3^2 + 2^2 + 2^2$, both $L(17,2)$ and $L(17,3)$ are true. We also continue the notation from Exercise 1.7.14. Use this notation and logical symbols to express the following. (Some of the statements are not true.)
(a) There are natural numbers that can be written as the sum of three squares.
(b) Every natural number can be written as the sum of four squares.
(c) There is a natural number that can be written as the sum of any number of squares.
(d) For a prime number p, if 4 divides $p - 1$, then p can be written as the sum of two squares.
(e) For every natural number k, there is a natural number that can be written as the sum of k squares.
(f) If two integers are relatively prime and each can be written as the sum of two squares, then their product can be written as the sum of four squares.

Exercise 1.7.16   For each of the parts of Exercises 1.7.14 and 1.7.15, write the negation of your expression with symbols. Follow the rule that the negation symbol $\neg$ never immediately precedes a parenthesis or bracket.

Exercise 1.7.17 Sometimes, but not always, quantifiers distribute over logical operations. Determine which of the following pairs of statements are equivalent. In the case of nonequivalent pairs, give an example of propositional functions $P(x)$ and $Q(x)$ for which the paired statements are not equivalent.

(a) $(\forall x)[P(x) \wedge Q(x)]$ and $(\forall x)[P(x)] \wedge (\forall x)[Q(x)]$.
(b) $(\exists x)[P(x) \wedge Q(x)]$ and $(\exists x)[P(x)] \wedge (\exists x)[Q(x)]$.
(c) $(\forall x)[P(x) \vee Q(x)]$ and $(\forall x)[P(x)] \vee (\forall x)[Q(x)]$.
(d) $(\exists x)[P(x) \vee Q(x)]$ and $(\exists x)[P(x)] \vee (\exists x)[Q(x)]$.
(e) $(\forall x)[P(x) \Rightarrow Q(x)]$ and $(\forall x)[P(x)] \Rightarrow (\forall x)[Q(x)]$.
(f) $(\forall x)[P(x) \Leftrightarrow Q(x)]$ and $(\forall x)[P(x)] \Leftrightarrow (\forall x)[Q(x)]$.

Exercise 1.7.18 For each of the following statements, define appropriate propositional functions and variables, then write the expression with logical symbols and the propositional functions you defined. Write the negation of each expression with symbols *and* as an English sentence.

(a) Every cloud has a silver lining.
(b) Nobody doesn't like Sara Lee.
(c) Everybody loves Raymond.
(d) There's no friend like an old friend.

Exercise 1.7.19 Consider the following sentence:

Every Monday, I drink coffee or tea.

For each of the following sentences, say whether it is
1. equivalent to the given sentence,
2. equivalent to the negation of the given sentence, or
3. neither of the above.

(a) Every Monday I drink neither coffee nor tea.
(b) Every Monday, if I don't drink coffee, then I drink tea.
(c) Some Mondays I drink neither coffee nor tea.
(d) If I drink neither coffee nor tea, then it isn't Monday.
(e) A sufficient condition for me to drink coffee or tea is that it be Monday.
(f) If it isn't Monday, then I drink neither coffee nor tea.

Exercise 1.7.20 Consider the saying "All that glitters is not gold." What about, "Not all that glitters is gold?" Which is the true statement? Are the two statements negations of each other? Write the negation of each statement.

Exercise 1.7.21 (a) The first line of a Dean Martin standard goes, "Everybody loves somebody sometime." Let $L(x, y, t)$ mean "Person x loves person y at time t," and express this romantic line in formal logic with quantifiers. Discuss how the meaning of this line is changed (sometimes humorously) if the order of the quantifiers is changed.
(b) A line from the song "Heartache Tonight" by the Eagles goes, "Somebody's gonna hurt someone before the night is through." Let $H(x, y, t)$ mean "Person x is gonna hurt person y at time t." Use appropriate quantifiers and this propositional function to express this line in symbols.

Chapter 2

Numbers

NUMBER THEORY studies the arithmetic of the integers. You've been familiar with many of these properties since you were a young child. For example, Proposition 1.0.1 states a fact from number theory. While this book is not a text for a course in number theory, this very fundamental and useful material provides a bounty of practice for proof writing. We begin with some basic concepts and notation about sets to better express notions about numbers.

2.1   Basic Ideas of Sets

A **set** is *any* collection of *any* kind of objects. For mathematicians, these collections are usually of numbers, other mathematical objects, or even collections of other sets. The usual notation is to label a set with an uppercase letter from the Latin alphabet and to list the contents of the set in some clear way within braces like this:

$$B = \{2, 4, 6, 8, 10\},$$

or

$$X = \{\text{all functions whose derivative is } e^{3x} - x^2\}.$$

In a set, the order of the objects is not relevant, and it is not important whether an object in a set is listed more than once. So the set B above could be written as

$$B = \{8, 6, 6, 2, 4, 6, 10, 8, 4\}.$$

The objects in a set are the **elements** of the set. For example, 2 is an element of B, and $\frac{1}{3}e^{3x} - \frac{x^3}{3} + 13$ is an element of X. The symbol $\in$ is used in place of the words "is an element of," as in

$$2 \in B \qquad \text{and} \qquad \frac{1}{3}e^{3x} - \frac{x^3}{3} + 13 \in X.$$

The symbol $\notin$ is used to indicate that an object is not an element of a set. For example,

$$17 \notin B \qquad \text{and} \qquad e^{3x} - x^2 + 13 \notin X.$$

Thus $17 \notin B$ is shorthand for the statement $\neg[17 \in B]$.

Logical problems can arise if absolutely *anything* is permitted to be collected into a set. In particular, a set is not allowed to be an element of itself.[1]

Often, it is not practical or even possible to list all of the elements of a set. Certainly one cannot list *all* of the elements in the set X above, but it is clear what the elements of X are. More precisely, it is clear what a function must look like in order to be an element of X. We wrote out in English the membership requirements for X, but there is a symbolic way to write what we mean that is not specific to any spoken language. Here is the way any mathematician can write the set X:

$$X = \{f : f'(x) = e^{3x} - x^2\}.$$

This time the set X has been given in **set-builder notation**. The way to read this notation (since we know from the context that f denotes a function) is,

   X is the set of functions f such that f prime of x equals $e^{3x} - x^2$.

---

[1]Bertrand Russell (1872–1970) was a British philosopher and logician who stated what became known as Russell's Paradox: Let B be the set of all sets that are not elements of themselves. Is B an element of itself?

The colon used in set-builder notation is spoken and read as "such that." Equivalently, since we know from calculus what these functions are, we also may write

$$X = \left\{ \frac{1}{3}e^{3x} - \frac{1}{3}x^3 + C : C \text{ is a real number} \right\}.$$

We might write the set $D = \{1, 2, 3, 4, 6, 8, 12, 24\}$ as

$$D = \{k : k \text{ is a positive divisor of } 24\}$$

or as

$$D = \left\{ k : \text{Both } k \text{ and } \frac{24}{k} \text{ are positive integers} \right\}.$$

Mathematicians often agree on shorthand notation for frequently used expressions. For example, instead of writing $(a \in X) \wedge (b \in X)$, we may write $a, b \in X$. However, $a \wedge b \in X$ is meaningless, because the logical connective $\wedge$ may be placed *only* between two statements and never between two elements or between an element and a statement. There is no analogous shorthand convention for $(a \in X) \vee (b \in X)$.

2.2 Sets of Numbers

We all develop a sense of numbers at an early age. We collect the "counting numbers," or **natural numbers**, into a set denoted by $\mathbb{N}$:

$$\mathbb{N} = \{1, 2, 3, 4, 5, 6, 7, \ldots\}.$$

Thus the set $D = \{1, 2, 3, 4, 6, 8, 12, 24\}$ may also be written as

$$D = \left\{ k : k \in \mathbb{N} \wedge \frac{24}{k} \in \mathbb{N} \right\}.$$

There are other important sets of numbers. For example, the set of positive even numbers is

$$\mathbb{E} = \{2, 4, 6, 8, 10, 12, 14, \ldots\},$$

or, in set-builder notation,

$$\mathbb{E} = \big\{ n \in \mathbb{N} : (\exists k \in \mathbb{N})[n = 2k] \big\}.$$

Exercise 2.2.1   List some elements in each of the following sets.
(a) $\big\{ x \in \mathbb{N} : (\exists k \in \mathbb{N})[x = 7k] \big\}$
(b) $\big\{ n \in \mathbb{N} : n^2 + n - 12 = 0 \big\}$
(c) $\big\{ y \in \mathbb{N} : (\exists \ell \in \mathbb{N})[y = \ell^2] \big\}$
(d) $\big\{ s \in \mathbb{N} : \sqrt[3]{s} \in \mathbb{N} \big\}$
(e) $\big\{ t \in \mathbb{N} : (\exists q \in \mathbb{N})[t = 4q + 1] \big\}$

Here is the standard notation for some other sets of numbers. The set of **integers** is denoted by

$$\mathbb{Z} = \big\{ \ldots, -3, -2, -1, 0, 1, 2, 3, \ldots \big\}.$$

The ellipsis (three dots) suggests what the other elements in the set are. We could have equally well written $\mathbb{Z} = \{ \ldots, -4, -3, -2, -1, 0, 1, 2, 3, 4, \ldots \}$ or $\mathbb{Z} = \{ \ldots, -2, -1, 0, 1, 2, 3, \ldots \}$. Generally, just enough elements are included so that an intelligent reader (like you) can make a very good guess as to what the unwritten elements ought to be.

The set $\mathbb{Q}$ of **rational numbers**[2] is

$$\mathbb{Q} = \Big\{ \frac{a}{b} : a, b \in \mathbb{Z} \text{ and } b \neq 0 \Big\}.$$

Note that every integer z is also a rational number, since z can be expressed as $\dfrac{z}{1}$.

The set $\mathbb{R}$ of **real numbers** corresponds to the collection of all points on the number line. In terms of the real numbers, the set of **complex numbers** (see Exercise 1.7.10) is

$$\mathbb{C} = \big\{ a + bi : a, b \in \mathbb{R} \big\}, \quad \text{where } i^2 = -1.$$

---

[2]The letter $\mathbb{Q}$ stands for *quotient*. The letter $\mathbb{Z}$ comes from the German word *Zahl*, meaning *number*.

The symbols $\mathbb{N}, \mathbb{Z}, \mathbb{Q}, \mathbb{R}$, and $\mathbb{C}$ have the meanings just described in any mathematical writing in every human language.[3] Mathematics is indeed an international language.

If $\mathbb{S}$ is any of the sets $\mathbb{Z}, \mathbb{Q}$, or $\mathbb{R}$, then we define

$$\mathbb{S}^+ = \{x \in \mathbb{S} : x > 0\} \quad \text{and} \quad \mathbb{S}^- = \{x \in \mathbb{S} : x < 0\}.$$

For example, $\mathbb{R}^+$ is another notation for the positive ray $(0, \infty)$ on the number line. Since $\mathbb{Z}^+$ is also denoted by $\mathbb{N}$, we prefer to use the symbol $\mathbb{N}$ when needed.

Note the different uses of the set-builder notation. The set

$$\mathbb{E} = \{n \in \mathbb{N} : (\exists k \in \mathbb{N})[n = 2k]\}$$

is described by using the initial statement "$n \in \mathbb{N}$" as first screening: "Those natural numbers that meet the following membership criterion." We need consider only natural numbers for candidates. Whereas the set

$$\mathbb{Q} = \left\{\frac{a}{b} : a, b \in \mathbb{Z} \text{ and } b \neq 0\right\}$$

is described first by giving the structure of the elements and then the restrictions within the structure.

Exercise 2.2.2   List some elements in each of the following sets.

(a) $\left\{\begin{bmatrix} a & b \\ c & d \end{bmatrix} : a, b, c, d \in \mathbb{Z} \wedge ad - bc = 1\right\}$

(b) $\left\{2^{r+1} - 1 : r \in \mathbb{E}\right\}$

(c) $\left\{3x + 2y : x, y \in \mathbb{Z}\right\}$ [Is 1 an element of this set?]

Exercise 2.2.3   Use symbols and set-builder notation (use no words in your answers) to denote each of the following sets.

(a) $\{1, 8, 27, 64, 125, \ldots\}$

(b) $\{0, \pm 1, \pm 8, \pm 27, \pm 64, \pm 125, \ldots\}$

---

[3]There is one exception to the universality of these symbols. Sometimes $\mathbb{N}$ is defined to include 0; that is *not* the convention of this book.

(c) The set of all functions whose graph passes through the point $(3, 0)$ [Use $\mathcal{F}$ to denote the set of functions.]

(d) The set of all functions f whose graphs have a horizontal tangent line at the point $\big(3, f(3)\big)$

(e) The set of all natural numbers that are either a divisor of 100 or a multiple of 100

(f) $\left\{\ldots, \frac{1}{8}, \frac{1}{4}, \frac{1}{2}, 1, 2, 4, 8, 16, \ldots\right\}$

(g) $\{\pm 5, \pm 15, \pm 25, \pm 35, \ldots\}$

(h) $\{1, 3, 6, 10, 15, 21, 28, \ldots\}$

2.3   Some Properties of $\mathbb{N}$ and $\mathbb{Z}$

We begin with some basic properties of the integers.

Definition 2.3.1 *Let $n \in \mathbb{Z}$. Then n is **even** whenever there exists some $k \in \mathbb{Z}$ such that $n = 2k$, and n is **odd** whenever there exists some $k \in \mathbb{Z}$ such that $n = 2k + 1$.*

Proposition 2.3.2 *Let $n \in \mathbb{Z}$. If n is even, then n^2 is even.*

Proof. Let n be even. By Definition 2.3.1, there exists $k \in \mathbb{Z}$ such that $n = 2k$. Then
$$n^2 = (2k)^2 = 4k^2 = 2(2k^2).$$

By Definition 2.3.1, since $2k^2 \in \mathbb{Z}$, n^2 is even. [Elementary proofs often are no more complicated than this: translate the hypothesis with a definition, then perform some mathematically correct manipulation, and, finally, translate again with a definition to obtain the conclusion.] $\square$

The set of even numbers also has what is called a *closure property* with respect to addition, as we now show.

Proposition 2.3.3 *Let $m, n \in \mathbb{Z}$. If both m and n are even, then so is $m + n$.*

Proof. Suppose that m and n are even integers. By Definition 2.3.1, there exist integers k and ℓ such that $m = 2k$ and $n = 2\ell$. [Do you see why it is essential to introduce not one but two new variables, k and ℓ?] Then

$$m + n = 2k + 2\ell = 2(k + \ell),$$

and $k + \ell \in \mathbb{Z}$. It follows that $m + n$ is even. $\square$

Exercise 2.3.4 Let $n, m \in \mathbb{Z}$. Prove the following.
(a) If both m and n are even, then so is mn.
(b) If n is odd and m is even, then $m + n$ is odd and mn is even.
(c) If both m and n are odd, then $m + n$ is even and mn is odd.

The next definition is a fundamental idea in the multiplicative theory of $\mathbb{Z}$.

Definition 2.3.5 *Let* $a, b \in \mathbb{Z}$ *with* $a \neq 0$. *Then* a **divides** b, *written* $a \mid b$, *when there exists an integer* k *such that* $b = ak$. *Equivalently, we may say that* b *is* **divisible by** a, *or that* b *is a* **multiple** *of* a, *or that* a *is a* **divisor** *of* b. *If* $a \mid b$ *and* $1 < a < |b|$, *then* a *is a* **proper divisor** *of* b. *We write* $a \nmid b$ *when* a *does not divide* b.

For example, since $72 = 9 \cdot 8$, we have that $8 \mid 72$ and $9 \mid 72$. The equation $9k = 37$ does not have an integral solution, so $9 \nmid 37$.

Remark on notation. Do not confuse "divides," written $\mid$, with "divided by," written $/$. The *statement* $a \mid b$ is either true or false; it is *not* a number. The *number* a/b, also written as $\dfrac{a}{b}$, is the number that is the solution to the equation $bx = a$.

Given integers a and b, any number of the form $ax + by$, where x and y are also integers, is a **linear combination of** a **and** b. For example, 7 is a linear combination of 5 and 6, because we can write $7 = 5 \cdot 5 + 6 \cdot (-3)$. We can also write $7 = 5 \cdot (-1) + 6 \cdot 2$. However, 7 is not a linear combination of 4 and 6. [Why not? What do the previous results and exercises say about sums and products of even numbers?]

Theorem 2.3.6 *The following statements hold for all $a, b, c, d \in \mathbb{Z}$.*
(i) $a \mid 0$, $1 \mid a$, and $a \mid a$.
(ii) $a \mid 1$ if and only if $a = \pm 1$.
(iii) If $a \mid b$ and $c \mid d$, then $ac \mid bd$.
(iv) If $a \mid b$ and $b \mid c$, then $a \mid c$.
(v) If $a \mid b$ and $a, b > 0$, then $a \leq b$.
(vi) If $a \mid b$ and $a \mid c$, then a divides every linear combination of b and c.

Proof. We prove parts (i), (v), and (vi). The rest are left as Exercise 2.3.7.

Note that
$$a \cdot 0 = 0, \quad 1 \cdot a = a, \quad \text{and} \quad a \cdot 1 = a.$$
This proves part (i).

For part (v), we have the additional hypothesis $a, b > 0$, so we assume that there exists some $\ell \in \mathbb{N}$ such that $a\ell = b$. Since $\ell \geq 1$, we conclude that $a \leq a\ell = b$.

To prove part (vi), assume that there exist integers k and ℓ such that $ak = b$ and $a\ell = c$. Then for arbitrary $x, y \in \mathbb{Z}$, we have

$$\begin{aligned} bx + cy &= (ak)x + (a\ell)y \\ &= a(kx + \ell y). \end{aligned}$$

Since $kx + \ell y \in \mathbb{Z}$, we see that $a \mid bx + cy$. $\square$

Exercise 2.3.7   Write proofs for parts (ii), (iii), and (iv) of Theorem 2.3.6.

Exercise 2.3.8   Prove the following corollary to Theorem 2.3.6:   *Let $a, b \in \mathbb{N}$. If $a \mid b$ and $b \mid a$, then $a = b$.*

There is an intuitively reasonable assumption called the Well Ordering Principle needed for the next proof. It will be presented in more generality in Section 5.2. It is an intrinsic axiom of the natural numbers, and we accept it without proof.

The Well Ordering Principle. *Any set of natural numbers with at least one element has a smallest element.*

The next theorem is the mathematical formulation of a familiar fact about division with remainder. The choice of symbols q and r in the statement of the theorem suggests the words *quotient* and *remainder*, respectively.

Theorem 2.3.9 (Division Algorithm) *If $a \in \mathbb{Z}$ and $b \in \mathbb{N}$, then there exist $q, r \in \mathbb{Z}$ such that $a = qb + r$ and $0 \le r < b$. Furthermore, this representation of a is unique.*

Proof. Let $a \in \mathbb{Z}$ and $b \in \mathbb{N}$ be given, and let

$$S = \{a + xb : x \in \mathbb{Z} \ \wedge \ a + xb \ge 0\}.$$

Note that there is an element in S. (If $a \ge 0$, pick $x = 0$, and so $a \in S$; if $a < 0$, pick $x = -a$, and so $a - ab = a(1 - b) \ge 0$.) Thus, by the Well Ordering Principle, S has a least element, which we denote by r. Since $r \in S$, $r = a - qb$ for some $q \in \mathbb{Z}$. By definition, $r \ge 0$.

Suppose that $r \ge b$. [In order to deduce that $r < b$, we assume that $r \ge b$ and derive a contradiction.] Then

$$a - (q + 1)b = a - qb - b$$
$$= r - b$$
$$\ge 0,$$

and $a - (q + 1)b = r - b < r$, since $b > 0$. This gives an element of S that is strictly less than r, contradicting the minimality of r. [This is the contradiction: r is the least element of S, and there is an element of S less than r.] Thus $r < b$. This yields the representation $a = qb + r$ with $0 \le r < b$.

To show that the representation is unique, suppose that we have two such representations for a,

$$a = qb + r \quad \text{and} \quad a = q_1 b + r_1.$$

Then

$$b(q - q_1) = r_1 - r.$$

We take the absolute value of each side and note that $b > 0$ to see that

$$b\,|q - q_1| \;=\; |r_1 - r|. \tag{2.3.1}$$

By hypothesis, $0 \le r < b$ and $0 \le r_1 < b$. We rewrite the first inequality as $-b < -r \le 0$ and then add the second to it to obtain

$$-b < r_1 - r < b,$$

which is equivalent to

$$|r_1 - r| < b.$$

This, together with equation (2.3.1), implies that $b\,|q - q_1| < b$. Since $b > 0$, we have $0 \le |q - q_1| < 1$. But $q - q_1 \in \mathbb{Z}$, and so $q - q_1 = 0$. Therefore $q = q_1$. It follows immediately that $r = r_1$. Thus the representation is unique. $\square$

Example 2.3.10   Let $a = 39$ and $b = 7$. Then we can write $39 = 5 \cdot 7 + 4$. (A fourth grader would respond to "$39 \div 7$" by saying, "5 remainder 4.") Similarly $-39 = (-6) \cdot 7 + 3$.

Exercise 2.3.11   Apply the Division Algorithm to $a = 213$ and $b = 19$. Do this also for $a = -213$ and $b = 19$.

Proposition 2.3.12   *Let $n \in \mathbb{Z}$. Then n is either even or odd, but not both.*

Proof. Apply the Division Algorithm to n and 2. Then either for some $q \in \mathbb{Z}$ it holds that $n = 2q + 0 = 2q$ or for some $q' \in \mathbb{Z}$ it holds that $n = 2q' + 1$. In the first case, n is even, and in the second case, n is odd. If n is both even and odd, then by the uniqueness of the representation, $2q = 2q' + 1$. But then $1 = 2(q - q')$, implying that $2 \mid 1$. By Theorem 2.3.6(v), $2 \le 1$, clearly a contradiction. Hence no integer is both even and odd. $\square$

Exercise 2.3.13   Prove that an integer is odd if and only if its square is odd.

Exercise 2.3.14   Prove that any odd number is either of the form $4k + 1$ or of the form $4k + 3$, and every even number is of the form $4k$ or $4k + 2$, where $k \in \mathbb{Z}$.

Exercise 2.3.15 (a) Use the Division Algorithm to prove that the 1's digit of a perfect square is never $2, 3, 7,$ or 8. (Recall that an integer s is a **perfect square** if there exists $k \in \mathbb{N}$ such that $s = k^2$.)
(b) Prove that when a perfect square is divided by 9, the remainder is never $2, 3, 5, 6,$ or 8.
(c) What are the possible remainders when a perfect square is divided by 11?

2.4 Prime Numbers

Natural numbers p whose only divisors are 1 and p have long been of particular interest.

Definition 2.4.1 *The number $p \in \mathbb{N}$ is **prime** if p has no proper divisor. An equivalent, symbolic formulation is that p is prime if the following statement is true:*

$$p > 1 \wedge (\forall n \in \mathbb{N})\big[n \mid p \Rightarrow (n = 1) \vee (n = p)\big].$$

*An integer at least 2 that is not prime is **composite**. (The integer 1 is neither prime nor composite.) A **prime factorization** of any integer n is a representation of n as a product $n = (\pm 1)p_1 \, p_1 \, \cdots \, p_k$ whose factors are prime numbers, not necessarily distinct.*

The significance of the prime numbers as the basic structural components of the natural numbers is expressed in the following theorem. The proof of this result must wait until Chapter 5, where it appears as Theorem 5.3.3.

The Fundamental Theorem of Arithmetic. *Every integer greater than 1 has a prime factorization that is unique up to the order in which the factors occur.*

The surprising part of the Fundamental Theorem of Arithmetic is not that a prime factorization of every natural number *exists* but rather that the factorization is *unique*. There are important algebraic structures that have prime elements but do not have unique factorization into prime elements. See Exercises 2.4.4 and 2.7.18.

More than 2000 years ago, Euclid[4] proved that there are infinitely many prime numbers. His proof still remains a model of mathematical elegance. We present Euclid's proof, which is an excellent example of a proof by contradiction.

Theorem 2.4.2   *There are infinitely many prime numbers.*

Proof. Suppose that there are only finitely many, say k, prime numbers, and here is the complete list:

$$2, 3, 5, 7, \ldots, p_{k-1}, p_k.$$

Let $q = (2 \cdot 3 \cdot 5 \cdot \ldots \cdot p_k) + 1$. Since q is greater than each of the numbers on this list, q cannot be prime. By the Fundamental Theorem of Arithmetic, q must then be a product of prime numbers. Therefore, there is a prime number p_i on the list such that $p_i \mid q$. By Definition 2.3.5, $p_i \mid 2 \cdot 3 \cdot 5 \cdot \ldots \cdot p_k$ since p_i is itself one of these prime numbers. Then by Theorem 2.3.6(vi), $p_i \mid q - (2 \cdot 3 \cdot 5 \cdot \ldots \cdot p_k)$. But $q - (2 \cdot 3 \cdot 5 \cdot \ldots \cdot p_k) = 1$, and the claim that $p_i \mid 1$ contradicts Theorem 2.3.6(v) since $p_i > 1$. Thus the assumption that there are finitely many prime numbers is false. $\square$

Although there are infinitely many prime numbers, there are arbitrarily large gaps between consecutive prime numbers (recall Theorem 1.1.5).

Pairs of prime numbers that differ by 2 are called **twin primes**. Examples of such pairs are (3,5), (5,7), (11,13), (101,103), and many, many more. Just how many more is another matter. Although the set of all prime numbers was easily shown to be infinite, it is still unknown as of this writing whether there exist infinitely many twin primes. Another famous unresolved question[5] in number theory is stated in the next exercise.

---

[4]Little is known about Euclid's life. Most scholars agree that Euclid was Greek and lived in Alexandria, Egypt, around 300 BCE. He is credited with writing *The Elements*, a collection of books on geometry and number theory that includes the proof on the infinitude of the prime numbers.

[5]If you resolve either of these two problems and are under the age of 40, you would receive serious consideration for the Fields Medal. The Fields Medal is regarded as the highest professional honor that a mathematician can receive. It is generally viewed as the equivalent to the Nobel Prize for mathematicians (there is no Nobel Prize for Mathematics). There is no age limit for the Cole Prize, number theory's most prestigious award.

Exercise 2.4.3 It has been conjectured that there are infinitely many prime numbers of the form $n^2 + 1$ for $n \in \mathbb{N}$.

(a) Find at least six such prime numbers.

(b) Prove that if $n^2 + 1$ is a prime number greater than 5, then the digit in the 1's place of n is 0, 4, or 6. [Hint: Try to use Exercise 2.3.15(a).]

(c) Why might you suspect that the converse of the statement in part (b) is false?

Exercise 2.4.4 A rational number of the form $\dfrac{a}{2^n}$, where $a \in \mathbb{Z}$ and $n \in \mathbb{N}$, is called a **diadic rational**. Let D be the set of all diadic rational numbers.

(a) Prove that if $r, s \in D$, then $rs \in D$.

(b) A **diadic prime** is an element of D of the form $\dfrac{p}{2^n}$ where p is prime. Show that there are elements of D that do not have a unique prime factorization into diadic primes.

2.5 gcds and lcms

The twin notions of the greatest common divisor and the least common multiple of a pair of integers are known to most people since elementary school. Indeed, we use these notions to reduce a fraction to lowest terms or to add two fractions with different denominators. However, these notions have some interesting properties of their own.

Definition 2.5.1 *Let $a, b \in \mathbb{Z}$ with a and b not both 0. Then $c \in \mathbb{N}$ is a* **common divisor** *of a and b whenever $c \mid a$ and $c \mid b$.*

Example 2.5.2 The positive divisors of 24 are 1, 2, 3, 4, 6, 8, 12, and 24. The positive divisors of 84 are 1, 2, 3, 4, 6, 7, 12, 14, 21, 28, 42, and 84. The common divisors of 24 and 84 are

$$1, 2, 3, 4, 6, \text{ and } 12;$$

of these, 12 is clearly the greatest.

Definition 2.5.3 *Let $a, b \in \mathbb{Z}$ with a and b not both 0. Let $C(a, b)$ be the set of common divisors of a and b; that is,*

$$C(a, b) = \{c \in \mathbb{N} : c \mid a \ \wedge \ c \mid b\}.$$

The **greatest common divisor of** a **and** b, *denoted* $\gcd(a,b)$, *is the largest element of* $C(a,b)$. *We denote this element by* $\gcd(a,b)$. *Thus,*

$$\big(\forall c \in C(a,b)\big)[c \le \gcd(a,b)].$$

By Theorem 2.3.6(i), the number 1 is always a common divisor of a and b and thus is always an element of $C(a,b)$. So, for all $a,b \in \mathbb{Z}$, $\gcd(a,b) \ge 1$. When $\gcd(a,b) = 1$, we say that a and b are **relatively prime**.

You are no doubt familiar with finding $\gcd(a,b)$ by comparing the prime factorizations of a and b. We present a different approach that develops the properties of $\gcd(a,b)$ without requiring any factorization of any integers.

Proposition 2.5.4 *Suppose* $a \mid b$ *with* $a > 0$. *Then* $\gcd(a,b) = a$.

Proof. By the hypothesis and Theorem 2.3.6(i), a is a common divisor of a and b. Let $c \in \mathbb{N}$ be a common divisor of a and b. Since $c \mid a$, by Theorem 2.3.6(v), $c \le a$. Since c is an arbitrary common divisor of a and b, $\gcd(a,b) = a$. $\qquad\square$

The next theorem is the foundation of our study of the greatest common divisor.

Theorem 2.5.5 *Let* $a,b \in \mathbb{Z}$ *with* a,b *not both* 0. *Then* $\gcd(a,b)$ *is the least positive linear combination of* a *and* b.

Proof. Let S denote the set of all positive linear combinations of a and b. Because not both a and b are 0, we have $a^2 + b^2 > 0$, and so $a^2 + b^2 \in S$. [Why?] That means that S has an element. By the Well Ordering Principle, S has a least element ℓ, and so $\ell = ax_0 + by_0$ for some $x_0, y_0 \in \mathbb{Z}$.

For brevity, let $d = \gcd(a,b)$. We must show that $d = \ell$. [Our strategy is to prove first that $d \le \ell$ and then that $\ell \le d$.]

By definition of gcd, $d \mid a$ and $d \mid b$. By Theorem 2.3.6(vi), d divides every linear combination of a and b. In particular, $d \mid \ell$. By Theorem 2.3.6(v), $d \le \ell$.

By the Division Algorithm (Theorem 2.3.9) applied to a and ℓ, there exist $q, r \in \mathbb{Z}$ with $0 \le r < \ell$ such that $a = q\ell + r$. Thus

$$r = a - q\ell$$
$$= a - q(ax_0 + by_0)$$
$$= a(1 - qx_0) + b(-qy_0),$$

which shows that r is a linear combination of a and b. However, r cannot belong to S, because $r < \ell$ and ℓ is by definition the least element of S. It follows that r is not positive, and so $r = 0$. Therefore $a = q\ell$ and so $\ell \mid a$.

We can repeat this very same argument, applying the Division Algorithm instead to b and ℓ, to conclude that $\ell \mid b$. Thus ℓ is a common divisor of a and b. Since $d = \gcd(a, b)$, it follows that $\ell \le d$. Since $d \le \ell$ and $\ell \le d$, it follows that $d = \ell$. $\qquad\square$

Example 2.5.6 Elementary arithmetic yields that $\gcd(32, 20) = 4$. We can write

$$4 = 32 \cdot 2 + 20 \cdot (-3).$$

This linear combination is not unique since

$$4 = 32 \cdot 2 + 20 \cdot (-3)$$
$$= 32 \cdot 2 - 32 \cdot 20 + 32 \cdot 20 + 20 \cdot (-3)$$
$$= 32 \cdot (-18) + 20 \cdot 29.$$

The greatest common divisor $d = \gcd(a, b)$ of a and b is both a "least" and a "greatest." By definition, d is the greatest integer that divides both a and b. At the same time, by Theorem 2.5.5, d is the least positive linear combination of a and b. Because 1 *is* the least positive integer, when we find a linear combination $ax + by = 1$, we can immediately conclude that a and b are relatively prime.

Example 2.5.7 We prove that any two consecutive integers are relatively prime. Let $n \in \mathbb{Z}$. Then $n \cdot (-1) + (n + 1) \cdot (1)$ is a linear combination of n and $n + 1$ that equals 1. By Theorem 2.5.5, $\gcd(n, n + 1) = 1$.

An important corollary to Theorem 2.5.5 is the following.

Corollary 2.5.8   *Let $a, b \in \mathbb{Z}$ with a and b not both 0. Then the numbers*

$$\frac{a}{\gcd(a, b)} \quad and \quad \frac{b}{\gcd(a, b)}$$

are relatively prime.

Proof. Let $d = \gcd(a, b)$. By Theorem 2.5.5, for some $x, y \in \mathbb{Z}$, we have

$$d = ax + by,$$

and so

$$1 = \frac{a}{d}x + \frac{b}{d}y.$$

Because d is a common divisor of a and b, both $\frac{a}{d}$ and $\frac{b}{d}$ are integers. Thus, by Theorem 2.5.5,

$$\gcd\left(\frac{a}{d}, \frac{b}{d}\right) = 1.$$

$\square$

Notice how, in the proofs of these results, we proceed by expressing the greatest common divisor as a linear combination and then manipulating that linear combination.

Exercise 2.5.9   Prove the following.
(a) For all $n \in \mathbb{N}$, $\gcd(2n + 1, 9n + 4) = 1$.
(b) For all $n \in \mathbb{N}$, $\gcd(5n + 8, 3n + 5) = 1$.

Exercise 2.5.10   Prove that $\gcd(a, m) = 1$ and $\gcd(b, m) = 1$ if and only if $\gcd(ab, m) = 1$.

Exercise 2.5.11   (a) Prove **Euclid's Lemma:** *If $a \mid bc$ and $\gcd(a, b) = 1$, then $a \mid c$.*
(b) Show that the converse of Euclid's lemma is false by giving some examples of integers a, b, c such that $a \nmid b$ and $a \nmid c$, but still $a \mid bc$. In your examples, must $\gcd(a, b) > 1$ hold?

Definition 2.5.12 *Let a, b be nonzero integers. Then $m \in \mathbb{N}$ is a* **common multiple** *of a and b if $a \mid m$ and $b \mid m$.*

Example 2.5.13 The first few multiples of 12 are 12, 24, 36, 48, 60, 72, and 84. Some small multiples of 8 are 8, 16, 24, 32, 40, 48, and 56. The common multiples of 8 and 12 include 24 and 48; of course there are infinitely many more, but note that 24 is the least of them.

Definition 2.5.14 *Let a, b be nonzero integers. Let $M(a, b)$ be the set of common multiples of a and b; that is,*

$$M(a, b) = \{m \in \mathbb{N} : a \mid m \ \wedge \ b \mid m\}.$$

The **least common multiple of a and b**, *denoted* $\mathrm{lcm}(a, b)$, *is the smallest element of $M(a, b)$. Thus*

$$\big(\forall m \in M(a, b)\big)[\mathrm{lcm}(a, b) \leq m].$$

Note that $M(a, b)$ must have at least one element—namely, ab. (Why?) Thus by the Well Ordering Principle, there is a smallest element of $M(a, b)$. Of course, ab is not necessarily the smallest element of $M(a, b)$.

Exercise 2.5.15 (a) Find $\mathrm{lcm}(35, 49)$.
(b) Find $\mathrm{lcm}(35, 90)$.
(c) Find $\mathrm{lcm}(35, 91)$.

Exercise 2.5.16 Prove that $\mathrm{lcm}(n, kn) = kn$, for $n, k \in \mathbb{N}$.

Lemma 2.5.17 *If $a, b \in \mathbb{N}$ and c is any common multiple of a and b, then $\mathrm{lcm}(a, b) \mid c$.*

Proof. Assume c is a common multiple of a and b but that $\mathrm{lcm}(a, b) \nmid c$. [We seek a contradiction.] By the Division Algorithm (Theorem 2.3.9), we have

$$c = q \cdot \mathrm{lcm}(a, b) + r,$$

where $q, r \in \mathbb{Z}$ with $0 < r < \mathrm{lcm}(a, b)$. Since each of a and b divides both c and $\mathrm{lcm}(a, b)$, each of a and b must divide $c - q \cdot \mathrm{lcm}(a, b) = r$. Thus r is a common multiple of a and b. But $r < \mathrm{lcm}(a, b)$, contrary to the definition of lcm. We conclude $\mathrm{lcm}(a, b) \mid c$. $\square$

There is a simple identity that relates the $\gcd(a, b)$ to $\text{lcm}(a, b)$.

Proposition 2.5.18   *For all $a, b \in \mathbb{N}$,*

$$ab = \text{lcm}(a, b) \cdot \gcd(a, b).$$

Proof. Let $\text{lcm}(a, b) = m$ and $\gcd(a, b) = d$. [We repeat our strategy of the proof of Theorem 2.5.5. First we show $md \le ab$, and then we show $ab \le md$.] By definition, $\frac{a}{d}, \frac{b}{d} \in \mathbb{N}$. Thus $\frac{ab}{d} = a \cdot \frac{b}{d} = \frac{a}{d} \cdot b$ is a common multiple of a and b. This means that $m \le \frac{ab}{d}$, and so $md \le ab$.

On the other hand, by Lemma 2.5.17, $m \mid ab$, so that $\frac{ab}{m} \in \mathbb{N}$. Then, since $m = ak$ and $m = b\ell$ for some $k, \ell \in \mathbb{N}$, we have $\frac{ab}{m} = \frac{ab}{b\ell} = \frac{a}{\ell} \in \mathbb{N}$. Similarly, $\frac{b}{k} \in \mathbb{N}$. Since $\frac{a}{\ell} \cdot \ell = a$, we have $\frac{a}{\ell} \mid a$; in other words, $\frac{ab}{m} \mid a$. A similar argument shows that $\frac{ab}{m} \mid b$. Thus $\frac{ab}{m}$ is a common divisor of a and b. Hence $\frac{ab}{m} \le d$, which implies $ab \le md$. $\square$

Exercise 2.5.19   (a) Determine a formula for the least common multiple of two consecutive integers.
(b) Determine a formula for the least common multiple of two integers whose difference is a prime number.

Exercise 2.5.20   (a) Prove that if $\gcd(a, b) = k$ and $\gcd(b, c) = k$, then $\gcd(a, c) \ge k$.
(b) Give examples of integers a, b, c such that $\gcd(a, b) = \gcd(b, c)$ and $\gcd(a, c) > \gcd(a, b)$.

2.6 Rational Numbers and Algebraic Numbers

In Section 2.2, we introduced the set $\mathbb{Q}$ of rational numbers. A rational number q is written **in lowest terms** when $q = \dfrac{a}{b}$ and a, b are integers such that $\gcd(|a|, |b|) = 1$. Since, by Corollary 2.5.8, the fraction $\dfrac{a/\gcd(|a|, |b|)}{b/\gcd(|a|, |b|)}$ is always in lowest terms, any rational number $\dfrac{a}{b}$ can be written in lowest terms.

We define the set $\mathbb{I}$ of **irrational numbers** by $\mathbb{I} = \{x \in \mathbb{R} : x \notin \mathbb{Q}\}$.

The next theorem shows that irrational numbers exist.[6]

Theorem 2.6.1 $\sqrt{2} \in \mathbb{I}$.

Proof. Suppose $\sqrt{2} \in \mathbb{Q}$. [We seek a contradiction.] By definition of $\mathbb{Q}$, $\sqrt{2} = \dfrac{a}{b}$ for some $a, b \in \mathbb{N}$ with $b \neq 0$. We may assume that $\gcd(a, b) = 1$, because if $\gcd(a, b) > 1$, then as just mentioned, both a and b are divisible by $\gcd(a, b)$, giving a fraction in lowest terms. Then we have $\sqrt{2}\, b = a$, and so $2b^2 = a^2$. Therefore a^2 is even, and so by Exercise 2.3.13 and Proposition 2.3.12, a is even. Then $a = 2k$ for some $k \in \mathbb{Z}$.

Substitution gives $2b^2 = (2k)^2$, and so $b^2 = 2k^2$. Then b^2 is even, and hence b is even. Since a and b are both even, $\gcd(a, b) \geq 2$. This contradicts our assumption that $\gcd(a, b) = 1$. Thus $\sqrt{2} \in \mathbb{I}$. $\qquad\square$

Not only is $\sqrt{2}$ irrational, but the square root of any natural number that is not a perfect square is irrational, too.

---

[6]The idea that irrational numbers exist was appalling to the followers of Pythagoras, the Greek mathematician for whom the famous theorem is named. The Pythagoreans believed that all numbers were rational. According to some legends, upon seeing a proof of the next theorem, some Pythagoreans threw the author of the proof off a boat to his demise.

Theorem 2.6.2   *Let $k \in \mathbb{N}$. If $\sqrt{k} \notin \mathbb{N}$, then $\sqrt{k} \in \mathbb{I}$.*

Proof. We prove the contrapositive. Assume that $\sqrt{k} \notin \mathbb{I}$. Then, as in the previous proof, since $\sqrt{k} > 0$, there exist $a, b \in \mathbb{N}$ with $b \neq 0$ such that $\sqrt{k} = \dfrac{a}{b}$ and $\gcd(a, b) = 1$. By Theorem 2.5.5, there exist $x, y \in \mathbb{Z}$ such that $ax + by = 1$, and so $\sqrt{k}\, ax + \sqrt{k}\, by = \sqrt{k}$.

By our assumption, $\sqrt{k}\, b = a$ and $\sqrt{k}\, a = kb$ (verify these facts). By substitution,

$$kbx + ay = \sqrt{k}.$$

Since $k, b, x, a, y \in \mathbb{Z}$, it follows that $\sqrt{k} \in \mathbb{Z}$. In fact, $\sqrt{k} \in \mathbb{N}$ since $\sqrt{k}$ is positive. $\square$

Exercise 2.6.3   Let $x \in \mathbb{Q}$ and $y \in \mathbb{R}$, with $y \neq 0$. Prove the following.
(a) $x + y \in \mathbb{Q}$ if and only if $y \in \mathbb{Q}$.
(b) $xy \in \mathbb{Q}$ if and only if $x = 0$ or $y \in \mathbb{Q}$.
(c) $1/y \in \mathbb{Q}$ if and only if $y \in \mathbb{Q}$.

Example 2.6.4   Is it possible to have $a^b \in \mathbb{Q}$ even when both a and b are irrational? We propose two candidates: $\sqrt{2}^{\sqrt{2}}$ and $\left(\sqrt{2}^{\sqrt{2}}\right)^{\sqrt{2}}$.

If $\sqrt{2}^{\sqrt{2}} \in \mathbb{Q}$, then the first candidate gives an affirmative answer by Theorem 2.6.1. Otherwise, $\sqrt{2}^{\sqrt{2}} \in \mathbb{I}$, in which case

$$\left(\sqrt{2}^{\sqrt{2}}\right)^{\sqrt{2}} = \sqrt{2}^{\sqrt{2}\cdot\sqrt{2}} = \sqrt{2}^{2} = 2 \in \mathbb{Q}.$$

Note that the question of whether $\sqrt{2}^{\sqrt{2}}$ is rational or irrational remains unresolved here. (In fact, $\sqrt{2}^{\sqrt{2}} \in \mathbb{I}$, but the mathematics behind the proof is very deep.)

The usual discussion in secondary school about rational and irrational numbers concerns the decimal expansion of a number. It is more traditional in the mathematical community to view rational and irrational numbers as we have defined them here. We demonstrate the equivalence of these two approaches.

Theorem 2.6.5 *A real number is rational if and only if its decimal expansion terminates or has an infinitely repeating sequence of digits.*

Proof. Let $r \in \mathbb{R}$. If $r \in \mathbb{Z}$, then r can be written as $r.0$, and so its decimal expansion clearly terminates. So assume that $r \in \mathbb{Q}$ but $r \notin \mathbb{Z}$ and write $r = \dfrac{a}{b}$ for some $a, b \in \mathbb{Z}, b \neq 0$. It suffices to assume that $r \in (0, 1)$. [The words "suffices to assume" mean that if this proof works when $r \in (0, 1)$, then the theorem is true for *all* $r \in \mathbb{R}$.] This is so because, given any $x \in \mathbb{R}$, either $x \in \mathbb{Z}$ or there is an integer k such that $x + k \in (0, 1)$. Clearly, x and $x + k$ have the same expansion after the decimal point. We convert r into its decimal expansion by long division in the usual way:

$$b \, \overline{)\, a.000 \cdots}.$$

If the division process terminates, then we are done. Otherwise, since each digit of the quotient determines in turn its successor, and since there are at most $b - 1$ possible nonzero remainders when dividing by b (by the Division Algorithm), some digit of the remainder must show up again, forcing a sequence of digits to repeat forever. (The length of the repeating cycle is at most $b - 1$.)

For the converse, first suppose that the decimal expansion of r terminates— that is, that $r = 0.a_1 a_2 \cdots a_k$, where each $a_i \in \{0, 1, 2, 3, 4, 5, 6, 7, 8, 9\}$ and $a_k \neq 0$. Then

$$r = \frac{a_1 10^{k-1} + a_2 10^{k-2} + \cdots + a_k}{10^k}$$

satisfies the definition of a rational number.

Next, we suppose that the decimal expansion of r has an infinitely repeating sequence of digits that begins immediately after the decimal point. We write $r = 0.\overline{b_1 b_2 \cdots b_k}$, where the overline indicates that the sequence of digits beneath it is repeated forever. Then

$$10^k r = b_1 b_2 \cdots b_k \, . \, b_1 b_2 \cdots b_k \overline{b_1 b_2 \cdots b_k}.$$

So

$$10^k r - r = b_1 b_2 \cdots b_k,^*$$

giving

$$r = \frac{b_1 b_2 \cdots b_k}{10^k - 1} \in \mathbb{Q}.$$

Suppose r has an initial sequence of digits before the repeating sequence: $r = 0.a_1 a_2 \cdots a_\ell \overline{b_1 b_2 \cdots b_k}$. By the previous case, $r' = 0.\overline{b_1 b_2 \cdots b_k} \in \mathbb{Q}$. It is easy to verify that

$$r = \frac{r' + a_1 a_2 \cdots a_\ell}{10^\ell}.$$

By the previous case and Exercise 2.6.3, $r \in \mathbb{Q}$. $\square$

Example 2.6.6 What rational number is $r = 0.7\overline{461538}$? This is the last case of the proof. Here $\ell = 1, k = 6$, $a_1 = 7$, and

$$r' = .\overline{461538} = \frac{461538}{10^6 - 1} = \frac{461538}{999999} = \frac{6}{13}.$$

So

$$r = \frac{6/13 + 7}{10} = \frac{97}{130}$$

when written in lowest terms.

We restate the previous theorem in terms of irrational numbers.

Corollary 2.6.7 *Let $x \in \mathbb{R}$. Then $x \in \mathbb{I}$ if and only if the decimal expansion of x is nonterminating and nonrepeating.*

We have seen that, for all $k \in \mathbb{N}$, $\sqrt{k}$ is either an integer or irrational. Other well-known irrational numbers include π and e. Proofs of the irrationality of π and e are beyond the scope of this book.

---

*When we write $b_1 b_2 \cdots b_k$, we mean $b_1 10^{k-1} + b_2 10^{k-2} + \cdots + b_{k-1} 10^1 + b_k$.

Notation. The set of all polynomials in x with coefficients from $\mathbb{Z}$ is denoted by $\mathbb{Z}[x]$. Thus, each element $p \in \mathbb{Z}[x]$ has the form

$$p(x) = c_n x^n + c_{n-1} x^{n-1} + \ldots + c_1 x + c_0,$$

where n is a nonnegative integer, $c_i \in \mathbb{Z}$ for each $i \in \{0, 1, 2, \ldots n\}$, and $c_n \neq 0$ if $n > 0$.

Definition 2.6.8 *A number s is an* **algebraic number** *when there exists some $p \in \mathbb{Z}[x]$ such that $p(s) = 0$. Let us denote the set*

$$\mathbb{A} = \{x \in \mathbb{C} : x \text{ is algebraic}\}.$$

Proposition 2.6.9 *All rational numbers are algebraic.*

Proof. Let $q \in \mathbb{Q}$. Then $q = \dfrac{a}{b}$, for some $a, b \in \mathbb{Z}$, $b \neq 0$. The polynomial $p(x) = bx - a$ belongs to $\mathbb{Z}[x]$ and $p(q) = p\left(\dfrac{a}{b}\right) = 0$. Hence $q \in \mathbb{A}$. $\qquad\square$

Some algebraic numbers are irrational. Recall that $\sqrt{2} \in \mathbb{I}$. If $p(x) = x^2 - 2$, then $p(\sqrt{2}) = 0$, and so $\sqrt{2} \in \mathbb{A}$.

Example 2.6.10 From Theorem 2.6.2 we know that if $k \in \mathbb{N}$, then $\sqrt{k}$ is either in $\mathbb{N}$ or in $\mathbb{I}$. In both cases, $\sqrt{k}$ is algebraic. Consider the polynomial $p(x) = x^2 - k$. Then $p \in \mathbb{Z}[x]$ and $p(\sqrt{k}) = 0$.

Exercise 2.6.11 Prove that, if $a \in \mathbb{A}$ and $q \in \mathbb{Q}$, then $qa \in \mathbb{A}$.

A number that is not algebraic is called **transcendental**. That is, the set $\mathbb{T}$ of transcendental numbers satisfies

$$\mathbb{T} = \{x \in \mathbb{C} : x \notin \mathbb{A}\}.$$

By the way, e and π are not only irrational, they are, in fact, transcendental. This is even harder to prove.

Proposition 2.6.12 *If $t \in \mathbb{T}$ and $k \in \mathbb{Z}$, then $kt \in \mathbb{T}$.*

Proof. We prove the contrapositive. Suppose that $kt \notin \mathbb{T}$; that is, $kt \in \mathbb{A}$. By Definition 2.6.8, there exists a polynomial $p \in \mathbb{Z}[x]$ such that

$$p(kt) = c_n(kt)^n + c_{n-1}(kt)^{n-1} + \ldots + c_1(kt) + c_0 = 0,$$

where $c_i \in \mathbb{Z}$ for each $i \in \{0, 1, \ldots, n\}$. We can rewrite this equation as

$$(c_n k^n)t^n + (c_{n-1}k^{n-1})t^{n-1} + \ldots + (c_1 k)t + c_0 = 0.$$

The polynomial

$$q(x) = c_n k^n x^n + c_{n-1} k^{n-1} x^{n-1} + \ldots + c_1 k x + c_0$$

thus has the property that $q(t) = 0$. Since each of its coefficients $c_i k^i$ is an integer, $q \in \mathbb{Z}[x]$. Thus $t \in \mathbb{A}$, which means that $t \notin \mathbb{T}$. $\square$

Exercise 2.6.13 (a) Prove that if $t \in \mathbb{T}$ and $q \in \mathbb{Q}$ but $q \neq 0$, then $qt \in \mathbb{T}$.
(b) Prove that if $t \in \mathbb{T}$, then $1/t \in \mathbb{T}$.
(c) Give examples of transcendental numbers t_1 and t_2 such that $t_1 t_2 \in \mathbb{Q}$.

2.7   Further Exercises

Exercise 2.7.1 Prove that, if an integer s is a perfect square, then there exists an integer q such that $s = 4q + r$ where $r = 0$ or 1.

Exercise 2.7.2 Let $k \in \mathbb{N}$ such that $k \geq 2$. Find $q, r \in \mathbb{Z}$ in terms of k such that $0 \leq r < k + 1$ and $3k = q(k + 1) + r$.

Exercise 2.7.3 Given that $61 \mid (16! + 1)$, prove that $61 \mid (18! + 1)$.

Exercise 2.7.4 Prove that the following divisibility tests are valid.
(a) A number n is divisible by 3 if and only if the sum of the digits in the decimal expansion of n is divisible by 3.
(b) A number n is divisible by 9 if and only if the sum of the digits in the decimal expansion of n is divisible by 9.
[Hint for both parts: Write $n = 10^{k-1}d_k + 10^{k-2}d_{k-1} + \cdots + 10d_2 + d_1$, where $d_i \in \{0, 1, 2, \ldots, 9\}$ and $d_k \neq 0$, and consider $n - (d_k + d_{k-1} + \cdots + d_2 + d_1)$.]

Exercise 2.7.5 Prove that the following test for divisibility by 7 is valid. Let $n \in \mathbb{N}$. Write $n = 10a + b$, where $0 \leq b \leq 9$ and $b \in \mathbb{N}$. Then n is divisible by 7 if and only if $a - 2b$ is divisible by 7.

For example, let $n = 37394$.
Write $37394 = 3739 \cdot 10 + 4$. Compute $3739 - 2 \cdot 4 = 3731$.
Now write $3731 = 373 \cdot 10 + 1$, and compute $373 - 2 \cdot 1 = 371$;
then write $371 = 37 \cdot 10 + 1$, and finally $37 - 2 \cdot 1 = 35$.
Since 35 is divisible by 7, 371 is divisible by 7, 3731 is divisible by 7, and finally we conclude that 37394 is divisible by 7.

Exercise 2.7.6 Prove or disprove the following statements.
(a) $\gcd(n, n + 2) = 1$ or 2 for every $n \in \mathbb{N}$.
(b) If n is odd, then n and $n + 2$ are relatively prime. (Compare Exercise 2.5.19(b).)
(c) For any three distinct odd integers, if a and b are relatively prime and if b and c are relatively prime, then a and c are relatively prime.
(d) For any distinct nonzero integers a and b, it holds that $\gcd(a, b) \leq |a - b|$.

Exercise 2.7.7 Assess the correctness (that is, find the error(s), if any) of each of the proposed proofs and counterexamples for the claim

$$\text{For all } a, b, c \in \mathbb{N}, \text{ if } a^2 \mid bc, \text{ then } a \mid b \text{ or } a \mid c.$$

(a) *Counterexample.* $2^2 \mid 20 = 5 \cdot 4$, but $2 \nmid 5$.

(b) *Proof.* If $a \mid b$ and $a \mid c$, then there exist integers k and ℓ such that $b = ak$ and $c = a\ell$. Thus $bc = (ak)(a\ell) = a^2(k\ell)$, and so $a^2 \mid bc$.

(c) *Proof.* If $a \mid b$, then the "or" statement is true and we are done, and the same argument holds if $a \mid c$. Since $a \mid b$ or $a \mid c$ is true, then we have proved the result.

(d) *Counterexample.* We have $3^2 \mid 12 \cdot 3$, but $9 \nmid 12$ and $9 \nmid 3$.

(e) *Proof.* By the Division Algorithm, there exist $q_1, q_2, r_1, r_2 \in \mathbb{N}$ such that

$b = aq_1 + r_1$, $c = aq_2 + r_2$, $0 \leq r_1 < a$, and $0 \leq r_2 < a$. Thus

$$bc = q_1 q_2 a^2 + (q_1 r_2 + q_2 r_1)a + r_1 r_2. \tag{2.7.1}$$

To prove the contrapositive, assume that $a \nmid b$ and $a \nmid c$. That implies that $r_1 r_2 \neq 0$. But $a > r_1$ and $a > r_2$, and so a cannot be a divisor of $r_1 r_2$. By equation (2.7.1), $a^2 \nmid bc$.

(f) *Counterexample.* $36 \mid 360$ but $6 \nmid 45$ and $6 \nmid 8$.

Exercise 2.7.8   Find all positive integers a, b such that both $\gcd(a, b) = 5$ and $\operatorname{lcm}(a, b) = 50$ hold.

Exercise 2.7.9   Suppose that a and b are positive integers both divisible by 19. Is it possible to find integers x and y such that $0 < ax + by < 19$? Why or why not?

Exercise 2.7.10   Prove that if $a \mid c$ and $b \mid c$ and $\gcd(a, b) = 1$, then $ab \mid c$. Find counterexamples if $\gcd(a, b) > 1$.

Exercise 2.7.11   Let $a, b \in \mathbb{N}$ and $m = \operatorname{lcm}(a, b)$. Prove that

$$\gcd\left(\frac{m}{a}, \frac{m}{b}\right) = 1.$$

Exercise 2.7.12   Let $a, b \in \mathbb{N}$. Prove that $\gcd(a, b) = \operatorname{lcm}(a, b)$ if and only if $a = b$.

Exercise 2.7.13   Let p be a prime number greater than 2. Prove or disprove each of the following statements.
(a) Every prime divisor of $p^2 - 1$ is less than p.
(b) There is a prime divisor of $p^4 - 1$ that is greater than p.

Exercise 2.7.14   Prove that if $p \geq 5$ is prime, then $p^2 + 2$ is composite. In fact, $3 \mid p^2 + 2$. [Hint: First show that any prime number $p \geq 5$ has the form $6\ell + 1$ or $6\ell + 5$ for some $\ell \in \mathbb{N}$.]

Exercise 2.7.15 Prove that if $p \geq q \geq 5$ and p and q are prime, then $24 \mid p^2 - q^2$. [Hint: See the hint in Exercise 2.7.14 and also consider the form of any prime number with respect to division by 4.]

Exercise 2.7.16 (a) Prove that if n is a composite number, it must have a prime factor $p \leq \sqrt{n}$.
(b) Prove or disprove: If n is a composite number, it must have a prime factor $p > \sqrt{n}$.

Exercise 2.7.17 (a) Prove that for all $a, b \in \mathbb{Z}$, the two inequalities

$$a < b + 1 \qquad \text{and} \qquad a \leq b$$

are equivalent. [Hint: Consider the cases $a \leq b$ and $a > b$.]
(b) Show that part (a) is false if $\mathbb{Z}$ is replaced by $\mathbb{Q}$.

Exercise 2.7.18 Let $m \in \mathbb{N}$ such that $m \geq 2$ and consider the set

$$S_m = \{mn + 1 : n \text{ is a nonnegative integer}\}.$$

A number $r \in S_m$ is an S_m-**prime** if $r > 1$ and the only way to express r as a product of elements from S_m is as $1 \cdot r$.

(a) Prove that the product of any two elements of S_m is also an element of S_m.
(b) Show that 4, 7, 10, and 22 are S_3-primes but that 16 is not an S_3-prime.
(c) Show that 220 can be expressed in two different ways as a product of S_3-primes.
(d) Why do all elements of S_2 have a unique factorization as a product of S_2-primes?
(e) Consider some values of $m \geq 4$ and determine whether elements of S_m have a unique factorization as a product of S_m-primes.

Exercise 2.7.19 Express the real numbers $0.40\overline{1683}$ and $3.141\overline{592}$ as ratios of integers in lowest terms, thereby showing that they are rational.

Exercise 2.7.20 Let $a, b \in \mathbb{R}$, where $a < b$. Prove that there exist a rational number c and an irrational number d such that $a < c < b$ and $a < d < b$. [Hint: Consider decimal expansions of a and b.]

Exercise 2.7.21   Prove that if $y, z \in \mathbb{Q}$, then $y^z \in \mathbb{A}$.

Exercise 2.7.22   Let $q \in \mathbb{Q}$ with $q \neq 0$. Determine whether the line in the plane whose equation is

$$y = \sqrt{2}\,x + q$$

passes through any points (x_0, y_0) such that both x_0 and y_0 are rational numbers. [Hint: Use Exercise 2.6.3.]

Chapter 3

Sets

A MOVEMENT BEGAN in the mathematics community toward the end of the nineteenth century whose goal was to build all of mathematics on the foundation of set theory. Whether this goal was achieved, or deserved to be achieved, remains debatable. In any case, a solid knowledge of the principles of set theory is necessary for the study of advanced mathematics. This chapter introduces the basics.

3.1   Subsets

In Section 2.2, we presented the sets $\mathbb{N}$ and $\mathbb{E}$. You certainly noticed that every element of $\mathbb{E}$ is also an element of $\mathbb{N}$, or equivalently, that $\mathbb{E}$ is somehow contained inside of $\mathbb{N}$. We express this notion by saying that $\mathbb{E}$ is a *subset* of $\mathbb{N}$.

Example 3.1.1   Consider the sets $X = \{2, 3, 4, 5, 6\}, Y = \{1, 2, 3, 4\}$ and $Z = \{4, 5\}$. Then Z is a subset of X since each element of Z is also an element of X. But Y is not a subset of X since, for example, $1 \in Y$, but $1 \notin X$. (See Figure 3.1.1.)

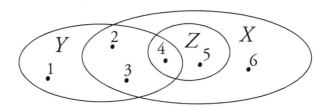

Figure 3.1.1: Example 3.1.1.

Definition 3.1.2   *Let A and B be sets. Then A is a **subset** of B, written A ⊆ B, when the statement* $(\forall x)\,[x \in A \Rightarrow x \in B]$ *is true.*

Notation. The symbol ⊆ is read "is a subset of" or, more informally, "is contained in." To indicate that A is not a subset of B, we write $A \nsubseteq B$. Equivalent to writing $A \subseteq B$, we write $B \supseteq A$ and say that B is a **superset** of A, or, more informally, "contains."

Frequently, all the sets in a given context are subsets of one particular set. For example, in a calculus course, most of the sets encountered (interval, domain, range, etc.) are subsets of $\mathbb{R}$. We call such a set the *universal set of discourse* or, for short, the **universal set**, or, even shorter, the *universe*.

With regard to the universal quantifier $\forall x$ in the definition of $A \subseteq B$, we need to consider only those x's that are elements of A because, for any x that is not in A, the hypothesis of the statement $x \in A \Rightarrow x \in B$ is false, and so the conditional itself is true. So in Example 3.1.1, for any element that we consider except 4 and 5, the statement $x \in Z$ is false. Thus the statement $x \in Z \Rightarrow x \in X$ is true. Note that $4 \in Z$ and $4 \in X$, so the statement $4 \in Z \Rightarrow 4 \in X$ is true, and the same holds for 5. Therefore the statement $(\forall x)[x \in Z \Rightarrow x \in X]$ is true, and we conclude that $Z \subseteq X$.

Note that for Y and X, we have $1 \in Y$, but $1 \notin X$. Therefore the statement $(\exists x)[x \in Y \wedge x \notin X]$ is true. Equivalently, its negation $(\forall x)\,[x \in Y \Rightarrow x \in X]$ is false, and so we conclude that $Y \nsubseteq X$.

To summarize, $A \nsubseteq B$ is the negation of $A \subseteq B$. Thus $A \nsubseteq B$ means $\neg(\forall x)\,[x \in A \Rightarrow x \in B]$, which is equivalent to $(\exists x)\,[x \in A \wedge x \notin B]$.

Exercise 3.1.3 Give examples of sets A and B to show that the statement $A \not\subseteq B$ is equivalent to neither $B \subseteq A$ nor to the case where A and B have no elements in common.

Proposition 3.1.4 *Let $A, B,$ and C be sets. If $A \subseteq B$ and $B \subseteq C$, then $A \subseteq C$.*

Proof. Assume $A \subseteq B$ and $B \subseteq C$. Let $x \in A$. [The most common strategy for proving that one set is a subset of another is to consider an arbitrary element of the first set and prove that that element must belong to the second set.] Since $A \subseteq B$, we know by Definition 3.1.2 that $(\forall x)\,[x \in A \Rightarrow x \in B]$ is true. Thus we conclude that $x \in B$. Since $B \subseteq C$ and we now know that $x \in B$, we conclude again by Definition 3.1.2 that $x \in C$. Thus $A \subseteq C$. $\quad\square$

Expressions of the form $(A \subseteq B) \wedge (B \subseteq C)$ occur so frequently that a shorter format is used; we say $A \subseteq B \subseteq C$ to mean exactly the same thing. (This is analogous to writing, for example, $3 \leq \pi \leq 4$ for real numbers.) Thus, from Section 2.2, we have

$$\mathbb{E} \subseteq \mathbb{N} \subseteq \mathbb{Z} \subseteq \mathbb{Q} \subseteq \mathbb{R} \subseteq \mathbb{C}.$$

One can define a set A for which the statement $x \in A$ is always false. For example, let $P(x)$ be any propositional function and let

$$A = \big\{x : P(x) \wedge \neg P(x)\big\}.$$

The statement $x \in A$ is indeed always false; that is, $(\forall x)[x \notin A]$, and so A is a set with no elements.

Definition 3.1.5 *A set with no elements is an* **empty set**.

Proposition 3.1.6 *If E is an empty set and A is any set, then $E \subseteq A$.*

Proof. Since E is an empty set, the statement $x \in E$ is false for all x. Therefore, the statement $(\forall x)[x \in E \Rightarrow x \in A]$ is true. [Remember the truth table for $P \Rightarrow Q$.] So, by definition, $E \subseteq A$. $\quad\square$

Exercise 3.1.7 Prove the following statements.
(a) If A is any set, then $A \subseteq A$.
(b) If E is an empty set and $A \subseteq E$, then A is an empty set.

Definition 3.1.8 *Let A and B be sets. Then A **equals** B, written $A = B$, when both $A \subseteq B$ and $B \subseteq A$. Thus the symbols A and B denote the same set.*

Equality of sets isn't as simple as it may seem. For sets like $A = \{1, 2, 3\}$ and $B = \{2, 3, 1\}$, it is trivial. However, there will be many instances where the equality of two sets is not so immediate. For example, if

$$A = \{3, 5, 11, 17, 29, 41, 59, 71\}$$

and

$$B = \{n \text{ is prime} : n < 100 \ \wedge \ n + 2 \text{ is prime}\},$$

then the fact that $A = B$ is less obvious. Similarly, in the universe $\mathcal{F}$ of all functions that are differentiable on $(-\infty, \infty)$, let

$$A = \{f \in \mathcal{F} : (\forall x \in \mathbb{R})[f'(x) = f(x)]\}$$

and

$$B = \{f \in \mathcal{F} : (\exists c \in \mathbb{R})[f(x) = ce^x]\}.$$

The fact that $A = B$ is a basic result in the study of differential equations.

The negation of $A = B$ is written simply as $A \neq B$.

Exercise 3.1.9 Prove that the statement $A \neq B$ is equivalent to the statement

$$(\exists x)[x \in A \wedge x \notin B] \vee (\exists x)[x \in B \wedge x \notin A].$$

Definition 3.1.10 *A set A is a **proper subset** of a set B, written $A \subset B$, when A is a subset[1] of B but $A \neq B$.*

---

[1]Some authors use $\subset$ to mean "is a subset of." For example, they would write $A \subset A$ and never use the symbol $\subseteq$, but that convention is not the usage of this book.

Proposition 3.1.11 *If A and B are both empty sets, then A = B.*

Proof. Assume that both A and B are empty sets. From Proposition 3.1.6, since A is empty, we have $A \subseteq B$. By the same proposition the other way around, since B is empty (and regardless of the status of A), we have $B \subseteq A$. Then, by Definition 3.1.8, we have that $A = B$. [Observe how this proof is short and simple because we made use of a previously proved proposition.] $\square$

The message of this proposition is that there is *only one* empty set. What we proved is that, if there were supposedly two empty sets, then they really are equal; in other words, they are the same set. Since there is a unique empty set, we follow established convention and denote *the* empty set by the symbol $\varnothing$. Do not confuse this symbol[2] with the Greek letter *phi*, written variously as Φ, ϕ, or φ. Although computer scientists sometimes write the similar symbol $\emptyset$ for the numeral 0 to distinguish it from the letter "O," mathematicians do not use this convention.

A statement of the form $(\forall x \in \varnothing)[P(x)]$ is a **vacuous statement**. Such statements are always true, although often not very informative. For example, let $P(x)$ mean, "x has red hair," and let S denote the set of all past and present emperors of the United States. Then, of course, $S = \varnothing$, but the statement $(\forall x \in S)[P(x)]$ is true. How do we see this? Were $(\forall x \in S)[P(x)]$ to be false, then its negation $(\exists x \in S)[\neg P(x)]$ would have to be true; that is, some emperor of the United States does (or did) not have red hair—and *that* is clearly false.

We observe that while $(\forall x \in \varnothing)[P(x)]$ is always true, the existential statement $(\exists x \in \varnothing)[P(x)]$ is always false.

Suppose that $A = \{a, b, c, d\}$. By Proposition 3.1.6 and Exercise 3.1.7(a),

---

[2]The symbol $\varnothing$ is a vowel in the Danish alphabet. It was selected by the German mathematician Georg Cantor, who will figure prominently in Chapter 7.

the sets $\varnothing$ and A are subsets of A. The complete list of subsets of A is

$$\varnothing,$$
$$\{a\}, \{b\}, \{c\}, \{d\},$$
$$\{a, b\}, \{a, c\}, \{a, d\}, \{b, c\}, \{b, d\}, \{c, d\},$$
$$\{a, b, c\}, \{a, b, d\}, \{a, c, d\}, \{b, c, d\},$$
$$\{a, b, c, d\}.$$

We may consider all of these sets to be the elements of a new set

$$\big\{\varnothing, \{a\}, \{b\}, \ldots, \{b, c, d\}, \{a, b, c, d\}\big\},$$

which may also be denoted by

$$\{S : S \subseteq A\}.$$

Definition 3.1.12 *Let A be a set. The set whose elements are all of the subsets of A is the **power set** of A, denoted $\mathscr{P}(A)$, and is defined by*

$$\mathscr{P}(A) = \{S : S \subseteq A\}.$$

Suppose $A = \{1, 2, 3\}$. It is extremely important to distinguish between the objects 2 and $\{2\}$. The integer 2 is an element of the set A. But $\{2\}$, the set whose only element is the integer 2, is an element of $\mathscr{P}(A)$. Thus $2 \neq \{2\}$. It is correct to write $2 \in \{2\}$, but $2 \not\subseteq \{2\}$ and $2 \notin 2$, since 2 is not a set and thus neither has nor fails to have elements. Therefore, 2 and $\{2\}$ must never be treated interchangeably; to do so leads to error. Similarly, the symbols $\in$ and $\subseteq$ (and likewise $\notin$ and $\not\subseteq$) must never be treated interchangeably. They are used only in the following contexts.

$$\text{(element)} \in \text{(set)}; \qquad \text{(set)} \subseteq \text{(set)}; \qquad \text{(set)} \in \text{(power set)}.$$

Be careful, though, because sometimes the elements of a set are sets themselves. For example, $\{2, 3\} \in \mathscr{P}(\{1, 2, 3\})$ since $\{2, 3\} \subseteq \{1, 2, 3\}$.

Exercise 3.1.13 (a) List the elements of $\mathscr{P}(A)$ if $A = \{1, 2, 3\}$.
(b) List the elements of $\mathscr{P}(B)$ if $B = \{b\}$.
(c) List the elements of $\mathscr{P}(\varnothing)$.

(d) For $B = \{b\}$, list the elements of $\mathscr{P}(\mathscr{P}(B))$.

(e) Let $A = \{1, \{2\}, \varnothing\}$. Which of the following are true? When the statement is false, state *why* it is false. Pay very close attention to the notation!

$1 \in A$	$1 \subseteq A$	$\{1\} \in A$	$\{1\} \subseteq A$
$1 \in \mathscr{P}(A)$	$\{1\} \in \mathscr{P}(A)$	$\{1\} \subseteq \mathscr{P}(A)$	$\varnothing \in A$
$\varnothing \subseteq A$	$\varnothing \subseteq \mathscr{P}(A)$	$\varnothing \in \mathscr{P}(A)$	$\{\varnothing\} \in \mathscr{P}(A)$
$2 \in A$	$\{2\} \in A$	$\{2\} \subseteq A$	$\{\{2\}\} \subseteq A$
$\varnothing \subseteq \mathscr{P}(\mathscr{P}(A))$	$A \in \mathscr{P}(A)$	$A \subseteq \mathscr{P}(A)$	$\mathscr{P}(A) \subseteq \mathscr{P}(A)$
$A \subseteq \mathscr{P}(\mathscr{P}(A))$	$A \in \mathscr{P}(\mathscr{P}(A))$	$\{A\} \in \mathscr{P}(\mathscr{P}(A))$	$\{A\} \subseteq \mathscr{P}(\mathscr{P}(A))$

Exercise 3.1.14 (a) Let a and b be integers, not both 0. Prove that the set of integer multiples of $\gcd(a, b)$ is precisely the set of all linear combinations of a and b. That is,

$$\{n \cdot \gcd(a, b) : n \in \mathbb{Z}\} = \{ak + b\ell : k, \ell \in \mathbb{Z}\}.$$

(b) Prove that if $\gcd(a, b) = 1$, then $\{ak + b\ell : k, \ell \in \mathbb{Z}\} = \mathbb{Z}$.

3.2 Operations with Sets

Consider the sets $A = \{1, 2, 3, 4, 5\}$ and $B = \{3, 4, 5, 6, 7\}$. The set $\{3, 4, 5\}$ is the set of elements that A and B have in common. The set $\{1, 2, 3, 4, 5, 6, 7\}$ consist of all of the elements that are in A or in B. These sets are important enough to merit definitions.

Definition 3.2.1 *Let A and B be sets.*

*The **intersection** of A and B, written $A \cap B$, is the set*

$$A \cap B = \{x : x \in A \wedge x \in B\}.$$

*The **union** of A and B, written $A \cup B$, is the set*

$$A \cup B = \{x : x \in A \vee x \in B\}.$$

Exercise 3.2.2 Let $A = \{a, b, c, f, g, i\}$, $B = \{b, f, h\}$, $C = \{a, k, l, m\}$.
List the elements of each of the following sets.
(a) $A \cap B$
(b) $B \cup C$
(c) $A \cup C$
(d) $B \cap C$
(e) $(A \cap B) \cup C$
(f) $A \cap (B \cup C)$

Proposition 3.2.3 *Let A, B, C be sets. Then all of the following hold.*
(i) $A \cap A = A$ and $A \cup A = A$.
(ii) $\emptyset \cap A = \emptyset$ and $\emptyset \cup A = A$.
(iii) $(A \cap B) \subseteq A$.
(iv) $A \subseteq (A \cup B)$.
(v) $A \cap (B \cap C) = (A \cap B) \cap C$.
(vi) $A \cup (B \cup C) = (A \cup B) \cup C$.
(vii) $A \cap (B \cup C) = (A \cap B) \cup (A \cap C)$. (Compare Proposition 1.3.9(iv).)
(viii) $A \cup (B \cap C) = (A \cup B) \cap (A \cup C)$. (Compare Proposition 1.3.9(v).)

Proof. We prove only the first part of (ii) and part of (viii), leaving the other parts and the reverse inclusion of (viii) as exercises.

For part of (ii), from Proposition 3.1.6, $\emptyset \subseteq \emptyset \cap A$. Conversely, let $x \in \emptyset \cap A$. This means that $x \in \emptyset$ and $x \in A$ by the definition of $\cap$. Since $x \in \emptyset$ is false, the conjunction $x \in \emptyset \wedge x \in A$ is false, and thus the statement $(\forall x)[x \in \emptyset \cap A \Rightarrow x \in \emptyset]$ is true. Therefore $\emptyset \cap A \subseteq \emptyset$. So, by Definition 3.1.8, we conclude that $\emptyset \cap A = \emptyset$.

For part (viii), we prove only that $A \cup (B \cap C) \subseteq (A \cup B) \cap (A \cup C)$. (We assume that part (iv) has already been proved.) Let $x \in A \cup (B \cap C)$. By definition of $\cup$, we have $x \in A$ or $x \in B \cap C$, and we consider each possibility in turn. If $x \in A$, then, by part (iv) of this proposition, x is an element of both $A \cup B$ and $A \cup C$. By definition of $\cap$, $x \in (A \cup B) \cap (A \cup C)$. On the other hand, if $x \in B \cap C$, then by definition of $\cap$, $x \in B$ and $x \in C$. Part (iv) of this proposition is now applied again (but to different sets); we have $x \in A \cup B$ and $x \in A \cup C$. Again, $x \in (A \cup B) \cap (A \cup C)$. $\qquad\square$

Rarely does a mathematical statement have only one correct proof. Let's look at another proof of part (viii) of Proposition 3.2.3. This one relies on a result from Chapter 1. Let x be an arbitrary element of some universal set that contains sets A, B, and C. Consider the statements

$$P : x \in A; \qquad Q : x \in B; \qquad R : x \in C.$$

To say that x belongs to the left-hand side of this set-equation is the statement $P \vee (Q \wedge R)$. To say that x belongs to the right-hand side of this set-equation is the statement $(P \vee Q) \wedge (P \vee R)$. This follows directly from the definitions of $\cup$ and $\cap$. To say that x belongs to one side if and only if x belongs to the other side is to say that these two logical statements are equivalent. But this equivalence is precisely Proposition 1.3.9(v).

Exercise 3.2.4 (a) Prove parts (i), (iii), (iv), (v), (vi), (vii), and the remainder of part (ii) of Proposition 3.2.3.
(b) Finish the proof of Proposition 3.2.3(viii) by showing that

$$(A \cup B) \cap (A \cup C) \subseteq A \cup (B \cap C).$$

Exercise 3.2.5 Prove the following for any sets A, B, and C.
(a) $A \subseteq B \cap C$ if and only if $A \subseteq B$ and $A \subseteq C$.
(b) $A \cup B \subseteq C$ if and only if $A \subseteq C$ and $B \subseteq C$.

3.3   The Complement of a Set

Let $A = \{1, 3, 5, 9\}$ and $B = \{2, 3, 4, 5, 6, 7, 8\}$. Then $\{3, 5\} = A \cap B$ is the set of elements that are in A and in B, while $\{1, 9\}$ is the set of elements that are in A but not in B. There is a term for this latter set.

Definition 3.3.1 *Let A and B be sets. The* **complement**[3] *of B **relative to** A, written $A \setminus B$, is the set*

$$A \setminus B = \{x : x \in A \wedge x \notin B\}.$$

---

[3]Note the spelling! You could send a *compliment* to the chef for the delicious *complement* to the entree.

For the sets A and B above,

$$A \setminus B = \{1, 9\} \quad \text{and} \quad B \setminus A = \{2, 4, 6, 7, 8\}.$$

Informally, we can read $A \setminus B$ as "A minus B." However, this so-called subtraction is not completely analogous to the usual subtraction with real numbers, as will become apparent.

Exercise 3.3.2   Let $A = \{a, b, c, f, g, i\}$, $B = \{b, f, h\}$, $C = \{a, k, l, m\}$. List the elements in each of the following sets.
(a) $A \setminus B$
(b) $B \setminus C$
(c) $(A \cup C) \setminus (B \cup C)$
(d) Show that $\setminus$ is not associative by comparing $(A \setminus B) \setminus C$ with the set $A \setminus (B \setminus C)$.

The complement of a set relative to the universal set is a case of special importance.

Definition 3.3.3   *Let U be the universal set and let $A \subseteq U$. The **complement of A**, written A', is the set*

$$A' = U \setminus A = \{x \in U : x \notin A\}.$$

Example 3.3.4   If U denotes the universal set, then $U' = \emptyset$ and $\emptyset' = U$.

In the universe $\mathbb{N}$, the set of all odd natural numbers is

$$\mathbb{E}' = \{1, 3, 5, 7, 9, \ldots\}.$$

Proposition 3.3.5   *Let A and B be subsets of a universal set U. Then all of the following hold.*
(i) $A \setminus B = A \cap B'$.
(ii) $(B')' = B$.
(iii) $(A \cup B)' = A' \cap B'$.
(iv) $(A \cap B)' = A' \cup B'$.
(v) $A \subseteq B$ if and only if $B' \subseteq A'$.
(vi) $A \cup A' = U$.
(vii) $A \cap A' = \emptyset$.
(viii) $A \cap B = \emptyset$ if and only if $A \subseteq B'$.
(ix) $A \subseteq B$ if and only if $A \setminus B = \emptyset$.

Remark. Parts (iii) and (iv) are called **De Morgan's Laws**, just like their logical counterparts in Section 1.3.

Proof. First we prove part (i). [Remember that to show that these two sets are equal, we have to prove the two statements: $A \setminus B \subseteq A \cap B'$ and $A \cap B' \subseteq A \setminus B$. Since each statement is truly equivalent to the next, we can write the proof as follows.]

$$x \in A \setminus B \iff x \in A \wedge x \notin B$$
$$[\text{definition of } \setminus]$$
$$\iff x \in A \wedge x \in B'$$
$$[\text{definition of complement}]$$
$$\iff x \in A \cap B'$$
$$[\text{definition of } \cap].$$

Since each pair of steps is connected by a definition, the sequence of steps is reversible. [This means that we have accomplished the twofold task of showing $x \in A \setminus B \Rightarrow x \in A \cap B'$ and $x \in A \cap B' \Rightarrow x \in A \setminus B$.] We have proved that $A \setminus B = A \cap B'$.

To prove (v), assume that $A \subseteq B$. Let x be an arbitrary element of B'. By definition of complement, $x \notin B$. Since our assumption means $x \in A \Rightarrow x \in B$, its contrapositive gives us $x \notin A$. In other words, $x \in A'$. Thus $B' \subseteq A'$. The other direction is similar but requires the use of part (ii).

The remaining parts are left as an exercise. $\qquad\qquad\square$

Exercise 3.3.6 Write a proof for each of the remaining parts of Proposition 3.3.5.

Exercise 3.3.7 Prove that, for any sets A, B, and C, if $A \subseteq B$, then

$$A \setminus C \subseteq B \setminus C.$$

Exercise 3.3.8 Let A, B, C, and D be sets such that $A \subseteq C$ and $B \subseteq D$. Prove the following.
(a) $B \setminus C \subseteq D \setminus A$.
(b) If $C \cap D = \emptyset$, then $A \cap B = \emptyset$.

Exercise 3.3.9 For any sets A, B, and C, prove or disprove the following.
(a) $(A \setminus B) \setminus C = (A \setminus C) \setminus (B \setminus C)$.
(b) $A \setminus (B \setminus C) = (A \setminus B) \setminus (A \setminus C)$.

Exercise 3.3.10 Let A and B be subsets of some universal set. Prove that

$$(A \setminus B)' \setminus (B \setminus A)' = B \setminus A.$$

Exercise 3.3.11 Decide the truth value of each of the following statements. If the statement is true, write a proof. If the statement is false, prove that it is false by providing a specific counterexample.
(a) $A \subseteq B$ if and only if $\mathscr{P}(A) \subseteq \mathscr{P}(B)$.
(b) $\mathscr{P}(A \cup B) = \mathscr{P}(A) \cup \mathscr{P}(B)$.
(c) $\mathscr{P}(A \cap B) = \mathscr{P}(A) \cap \mathscr{P}(B)$.
(d) $\mathscr{P}(A \setminus B) = \mathscr{P}(A) \setminus \mathscr{P}(B)$.
For any statement that may be false, can it be corrected by replacing $=$ with $\subseteq$ or $\supseteq$? If so, write the new statement that is true and prove it.

3.4   The Cartesian Product

Let $A = \{1, 2, 3\}$ and $B = \{a, b\}$. Now form a new set whose elements are all of the possible ordered pairs with an element of A in the first position and an element of B in the second position. This is the new set:

$$\{(1, a), (1, b), (2, a), (2, b), (3, a), (3, b)\}.$$

Note that the ordered pairs $(2, 3), (b, b)$, and $(a, 2)$ are *not* elements of this set because they do not fulfill the membership requirement that the first object be from A and the second be from B.

Definition 3.4.1 *Let A and B be sets. The* **Cartesian**[4] **product of A by B,** *written $A \times B$, is the set*

$$A \times B = \{(a, b) : a \in A \wedge b \in B\}.$$

_____
[4]After *Renatus Cartesius*, the Latin form of the name of the French philosopher and inventor of analytic geometry, René Descartes (1596–1650).

Note that we are talking about *ordered* pairs. Even when A and B are the same set, the pairs (x, y) and (y, x) are the same ordered pair if and only if $x = y$. You have encountered ordered pairs ever since you first plotted points on a set of coordinate axes. Indeed, the Cartesian product $\mathbb{R} \times \mathbb{R}$ is the set of ordered pairs (x, y) where x and y are real numbers. This is the set of all points in the xy-plane. It is sometimes handy to view any Cartesian product geometrically in this manner, as in Figure 3.4.1.

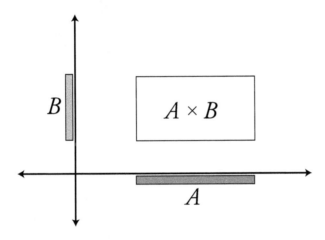

Figure 3.4.1: The Cartesian product $A \times B$.

Proposition 3.4.2 *Let A, B, C, and D be nonempty sets. Then the following hold.*
(i) $A \times (B \cup C) = (A \times B) \cup (A \times C)$.
(ii) $A \times (B \cap C) = (A \times B) \cap (A \times C)$.
(iii) $(A \times B) \cap (C \times D) = (A \cap C) \times (B \cap D)$.
(iv) $(A \times B) \cap (B \times A) = (A \cap B) \times (A \cap B)$.

Proof. We prove parts (i), (iii), and (iv) and leave (ii) as an exercise. [Bear in mind that an arbitrary element of a Cartesian product is an ordered pair.]

For part (i),

$$(x, y) \in A \times (B \cup C) \quad \Longleftrightarrow \quad x \in A \text{ and } y \in B \cup C$$
$$[\text{definition of } \times]$$
$$\Longleftrightarrow \quad x \in A \text{ and } (y \in B \text{ or } y \in C)$$
$$[\text{definition of } \cup]$$
$$\Longleftrightarrow \quad (x \in A \text{ and } y \in B) \text{ or } (x \in A \text{ and } y \in C)$$
$$[\wedge \text{ distributes over } \vee]$$
$$\Longleftrightarrow \quad (x, y) \in A \times B \text{ or } (x, y) \in A \times C$$
$$[\text{definition of } \times]$$
$$\Longleftrightarrow \quad (x, y) \in (A \times B) \cup (A \times C)$$
$$[\text{definition of } \cup].$$

Now (iii):

$$(x, y) \in (A \times B) \cap (C \times D) \quad \Longleftrightarrow \quad (x, y) \in A \times B \text{ and } (x, y) \in C \times D$$
$$\Longleftrightarrow \quad x \in A \text{ and } y \in B \text{ and } x \in C \text{ and } y \in D$$
$$\Longleftrightarrow \quad x \in A \text{ and } x \in C \text{ and } y \in B \text{ and } y \in D$$
$$\Longleftrightarrow \quad x \in A \cap C \text{ and } y \in B \cap D$$
$$\Longleftrightarrow \quad (x, y) \in (A \cap C) \times (B \cap D).$$

For part (iv), substitute $C = B$ and $D = A$ in part (iii). □

Exercise 3.4.3 Write out the proof of Proposition 3.4.2(ii), including the reasons for each step.

Exercise 3.4.4 (a) Let $A, B, C,$ and D be nonempty sets. (See Figure 3.4.2 to visualize the sets involved.) Prove that

$$(A \times B) \cup (C \times D) \subseteq (A \cup C) \times (B \cup D).$$

(b) Find specific sets $A, B, C,$ and D to show that the reverse inclusion of part (a) is false. (Such a counterexample demonstrates that the relation in part (a) cannot be strengthened to equality.)

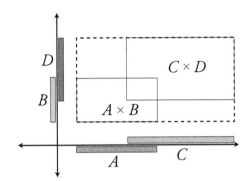

Figure 3.4.2: Exercise 3.4.4.

Exercise 3.4.5 Let A, B, C, and D be any nonempty sets. Prove the following statements.
(a) $A \times C \subseteq B \times D$ if and only if $A \subseteq B$ and $C \subseteq D$.
(b) $A \times \varnothing = \varnothing \times B = \varnothing$.
(c) $\varnothing \times \varnothing = \varnothing$.
(d) $A \times B = \varnothing$ if and only if $A = \varnothing$ or $B = \varnothing$.
(e) $(A \times B) \cup C \neq (A \cup C) \times (B \cup C)$. (If C is nonempty, equality or even subset inclusion would, in fact, be nonsense. Why?)
(f) $(A \setminus B) \times (C \setminus D) \subseteq (A \times C) \setminus (B \times D)$, but the reverse inclusion is false.
(g) $A' \times B' \subseteq (A \times B)'$, but the reverse inclusion is false.

Exercise 3.4.6 Let A and B be any sets. Explain why the statement

$$\mathscr{P}(A) \times \mathscr{P}(B) \subseteq \mathscr{P}(A \times B)$$

is not merely false but makes no sense at all.

3.5 Families of Sets

Let U be any set and let $\mathscr{A} \subseteq \mathscr{P}(U)$. Thus the elements of $\mathscr{A}$ are subsets of U. For example, if $U = \mathbb{R}$, then $\mathscr{A}$ could be the set of all closed intervals of length 1, or $\mathscr{A}$ could be the set of all open intervals whose left-hand endpoint is 3. As another example, we could have

$$U = \mathbb{Z} \quad \text{and} \quad \mathscr{A} = \{S_0, S_1, S_2, \ldots, S_{12}\}, \tag{3.5.1}$$

where for each subscript i, the set S_i consists of all integers leaving a remainder of i when divided by 13. Thus $37 \in S_{11}$, $S_{11} \subseteq \mathbb{Z}$, and $S_{11} \in \mathscr{A}$.

In these examples, $\mathscr{A}$ is what is called a **family of sets**. A family is really nothing other than a set, but we use this term frequently when we are talking about a set whose elements are sets. Just like any other set, the family $\mathscr{A}$ may be finite, infinite, or even empty. Note that to say that a family is finite or infinite says *absolutely nothing* about whether the sets that belong to the family are finite or infinite; it merely means that there are only finitely or infinitely many of them.

Choosing a convenient notation is an issue that arises with families of sets. Often, the sets in a family are "tagged" with an index, usually written as a subscript. The index belongs to a set of indices called an **index set**. In the example (3.5.1), the index set is $\{0, 1, 2, 3, 4, 5, 6, 7, 8, 9, 10, 11, 12\}$. To devise an index set for the first example, we have to be a little more creative. A typical closed interval in $\mathbb{R}$ of length 1 has the form $[x, x + 1]$, where $x \in \mathbb{R}$. So let us define $S_x = [x, x + 1]$ for each $x \in \mathbb{R}$. In this way, $\mathbb{R}$ also becomes the index set, and $\mathscr{A} = \{S_x : x \in \mathbb{R}\}$.

Let us consider a more complicated example. Let U be the xy-plane, and let $\mathscr{A}$ denote the set of all circles in U. So each element of $\mathscr{A}$ is a subset of U. How might we select an index set for this family of subsets? Any circle is determined by (1) its center and (2) its radius. The center is a point (x, y) in $U = \mathbb{R} \times \mathbb{R}$, and the radius is positive real number. So an appropriate index set would be $(\mathbb{R} \times \mathbb{R}) \times \mathbb{R}^+$. If the circle with center (x, y) and radius r is denoted by $C_{(x,y),r}$, then

$$\mathscr{A} = \left\{ C_{(x,y),r} : \big((x, y), r\big) \in (\mathbb{R} \times \mathbb{R}) \times \mathbb{R}^+ \right\}.$$

This notation, although bulky, has certain advantages. For example, one may easily denote the *subfamily* of circles of radius 1 by

$$\mathscr{A}_1 = \left\{ C_{(x,y),1} : (x, y) \in \mathbb{R} \times \mathbb{R} \right\}$$

and the *subfamily* of circles centered at the origin by

$$\mathscr{A}_{(0,0)} = \left\{ C_{(0,0),r} : r \in \mathbb{R}^+ \right\}.$$

[Be sure to note where and why the parentheses appear where they do in these expressions.] Thus $\mathbb{R} \times \mathbb{R}$ is the index set for $\mathscr{A}_1$, while $\mathbb{R}^+$ is the index set for $\mathscr{A}_{(0,0)}$.

Exercise 3.5.1 Select an appropriate index set for the sets in $\mathscr{A}$ for each of the following situations.
(a) The sets in $\mathscr{A}$ are of the form $\{pn : n \in \mathbb{Z}\}$, where p is a prime number.
(b) $\mathscr{A}$ is the family of all closed intervals of finite length in $\mathbb{R}$.
(c) The sets in $\mathscr{A}$ are subsets of $\mathbb{R} \times \mathbb{R}$ that make up the lines through the origin with negative slope.
(d) The sets in $\mathscr{A}$ are subsets of $\mathbb{R} \times \mathbb{R}$ that make up the graphs of all functions f, where f is of the form $f(x) = ax + b$ with $a, b \in \mathbb{Q}$.
(e) The same as part (d) except that f is of the form $f(x) = ax^2 + bx + c$, where $c \in \mathbb{R}$.
(f) The same as (d) except that f is of the form $f(x) = a\sin x + b\cos x$.
(g) $U = \mathbb{Z} \times (\mathbb{Z} \setminus \{0\})$, and the sets in $\mathscr{A}$ have the property that (a, b) and (c, d) belong to the same set in the family $\mathscr{A}$ if and only if $ad = bc$.

Now that we've seen that an index set can be just about anything, we let Λ denote the index set of the family $\mathscr{A} \subseteq \mathscr{P}(U)$. Thus we may write $\mathscr{A} = \{S_\lambda : \lambda \in \Lambda\}$.

For subsets S and T of a universe U, their union was defined in Definition 3.2.1: $S \cup T$ consists of all elements of U that belong to S or belong to T. We could as well have said, "$S \cup T$ is the set of elements of U that belong to at least one of S and T." This is the phrasing that enables us to speak of the union of all the sets S_λ where λ is in the index set Λ. Here is the formal definition, and while we're at it, here's the definition of the intersection.

Definition 3.5.2 Let $\mathscr{A} \subseteq \mathscr{P}(U)$, where $\mathscr{A} = \{S_\lambda : \lambda \in \Lambda\}$. The **union** of all the sets in $\mathscr{A}$ is

$$\bigcup_{\lambda \in \Lambda} S_\lambda = \{x \in U : (\exists \lambda \in \Lambda)[x \in S_\lambda]\},$$

and the **intersection** of all the sets in $\mathscr{A}$ is

$$\bigcap_{\lambda \in \Lambda} S_\lambda = \{x \in U : (\forall \lambda \in \Lambda)[x \in S_\lambda]\}.$$

Example 3.5.3   For each $x \in (0, 1)$, let S_x be the half-open interval $(0, x]$.
(We are denoting the index by x and are making the open interval $(0, 1)$
serve as the index set.) Then $\bigcup_{x \in (0,1)} S_x = (0, 1)$ and $\bigcap_{x \in (0,1)} S_x = \emptyset$. The
union should be clear, but why is the intersection empty? For any $x \in (0, 1)$,
there exists some y such that $0 < y < x$. Since $x \notin S_y$, x can't be in the
intersection of any family of sets that includes S_y. We can say more about
this intersection. Let L be any subset of $(0, 1)$. If there is some $w \in (0, 1)$ such
that $L \subseteq [w, 1)$, then $\bigcap_{x \in L} S_x \supseteq (0, w]$. However, if L contains arbitrarily
small positive numbers, then $\bigcap_{x \in L} S_x = \emptyset$. (We will consider the importance
of smallest elements again in Chapter 6.)

Exercise 3.5.4   Determine $\bigcup_{n \in \mathbb{N}} S_n$ and $\bigcap_{n \in \mathbb{N}} S_n$ in each of the following
situations. (Assume $S_n \subseteq \mathbb{R}$ in parts (a) through (d).)
(a) $S_n = [n, 2n]$.
(b) $S_n = \left(\frac{1}{n}, 1 + \frac{1}{n}\right)$.
(c) $S_n = \left[-\frac{1}{n}, n\right]$.
(d) $S_n = \left\{\frac{m}{10^n} : m \in \mathbb{Z}\right\}$.
(e) $S_n = \left\{(x, y) \in \mathbb{R} \times \mathbb{R} : x^2 + y^2 \le \frac{1}{n^2}\right\}$.
(f) $S_n = \left\{(x, y) \in \mathbb{R} \times \mathbb{R} : 0 \le x \le n; 0 \le y \le \frac{1}{n}\right\}$.

In the special case where a family of sets is finite or when the index set $\Lambda = \mathbb{N}$
or $\mathbb{Z}$, a simpler notation for their union and intersection is generally used.
If Λ is finite—that is, if Λ has n elements for some $n \in \mathbb{N}$—then we may
just as well consider Λ to *be* the set $\{1, 2, \ldots, n\}$. In this case, instead of
writing $\bigcup_{\lambda \in \Lambda} S_\lambda$, we write $\bigcup_{k=1}^{n} S_k$. If $\Lambda = \mathbb{N}$, we may write $\bigcup_{n=1}^{\infty} S_n$, and if
$\Lambda = \mathbb{Z}$, we may write $\bigcup_{n=-\infty}^{\infty} S_n$. (Of course, n never actually *equals* ∞ or
$-\infty$ because ∞ and $-\infty$ are merely symbols and not elements of the index
set $\mathbb{Z}$.) For example, suppose that S_n is the open interval $(n, n + 1)$ for all
$n \in \mathbb{Z}$. Then $\bigcup_{n=-\infty}^{\infty} S_n = \mathbb{R} \setminus \mathbb{Z}$. Everything said in this paragraph clearly
can be extended to intersections as well. However, when the index set is the
set $\mathbb{R}$, for example, then the simpler notation presented in this paragraph is
not possible for reasons that will be explored in Chapter 7.

An even simpler notation is often used when $\mathscr{A}$ is given and we don't care about what the index set may be. Then we write briefly

$$\bigcup_{S\in\mathscr{A}} S = \{x \in U : (\exists S \in \mathscr{A})[x \in S]\}$$

and

$$\bigcap_{S\in\mathscr{A}} S = \{x \in U : (\forall S \in \mathscr{A})[x \in S]\}.$$

We'll use these various notations interchangeably.

What are the union and intersection of an indexed family $\{S_\lambda : \lambda \in \Lambda\}$ of subsets of a nonempty set U when the index set Λ itself is empty? In this case, the statement

$$(\exists \lambda \in \emptyset)[x \in S_\lambda]$$

is false for every x in the universal set U. Since no x satisfies the condition in Definition 3.5.2 for belonging to $\bigcup_{\lambda\in\emptyset} S_\lambda$, clearly

$$\bigcup_{\lambda\in\emptyset} S_\lambda = \emptyset.$$

On the other hand, consider the condition $(\forall \lambda \in \emptyset)[x \in S_\lambda]$ in the intersection part of Definition 3.5.2. This is equivalent to saying $(\forall \lambda)[\lambda \in \emptyset \Rightarrow x \in S_\lambda]$. This conditional is true for all $x \in U$ because the hypothesis $\lambda \in \emptyset$, is always false. Therefore we have

$$\bigcap_{\lambda\in\emptyset} S_\lambda = U.$$

To conclude this section, we extend De Morgan's Laws to families of sets.

Theorem 3.5.5   *Let $\{S_\lambda : \lambda \in \Lambda\}$ be a family of subsets of some universal set U. Then*

$$\left(\bigcup_{\lambda\in\Lambda} S_\lambda\right)' = \bigcap_{\lambda\in\Lambda} S_\lambda' \quad \text{and} \quad \left(\bigcap_{\lambda\in\Lambda} S_\lambda\right)' = \bigcup_{\lambda\in\Lambda} S_\lambda'.$$

Proof. We present a proof only of the first statement, leaving the other as an exercise.

$$
\begin{aligned}
x \in \left(\bigcup_{\lambda \in \Lambda} S_\lambda \right)' \;\; &\Longleftrightarrow \;\; \neg[x \in \bigcup_{\lambda \in \Lambda} S_\lambda] \\
&\Longleftrightarrow \;\; \neg(\exists \lambda \in \Lambda)[x \in S_\lambda] \\
&\Longleftrightarrow \;\; (\forall \lambda \in \Lambda)\neg[x \in S_\lambda] \\
&\Longleftrightarrow \;\; (\forall \lambda \in \Lambda)[x \in S_\lambda'] \\
&\Longleftrightarrow \;\; x \in \bigcap_{\lambda \in \Lambda} S_\lambda'
\end{aligned}
$$

$\square$

Exercise 3.5.6   Complete the proof of Theorem 3.5.5; namely, prove that

$$
\left(\bigcap_{\lambda \in \Lambda} S_\lambda \right)' = \bigcup_{\lambda \in \Lambda} S_\lambda'.
$$

3.6   Further Exercises

Exercise 3.6.1   Determine which of the following sets are equal and which are proper subsets of which.

$$
A = \left\{ x \in \mathbb{R} : \sqrt{x^2} = x \right\} \qquad B = \left\{ x \in \mathbb{R} : \frac{1 + \sqrt{x}}{1 - \sqrt{x}} \in \mathbb{R} \right\}
$$

$$
C = \{ x \in \mathbb{R} : x > 0 \} \qquad D = \left\{ x \in \mathbb{R} : \frac{x}{(1 - x)^4} \in \mathbb{R} \right\}
$$

$$
E = \left\{ x^2 : x \in \mathbb{R} \right\}
$$

Exercise 3.6.2   Let A, B, C be sets. Identify a condition that, along with $A \cap C = B \cap C$, implies $A = B$. Prove this implication. Show that your condition is necessary by finding an example where $A \cap C = B \cap C$, but $A \neq B$.

Exercise 3.6.3 Let A, B, C be sets. Identify a condition that, along with $A \cup C = B \cup C$, implies $A = B$. Prove this implication. Show that your condition is necessary by finding an example where $A \cup C = B \cup C$, but $A \neq B$.

Exercise 3.6.4 Let $A = \{b, c\}$. Suppose that

$$A \cup B = \{a, b, c, e\} \text{ and } B \cup C = \{a, c, d, e, f\}.$$

Can one uniquely determine the sets B and C from this information? If not, what is the minimal additional information needed in terms of unions and intersections of the sets involved for B and C to be uniquely determined?

Exercise 3.6.5 Let A, B, C be sets. Prove the following. If $C \subseteq A$, then $(A \cap B) \cup C = A \cap (B \cup C)$. Prove or disprove the converse of this statement.

Exercise 3.6.6 Prove or disprove the following claim for sets A, B, C. If $C \subseteq B$, then $(A \cup B) \cap C = A \cup (B \cap C)$.

Exercise 3.6.7 For sets A, B, C, prove the following.
(a) $A \cap (B \setminus C) = (A \cap B) \setminus (A \cap C)$.
(b) $(A \cup B) \setminus C = (A \setminus C) \cup (B \setminus C)$.
(c) $(A \setminus B) \cap (C \setminus A) = \emptyset$.

Exercise 3.6.8 What can be concluded about sets A and B if it is known that $A \setminus B = B \setminus A$?

Exercise 3.6.9 For sets A and B, prove that if $A \cup B = A \cap B$, then $A \setminus B = \emptyset$.

Exercise 3.6.10 For sets A and B, prove or disprove the following.
(a) If $(A \cup B)' = A' \cup B'$, then $A = B$.
(b) If $(A \cap B)' = A' \cap B'$, then $A = B$.

Exercise 3.6.11 Let $A = \{w, \{x, y\}\}$, $B = \{w, y, \{y\}\}$ and $C = \{w, x, y\}$. Find each of the following sets explicitly.
(a) $A \cup C$
(b) $C \setminus B$
(c) $B \cap \mathscr{P}(B)$
(d) $(A \cap B) \cup (B \cap C) \cup (A \cap C)$

Exercise 3.6.12   Let A and B be sets. Define the **symmetric difference** of A and B, written $A + B$, by

$$A + B = (A \cup B) \setminus (A \cap B).$$

Let A, B, and C be subsets of universal set U. Prove the following statements.
(a) $A + \varnothing = A$, $A + A = \varnothing$, and $A + A' = U$.
(b) $A + B = A \cup B$ if and only if $A \cap B = \varnothing$.
(c) $A + B = B + A$.
(d) $A + B = (A \setminus B) \cup (B \setminus A)$
(e) If $B \subseteq A$, then $A + B = A \setminus B$.
(f) $A + (B + C) = (A + B) + C$.
(g) $A + (B + C) = B + (A + C) = C + (A + B)$.
(h) The statements $A + B = C$, $A + C = B$, and $B + C = A$ are equivalent to each other. [Suggestion: Assume that $A + B = C$. Then "add" $(B + C)$ to both sides of the equation, thus $(A + B) + (B + C) = C + (B + C)$. Then use parts (g) and (a) of this exercise.]

Exercise 3.6.13   Let A, B, and C be sets. Prove or disprove the following.
(a) $(A + B) \cap C = (A \cap C) + (B \cap C)$.
(b) $(A + B) \cup C = (A \cup C) + (B \cup C)$.
(c) $(A + B) \setminus C = (A \setminus C) + (B \setminus C)$.
(d) $(A \cap B) + C = (A + C) \cap (B + C)$.
(e) $(A \cup B) + C = (A + C) \cup (B + C)$.
(f) $(A \setminus B) + C = (A + C) \setminus (B + C)$.
(g) $\mathscr{P}(A + B) = \mathscr{P}(A) + \mathscr{P}(B)$.

Can any of these statements that are false be corrected by replacing $=$ with $\subseteq$ or $\supseteq$?

Exercise 3.6.14   Let A and B be sets such that $\mathscr{P}(A) = \mathscr{P}(B)$. Prove that $A = B$.

Exercise 3.6.15   Let A and B be sets. Prove that

$$\mathscr{P}(A \setminus B) \subseteq \big(\mathscr{P}(A) \setminus \mathscr{P}(B)\big) \cup \{\varnothing\}.$$

(Compare with Exercise 3.3.11(d).)

Exercise 3.6.16 Express the following subsets of the plane $\mathbb{R} \times \mathbb{R}$, shown as shaded regions in Figure 3.6.1, as unions or intersections or relative complements of Cartesian products of rays or intervals. (You may assume that the subsets include all the points on their boundaries.)

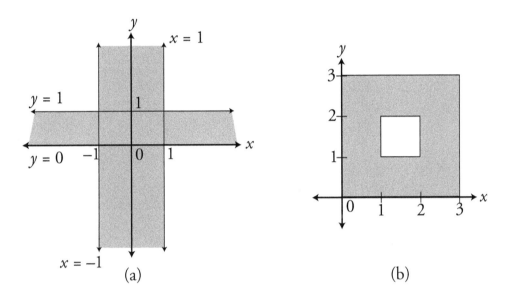

Figure 3.6.1: Exercise 3.6.16.

Exercise 3.6.17 For each $n \in \mathbb{N}$, let S_n denote the half-open interval $\left[-1 + \frac{1}{2n}, 1 + \frac{1}{2n}\right)$. Express each of the following sets in terms of rays or intervals. (The universe is the set $\mathbb{R} = (-\infty, \infty)$.)

(a) S_1, S_2, and S_3 (b) $\displaystyle\bigcup_{n \in \mathbb{N}} S_n$ (c) $\displaystyle\bigcap_{n \in \mathbb{N}} S_n$

(d) $\displaystyle\bigcap_{n \in \mathbb{N}} S_n'$ [Hint: Use De Morgan's Law and part (b).]

Exercise 3.6.18 Suppose that $\mathscr{A} \subseteq \mathscr{B} \subseteq \mathscr{P}(A)$. Prove the following.

(a) $\displaystyle\bigcup_{S \in \mathscr{A}} S \subseteq \bigcup_{S \in \mathscr{B}} S$.   (b) $\displaystyle\bigcap_{S \in \mathscr{A}} S \supseteq \bigcap_{S \in \mathscr{B}} S$.

(c) $\displaystyle\bigcup_{S \in \mathscr{A}} S' \subseteq \bigcup_{S \in \mathscr{B}} S'$.   (d) $\displaystyle\bigcap_{S \in \mathscr{A}} S' \supseteq \bigcap_{S \in \mathscr{B}} S'$.

Exercise 3.6.19   Suppose that $\mathscr{C}, \mathscr{D} \subseteq \mathscr{P}(A)$. Prove the following.

(a) $\displaystyle\bigcup_{S \in \mathscr{C} \cup \mathscr{D}} S = \left(\bigcup_{S \in \mathscr{C}} S\right) \cup \left(\bigcup_{S \in \mathscr{D}} S\right).$

(b) $\displaystyle\bigcap_{S \in \mathscr{C} \cap \mathscr{D}} S \supseteq \left(\bigcap_{S \in \mathscr{C}} S\right) \cup \left(\bigcap_{S \in \mathscr{D}} S\right).$

(c) $\displaystyle\bigcup_{S \in \mathscr{C} \cap \mathscr{D}} S \subseteq \left(\bigcup_{S \in \mathscr{C}} S\right) \cap \left(\bigcup_{S \in \mathscr{D}} S\right).$

(d) $\displaystyle\bigcap_{S \in \mathscr{C} \cup \mathscr{D}} S \subseteq \left(\bigcap_{S \in \mathscr{C}} S\right) \cup \left(\bigcap_{S \in \mathscr{D}} S\right).$

Chapter 4

Functions

AS A CALCULUS student, you developed an intuitive understanding of what a function is. There is the "sine function," the "exponential function," "linear functions," etc. In calculus, the emphasis is on processes (such as differentiation and integration) applied to specific functions. In this chapter, we explore the mathematics of functions from a more general standpoint, so that we can apply functions in a variety of settings beyond calculus. When functions are revisited in Section 6.6, they will be treated as a special case of relations. Although this latter approach is more rigorous, it lacks the intuition that you developed in your calculus courses and upon which we now build.

4.1   Functional Notation

We presume that you already know how to use the conventional function notation $f(x)$, where f denotes a function and x is an element of the domain of f. It is assumed, for example, that you know that if $f(x) = 4x^2 - 3x + 2$, then $f(-2) = 24$ and $f(a - 3) = 4(a - 3)^2 - 3(a - 3) + 2 = 4a^2 - 27a + 47$.

Definition 4.1.1   *Let X and Y be sets. A **function** f from X to Y, written*

$f : X \to Y$, *is a rule*[1] *that pairs an element $x \in X$ with an element $y \in Y$,
written $f(x) = y$, such that the following property holds.*

$$(\forall x \in X)(\exists! \, y \in Y)[f(x) = y]. \tag{4.1.1}$$

The set X is the **domain** *of f, and the set Y is the* **codomain** *of f. If
$f(x) = y$, then y is the* **image** *of x, and x is a* **preimage** *of y.*

Note the use of articles in the previous sentence: *the* image and *a* preimage.
As stated in the definition, each element of the domain has a *unique* image,
but there is no mention of any such condition being imposed on preimages of
elements of the codomain. The following example illustrates this important
point.

Example 4.1.2   Let $X = \{1, 2, 3, 4\}$ and $Y = \{a, b, c\}$. Let $f : X \to Y$ be
defined by

$$f(1) = b, \quad f(2) = b, \quad f(3) = c, \quad f(4) = c,$$

as indicated by Figure 4.1.1.

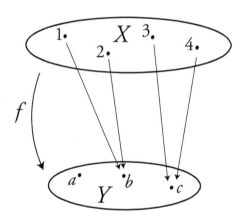

Figure 4.1.1: Example 4.1.2.

This is a function. Each element of X has exactly one image. However, the
element b of the codomain Y has two preimages, and the same holds for c,
while a has no preimage.

---

[1]The term "rule" in this context is undefined. This should not get in the way of
understanding the material that follows.

What about g defined by

$$g(1) = b, \; g(2) = a, \; g(3) = c\,?$$

As defined, g is not a function from X to Y because the element $4 \in X$ is not paired with an element from Y. Defined by this rule, however, g *is* a function from $\{1, 2, 3\}$ to Y.

On the other hand, consider h defined by

$$h(1) = a, \; h(1) = b, \; h(2) = b, \; h(3) = c, \; h(4) = a.$$

Do you see why h fails to satisfy the definition of a function?

Definition 4.1.3   *Two functions are* **equal** *when*
   (i) they have the same domain and the same codomain, and
   (ii) they agree at every element of their domain.

We interpret and apply the definition of equality of functions in the following way. Suppose that $f : X_1 \to Y_1$ and $g : X_2 \to Y_2$. Then $f = g$ precisely when $X_1 = X_2$ and $Y_1 = Y_2$ and $(\forall x \in X_1)[f(x) = g(x)]$.

Exercise 4.1.4   Let $f : A \to \mathbb{R}$ be defined by $f(x) = x^3 - 9x^2 + 23x - 12$, where $A = \{1, 3, 6\}$. Let $g : B \to \mathbb{R}$ be defined by $g(x) = x^2 - 4x + 6$, where

$$B = \big\{x \in \mathbb{N} : x \mid 6\big\} \setminus \big\{x : x \text{ is an even prime number}\big\}.$$

Prove that $f = g$.

The definition of a function places no restriction on the codomain. For example, the constant function $f : \mathbb{R} \to \mathbb{R}$ defined by $f(x) = 13$ uses only the single element 13 of the codomain $\mathbb{R}$, and yet it is still a reasonable and important (though simple) function. There is an important subset of the codomain that consists precisely of those elements that are actually paired with elements of the domain.

Definition 4.1.5   *Let $f : X \to Y$. The* **range** *of f is the set*

$$\big\{y \in Y : (\exists x \in X)[f(x) = y]\big\}.$$

Equivalently, the range of f is the set of all images of elements of the domain and may be indicated more briefly as

$$\{f(x) : x \in X\}.$$

Example 4.1.6 Let $f : \mathbb{N} \to \mathbb{N}$ be the function defined by the rule $f(n) = n^2$ for all $n \in \mathbb{N}$. The range of f is $\{1, 4, 9, 16, 25, \ldots\}$. Even though the integer 20 is in the codomain of f, 20 is not in the range of f, since there is no natural number whose square is 20.

Example 4.1.7 In Section 1.2, you encountered the term *propositional function*. Such an object really is a function. Its domain is some universal set, and its codomain is the set $\{\mathbf{T}, \mathbf{F}\}$. Any preimage of $\mathbf{T}$ is an element of the truth set of the propositional function. For example, if $P(n)$ means, "n is a prime number," then we have

$$P : \mathbb{N} \to \{\mathbf{T}, \mathbf{F}\},$$

and the set of all the preimages of $\mathbf{T}$ is the set of all prime numbers. The range of a tautology is the subset $\{\mathbf{T}\}$; the range of a contradiction is the subset $\{\mathbf{F}\}$.

In the calculus or precalculus setting, we encounter the notion of the "inverse" of a function. This notion makes precise, for example, the relationship between squaring and taking a square root or between the action of an exponential function and the action of a logarithmic function.

Definition 4.1.8 *Let $f : X \to Y$. The* **inverse** *of f (or f* **inverse***), denoted f^{-1}, is the pairing defined by the rule that, if $f(x) = y$, then $f^{-1}(y) = x$.*

Note that f^{-1} is defined as a "pairing" rather than as a function because f^{-1} is not necessarily a function from Y to X.

Example 4.1.9 Let $f : \{1, 2, 3\} \to \{a, b, c\}$ be defined by

$$f(1) = a, \quad f(2) = a, \quad f(3) = b.$$

Then we would have

$$f^{-1}(a) = 1, \quad f^{-1}(a) = 2, \quad f^{-1}(b) = 3.$$

The rule that pairs elements of $\{a, b\}$ with elements of $\{1, 2, 3\}$ is clear, but it is also clear that f^{-1} is not a function since the element of $\{1, 2, 3\}$ with which a is paired is not unique.

Exercise 4.1.10 Let $X = \{a, b, c, d\}$ and $Y = \{1, 2, 3\}$. Define $f : X \to Y$ by

$$f(a) = 1, \quad f(b) = 3, \quad f(c) = 2, \quad f(d) = 3.$$

List the pairings for f^{-1}. Is f^{-1} a function from Y to X? Explain why or why not.

4.2 Operations on Functions

In your first course in calculus, you encountered three operations on functions and called them *addition*, *multiplication*, and *composition*. In fact, you probably encountered more than just these three (e.g., *subtraction*), but for now, we will concentrate primarily just on these three. The motivation for introducing these operations in a calculus course is to be able to state more concisely some useful rules for differentiation, such as, "The derivative of the sum of two functions is the sum of their derivatives, but the derivative of their product is not the product of their derivatives." Both the domain and the codomain of the functions studied in a first course in calculus are subsets of $\mathbb{R}$. Here, as in Section 4.1, we treat functions with a variety of domains and codomains.

Suppose that sets X and Y are given. We impose no conditions on X, but let us for now require that Y has an operation that we denote by the symbol $+$. Here are some familiar examples of such a set Y.

- Y is the set $\mathbb{N}$ and $+$ denotes the addition that one learns in first-grade arithmetic.

- $Y = \mathbb{R} \times \mathbb{R}$ and, for $(x_1, y_1), (x_2, y_2) \in \mathbb{R} \times \mathbb{R}$, we have

$$(x_1, y_1) + (x_2, y_2) = (x_1 + x_2, y_1 + y_2).$$

[Those who have studied vectors will recognize this operation as "head-to-tail" vector addition in the plane.]

- Y is the set of 3×4 matrices[2] with entries in $\mathbb{Z}$ and $+$ denotes the standard entry-to-entry addition of same-size matrices.

Suppose that $f : X \to Y$ and $g : X \to Y$. We define a new function $f + g : X \to Y$ by the rule that, for all $x \in X$,

$$(f + g)(x) = f(x) + g(x). \qquad (4.2.1)$$

Beware of the double meaning of $+$ in statement (4.2.1)! The symbol $+$ occurs twice but with different meanings in its two occurrences. In the left-hand member, $+$ is part of the bigger symbol $f + g$, which denotes our new function. In the right-hand member, $+$ denotes whatever it is supposed to denote in the set Y; both $f(x)$ and $g(x)$ are elements of Y, and $+$ denotes the additive operation (i.e., the "arithmetic") of Y.

Example 4.2.1

1. Let $X = \mathbb{N}$ and $Y = \mathbb{Z}$. For all $n \in X$, let $f(n) = 2^n$ and $g(n) = 100 - 3^n$. Then $f + g$ is given by the rule that, for all $n \in \mathbb{N}$,

$$(f + g)(n) = f(n) + g(n) = 2^n + (100 - 3^n).$$

Thus, $(f + g)(1) = 99$, $(f + g)(2) = 95$, and $(f + g)(5) = -111$.

2. Let $X = \mathbb{R}$ and $Y = \mathbb{R} \times \mathbb{R}$. For all $x \in \mathbb{R}$, let $f(x) = (x/\pi, x^2)$ and $g(x) = (\sin x, \pi^2)$. Then for all $x \in \mathbb{R}$, $(f + g)(x) = (x/\pi + \sin x, x^2 + \pi^2)$. For example, $(f + g)(\pi) = (1, 2\pi^2)$.

3. Let X denote the collection of finite nonempty subsets of $\mathbb{N}$, and let $Y = \mathbb{Q}$. For each set $S \in X$, let $f(S)$ denote the average of all the elements of S, and let $g(S)$ denote the number of elements in S. Then

$$(f + g)\big(\{1, 2, 4, 8, 16, 32, 64, 128\}\big)$$
$$= f\big(\{1, 2, 4, 8, 16, 32, 64, 128\}\big) + g\big(\{1, 2, 4, 8, 16, 32, 64, 128\}\big)$$
$$= 31.875 + 8$$
$$= 39.875.$$

---

[2]If you haven't studied any linear algebra, feel free to ignore this and similar examples.

Notation. The expression $f + g$ denotes a function, but the expression $(f + g)(x)$ denotes an element of Y. Observe here the absence of parentheses in the first instance and the presence of two pairs of parentheses in the second instance. There's nothing random in this usage. If the first pair of parentheses were to be omitted in the second instance, we'd come up with the meaningless expression $f + g(x)$. Why does this expression have no meaning in this context? It looks like we're adding the function f to the element $g(x) \in Y$, while no such addition has been defined.

With addition of functions explained, it is but a short step to products of functions. Again, we have sets X and Y and functions $f, g : X \to Y$, but now we impose some additional structure upon the set Y. We assume that, in addition to addition, Y also has another operation called *multiplication*, where the *product* (the result of the multiplication) of $y_1, y_2 \in Y$ is denoted by $y_1 \cdot y_2$ or sometimes simply by $y_1 y_2$. Many mathematical objects have two such operations. Examples include $\mathbb{N}, \mathbb{Z}, \mathbb{Q}, \mathbb{R}$, and $\mathbb{C}$, as well as the set of $n \times n$ (square) matrices for each $n \in \mathbb{N}$. Here the order in which the elements appear may be important (as in the case of multiplication of matrices).

It is always assumed that *multiplication distributes over addition* in Y; that is, for all $y_1, y_2, y_3 \in Y$,

$$y_1 \cdot (y_2 + y_3) = y_1 \cdot y_2 + y_1 \cdot y_3$$

and (4.2.2)

$$(y_1 + y_2) \cdot y_3 = y_1 \cdot y_3 + y_2 \cdot y_3.$$

When Y satisfies (4.2.2), and if $f : X \to Y$ and $g : X \to Y$ are given, then we define the new function $f \cdot g$ (also denoted simply by fg) by the rule that, for all $x \in X$,

$$(f \cdot g)(x) = f(x) \cdot g(x).$$

Sometimes we write fg and sometimes $f \cdot g$, choosing the latter only if more clarification is needed. Of course, the notational convention concerning parentheses that was just mentioned in the context of addition of functions also applies to multiplication of functions.

Example 4.2.2 Let X, Y, f, and g be as in the first case in Example 4.2.1. Then for all $n \in \mathbb{N}$, we have $(f \cdot g)(n) = 2^n \cdot 100 - 6^n$.

A special case of multiplication of functions arises when the first function in the product is a *constant function*. You have certainly seen constant functions in previous courses; their graphs are horizontal lines.

Definition 4.2.3 *Let X and Y be any sets. A function $f : X \to Y$ is a* **constant function** *when the following property holds.*

$$(\exists\, a \in Y)(\forall\, x \in X)[f(x) = a].$$

Assume once again that Y is a set with addition and multiplication. Suppose that $f : X \to Y$ is the constant function given by $(\forall x \in X)[f(x) = a]$, where a is some element of Y, and that g is any function from X into Y. Then fg may be written as ag. In particular, if Y is a set of numbers containing 1 and -1, then the function $(-1)g$ is written as $-g$ and is called the **negative** of g.

Using the definitions and notational conventions of this section, let us prove that functions satisfy a distributive law akin to the distributive law of statement (4.2.2). This means that given the functions $f, g, h : X \to Y$ where $Y \subseteq \mathbb{R}$, then $h(f + g) = hf + hg$. We must prove that the two functions $h(f+g)$ and $hf+hg$ are indeed the same function. So we proceed as follows.

Let x be an arbitrary element of X. Then

$$
\begin{aligned}
[h(f + g)](x) &= h(x)[(f + g)(x)] && \text{[definition of product of functions]} \\
&= h(x)(f(x) + g(x)) && \text{[definition of sum of functions]} \\
&= h(x)f(x) + h(x)g(x) && \text{[distributive law in } \mathbb{R}] \\
&= (hf)(x) + (hg)(x) && \text{[definition of product of functions]} \\
&= (hf + hg)(x) && \text{[definition of sum of functions].}
\end{aligned}
$$

Since the equality $[h(f + g)](x) = (hf + hg)(x)$ (of numbers) holds for all $x \in X$, the equality $h(f + g) = hf + hg$ (of functions) holds.

Notation. In mathematical notation, parentheses may serve in many roles, and the preceding proof illustrates this point. We see the two expressions $h(f + g)$ and $h(x)$, each with a pair of parentheses. By $h(f + g)$, we mean the *function* $h \cdot (f + g)$, and the parentheses tell us that it is obtained by *first* adding f and g and *then* multiplying their sum by h. On the other hand, $h(x)$ is *not* a function but is the image in Y (with respect to the function h) of the element x of X. It is absolutely essential, when reading a mathematical argument, to bear constantly in mind *where* the various mathematical objects "live"; $h(f + g)$ lives in the set of functions from X to Y, while $h(x)$ lives in the set Y.

Exercise 4.2.4 Let X be a set, let $f, g : X \to \mathbb{R}$, and let $a, b \in \mathbb{R}$. Prove the following equalities.
(a) $1f = f$.
(b) $f + f = 2f$.
(c) $f + (-f) = \mathbf{0} = 0f$. (Here $\mathbf{0}$ denotes a particular constant function, not the number 0. What is that function?)
(d) $(a + b)f = af + bf$. (Does the symbol $+$ play the same role in its two occurrences here? Explain.)
(e) $a(f + g) = af + ag$. (Once again, does the symbol $+$ play the same role in its two occurrences here? Explain.)
(f) $(af) \cdot g = a(f \cdot g) = f \cdot (ag)$.

More notation. Instead of writing the sum of the functions f and $-g$ as $f + (-g)$, we write simply $f - g$. So *subtraction* of functions is merely a special case of addition.

If $f : X \to \mathbb{R}$, then $1/f$ denotes the function whose domain is

$$\{x \in X : f(x) \neq 0\}$$

and whose rule is that, for all x in its domain, $(1/f)(x) = 1/f(x)$. One *never* denotes $1/f(x)$ by $f^{-1}(x)$ because f^{-1} has the special meaning assigned to it in Section 4.1. However, it's perfectly all right to write $(1/f)(x) = [f(x)]^{-1}$ because $f(x)$ is a real number, not a function. The function $1/f$ is called the **reciprocal** of f, while f^{-1} was named the *inverse* of f in Section 4.1.

Exercise 4.2.5 Prove that if $f(x) \neq 0$ for all $x \in S$, then $1/(1/f) = f$. Why is this false if $f(x) = 0$ for some $x \in S$?

Definition 4.2.6 *Let $S \subseteq \mathbb{R}$ and let $f : S \to \mathbb{R}$. Then f is **increasing on** S if*

$$(\forall x_1, x_2 \in S)[x_1 < x_2 \implies f(x_1) < f(x_2)],$$

f is **decreasing on** S *if*

$$(\forall\, x_1, x_2 \in S)\big[x_1 < x_2 \;\Rightarrow\; f(x_1) > f(x_2)\big],$$

f is **nondecreasing on** S *if*

$$(\forall\, x_1, x_2 \in S)\big[x_1 < x_2 \;\Rightarrow\; f(x_1) \le f(x_2)\big],$$

and f is **nonincreasing on** S *if*

$$(\forall\, x_1, x_2 \in S)\big[x_1 < x_2 \;\Rightarrow\; f(x_1) \ge f(x_2)\big].$$

Note the use of the universal quantifier in these definitions. For example, for a given function f, being "increasing on S" is a property of the whole set S. If f is increasing on some subset of S and decreasing on some other subset of S, then f is neither increasing on S nor decreasing on S.

The same applies when we say that a function is **positive on** S; that means

$$(\forall x \in S)[f(x) > 0],$$

with a similar definition of f is **negative on** S. For example, if $f(x) = 2x - 4$, then f is positive on S if $S \subseteq (2, \infty)$ and f is negative on S if $S \subseteq (-\infty, 2)$, but if $S = (0, 4)$, then f is neither positive on S nor negative on S.

Exercise 4.2.7   Let $S \subseteq \mathbb{R}$ and let $f, g : S \to \mathbb{R}$.
(a) Prove that if f is increasing on S and g is nondecreasing on S, then $f + g$ is increasing on S.
(b) If both f and $f + g$ are increasing on S, then is g necessarily increasing on S? Prove this or give a counterexample.
(c) Prove or disprove that if both f and g are increasing on S and either both functions are positive on S or both are negative on S, then fg is increasing on S. What if exactly one of the functions is positive on S? [Use the definitions. Do not assume that these functions are differentiable.]

We now consider the third and perhaps most important operation on functions: *composition*. This time, the domains and codomains need not support any sort of algebraic structure at all, nor do they need to be the same set.

Definition 4.2.8 *Let X, Y, and Z be sets. Let functions $f : X \to Y$ and $g : Y \to Z$ be given. Then the* **composition of g with f** *(also called the* **composition of f by g***), written $g \circ f$, is defined by*

$$(\forall x \in X)[(g \circ f)(x) = g(f(x))].$$

In this situation, each element $x \in X$ is assigned by f to an element $f(x) \in Y$, which is assigned in turn by g to an element $g(f(x)) \in Z$. Thus we have

$$g \circ f : X \to Z.$$

This is indicated pictorially by Figure 4.2.1.

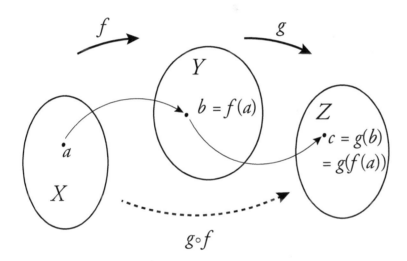

Figure 4.2.1: $(g \circ f)(a) = g(f(a)) = g(b) = c.$

If $X = Z$, then both $g \circ f : X \to X$ and $f \circ g : Y \to Y$ are functions too. However, in general, these two functions are not the same. For example, in the calculus context, suppose $f(x) = x - 2$ and $g(x) = 3x$ for all $x \in \mathbb{R}$. Then $(g \circ f)(x) = 3x - 6$ while $(f \circ g)(x) = 3x - 2$.

For another example, let $f, g : \mathbb{R} \to \mathbb{R}$ be given by $f(x) = x^3$ and $g(x) = 1-x$. Then, for all $x \in \mathbb{R}$, $(f \circ g)(x) = (1 - x)^3$ while $(g \circ f)(x) = 1 - x^3$.

So, unlike addition and multiplication of functions, composition of functions is not commutative. However, like both addition and multiplication of functions, you prove in Exercise 4.2.9 that composition of functions is associative. (Is subtraction associative?)

Exercise 4.2.9   Let $f : X \to Y$, $g : Y \to Z$, and $h : Z \to U$. Prove that for all $x \in X$,

$$[h \circ (g \circ f)](x) = [(h \circ g) \circ f](x).$$

In light of this exercise, we may, without risk of ambiguity, do without parentheses when writing a string of functions connected by composition. We may write simply $h \circ g \circ f$.

One might expect from the definition of $g \circ f$ that the domain of $g \circ f$ should be exactly the domain of f. However, in calculus, you have certainly seen situations where this is not so, and yet $g \circ f$ is treated as a well-defined function. Suppose, for example, that $X = \mathbb{R}$ and that f and g are given by $f(x) = x - 2$, and $g(x) = 1/x$. What then is $(g \circ f)(2)$? The problem in this case is that the range of f—namely, $\mathbb{R}$—is not contained in the domain of g, the latter being $\mathbb{R} \setminus \{0\}$. The conventional way to get out of messes like this is to replace X in Definition 4.2.8 by the set

$$\{x \in X : f(x) \text{ is in the domain of } g\}.$$

For our example here, the domain of $g \circ f$ is $\mathbb{R} \setminus \{2\}$.

4.3   Induced Set Functions

Recall the function in Example 4.1.6, $f : \mathbb{N} \to \mathbb{N}$ defined by $f(n) = n^2$. What *subset* of $\mathbb{N}$ ought to be matched with the *set* $\{3, 5, 9\}$ with respect to f? Since $f(3) = 9, f(5) = 25$, and $f(9) = 81$, the set $\{9, 25, 81\}$ makes some sense as the set that should be paired with the set $\{3, 5, 9\}$. This pairing motivates the next definition.

Definition 4.3.1 *Let* $f : X \to Y$. *The* **set function**[3] **induced by** f *is the function* $\overline{f} : \mathscr{P}(X) \to \mathscr{P}(Y)$ *defined by the rule that, for all* $A \in \mathscr{P}(X)$,

$$\overline{f}(A) = \big\{y \in Y : (\exists x \in A)[f(x) = y]\big\} = \big\{f(x) : x \in A\big\}.$$

Note that for any function $f : X \to Y$, we can denote the range of f by $\overline{f}(X)$. Also note that $\overline{f}(\varnothing) = \varnothing$ and that, if $f(x) = y$, we have that $\overline{f}(\{x\}) = \{y\}$.

Example 4.3.2 Let $g : \mathbb{R} \to \mathbb{R}$ be defined by $g(x) = 3x - 4$ and let $A = \big\{x \in \mathbb{R} : 1 < x \le 3\big\} = (1, 3]$. Then $\overline{g}(A) = (-1, 5]$. See Figure 4.3.1.

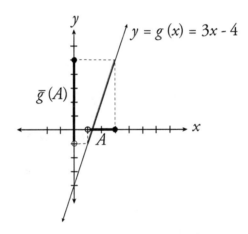

Figure 4.3.1: $\overline{g}(A) = (-1, 5]$.

Example 4.3.3 Let $h : \mathbb{R} \to \mathbb{R}$ be defined by $h(x) = 4 - x^2$. Then $\overline{h}\big((-1, 2]\big) = [0, 4]$. See Figure 4.3.2.

---

[3]Mathematicians usually make no notational distinction between the functions f and $\overline{f}$, even though they have different domains, different codomains, and different rules. For pedagogical purposes, we make this distinction here in § 4.3, in § 4.4, and in § 4.5. As you gain confidence working with induced set functions, you will find that the context makes clear whether f or $\overline{f}$ is intended.

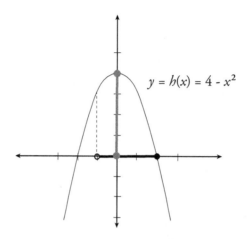

Figure 4.3.2: $\overline{h}\big((-1, 2]\big) = [0, 4]$.

(Note that, even though $h(-1) = 3$ and $h(2) = 0$, $\overline{h}\big((-1, 2]\big)$ is *not* the nonsense $(3, 0]$ and not even the more sensible $[0, 3)$.)

Here are some basic properties of induced set functions.

Theorem 4.3.4   *Let $f : X \to Y$ and let $A, B \in \mathscr{P}(X)$. Then the following hold.*

(i) $A \subseteq B \Rightarrow \overline{f}(A) \subseteq \overline{f}(B)$.

(ii) $\overline{f}(A \cap B) \subseteq \overline{f}(A) \cap \overline{f}(B)$.

(iii) $\overline{f}(A \cup B) = \overline{f}(A) \cup \overline{f}(B)$.

Proof. (i)   Assume that $A \subseteq B$, and let y be an arbitrary element of $\overline{f}(A)$. This means that there exists some $x \in A$ such that $y = f(x)$. Since $A \subseteq B$, we have $x \in B$. Since $x \in B$, we have $y = f(x) \in \overline{f}(B)$. Thus $\overline{f}(A) \subseteq \overline{f}(B)$.

(ii)   Let $y \in \overline{f}(A \cap B)$. Since $A \cap B \subseteq A$, we have $\overline{f}(A \cap B) \subseteq \overline{f}(A)$ by part (i). Similarly, since $A \cap B \subseteq B$, we have $\overline{f}(A \cap B) \subseteq \overline{f}(B)$. Hence $\overline{f}(A \cap B) \subseteq \overline{f}(A) \cap \overline{f}(B)$. (See Figure 4.3.3.)

(iii)   This proof is left as Exercise 4.3.5(b).   □

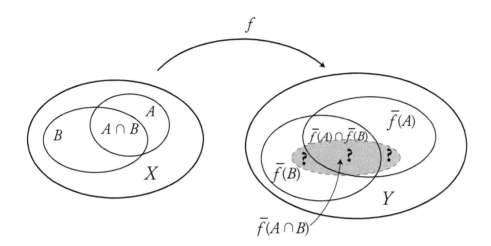

Figure 4.3.3: Theorem 4.3.4(ii).

The converse of the conditional in part (i) of Theorem 4.3.4 is false, and here is a counterexample.

Let $X = \{a, b, c, d\}$ and $Y = \{1, 2, 3\}$. Define $f : X \to Y$ by

$$f(a) = 1, \quad f(b) = 3, \quad f(c) = 2, \quad f(d) = 1.$$

Now let $A = \{c, d\}$ and $B = \{a, b, c\}$. Then

$$\overline{f}(A) = \{1, 2\} \quad \text{and} \quad \overline{f}(B) = \{1, 2, 3\}.$$

In this case, $\overline{f}(A) \subseteq \overline{f}(B)$ but $A \not\subseteq B$.

Exercise 4.3.5 (a) Show by example that the reverse inclusion in part (ii) of Theorem 4.3.4 does not necessarily hold.
(b) Give a proof of part (iii) of Theorem 4.3.4 in such a way that each step of your proof is reversible.

It is natural to ask, how does $\overline{f}(A \setminus B)$ compare with $\overline{f}(A) \setminus \overline{f}(B)$? Let $f : X \to Y$ be as in the example just presented, but now let $A = \{a, b, c\}$ and $B = \{c, d\}$. We have $A \setminus B = \{a, b\}$ and $\overline{f}(A \setminus B) = \{1, 3\}$. Also $\overline{f}(A) = \{1, 2, 3\}$ and $\overline{f}(B) = \{1, 2\}$. Thus $\overline{f}(A) \setminus \overline{f}(B) = \{3\}$. (See Figure 4.3.4.)

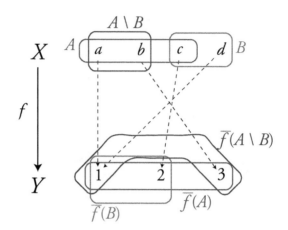

Figure 4.3.4: $\overline{f}(A \setminus B) \neq \overline{f}(A) \setminus \overline{f}(B)$.

Although these two sets need not be equal, the following subset inclusion still holds.

Proposition 4.3.6 *Let $A, B \in \mathscr{P}(X)$ and $f : X \to Y$. Then*

$$\overline{f}(A) \setminus \overline{f}(B) \subseteq \overline{f}(A \setminus B).$$

Proof. Let $y \in \overline{f}(A) \setminus \overline{f}(B)$. This means that $y \in \overline{f}(A)$ and $y \notin \overline{f}(B)$. So there exists $x \in A$ such that $f(x) = y$. If it were so that $x \in B$, then $y = f(x)$ would belong to $\overline{f}(B)$. But $y \notin \overline{f}(B)$, and so $x \notin B$. Thus $x \in A$ and $x \notin B$; that is, $x \in A \setminus B$, making $y \in \overline{f}(A \setminus B)$. Therefore $\overline{f}(A) \setminus \overline{f}(B) \subseteq \overline{f}(A \setminus B)$. $\square$

Exercise 4.3.7 Let $f : X \to Y$, and suppose that X and Y are universal sets. Let $A \subseteq X$.
(a) Prove that if $\overline{f}(X) = Y$ (that is, Y is the range of f), then

$$\left(\overline{f}(A)\right)' \subseteq \overline{f}(A').$$

[Hint: $A' = X \setminus A$ and use Proposition 4.3.6.]
(b) Show by a counterexample that the reverse inclusion can fail.

Recall that for any given function $f : X \to Y$, the pairing f^{-1} sometimes is and sometimes is not a function. However, f^{-1} always induces a set function $\overline{f^{-1}} : \mathscr{P}(Y) \to \mathscr{P}(X)$.

Definition 4.3.8 *Let $f : X \to Y$. For each set $B \in \mathscr{P}(Y)$, define the function $\overline{f^{-1}} : \mathscr{P}(Y) \to \mathscr{P}(X)$ by*

$$\overline{f^{-1}}(B) = \{x \in X : f(x) \in B\}.$$

Let us revisit the function f from Example 4.1.9 and its inverse f^{-1} (which is not a function). Recall that $f : \{1, 2, 3\} \to \{a, b, c\}$ was defined by $f(1) = a$, $f(2) = a$, and $f(3) = b$, so that

$$f^{-1}(a) = 1, \qquad f^{-1}(a) = 2, \qquad f^{-1}(b) = 3.$$

One should first verify that

$$\overline{f}(\varnothing) = \varnothing; \qquad \overline{f}(\{1\}) = \overline{f}(\{2\}) = \overline{f}(\{1,2\}) = \{a\};$$
$$\overline{f}(\{3\}) = \{b\}; \qquad \overline{f}(\{1,3\}) = \overline{f}(\{2,3\}) = \overline{f}(\{1,2,3\}) = \{a,b\}.$$

According to Definition 4.3.8, $\overline{f^{-1}}$ is defined on $\mathscr{P}(\{a, b, c\})$ as follows.

$$\overline{f^{-1}}(\varnothing) = \varnothing \qquad\qquad \overline{f^{-1}}(\{c\}) = \varnothing$$

$$\overline{f^{-1}}(\{a\}) = \{1, 2\} \qquad\qquad \overline{f^{-1}}(\{a, c\}) = \{1, 2\}$$

$$\overline{f^{-1}}(\{b\}) = \{3\} \qquad\qquad \overline{f^{-1}}(\{b, c\}) = \{3\}$$

$$\overline{f^{-1}}(\{a, b\}) = \{1, 2, 3\} \qquad\qquad \overline{f^{-1}}(\{a, b, c\}) = \{1, 2, 3\}$$

It is easily seen that, even though f^{-1} is not a function, $\overline{f^{-1}}$ *is a function* from $\mathscr{P}(Y)$ to $\mathscr{P}(X)$.

Exercise 4.3.9 Let $X = \{a, b, c, d\}$ and $Y = \{1, 2, 3\}$. Define $f : X \to Y$ by

$$f(a) = 1, \quad f(b) = 3, \quad f(c) = 2, \quad f(d) = 3,$$

as in Exercise 4.1.10. Write the eight pairings for the induced set pairing $\overline{f^{-1}}$ from $\mathscr{P}(Y)$ to $\mathscr{P}(X)$, thereby confirming that $\overline{f^{-1}}$ is indeed a function from $\mathscr{P}(Y)$ to $\mathscr{P}(X)$.

Exercise 4.3.10   Let $f\colon X \to Y$ and $E \subseteq Y$. Prove that

$$X \setminus \overline{f^{-1}}(E) \subseteq \overline{f^{-1}}(Y \setminus E).$$

Exercise 4.3.11   Suppose that $f : X \to Y$ and that $x \in X$. Justify the statement: $x \in \overline{f^{-1}}(\{f(x)\})$. Is it true that $\{x\} = \overline{f^{-1}}(\{f(x)\})$? Justify your answer.

The functions $f : X \to Y$ and $g : Y \to Z$ induce, respectively,

$$\overline{f} : \mathscr{P}(X) \to \mathscr{P}(Y) \quad \text{and} \quad \overline{g} : \mathscr{P}(Y) \to \mathscr{P}(Z).$$

Since $\overline{f}(A) \in \mathscr{P}(Y)$, $\overline{g}(\overline{f}(A))$ is a subset of Z. At the same time, we have the function $g \circ f : X \to Z$, which induces the function $\overline{g \circ f} : \mathscr{P}(X) \to \mathscr{P}(Z)$. From these considerations, it is straightforward to verify the following result.

Lemma 4.3.12   *Let X, Y, and Z be sets, and let the functions $f : X \to Y$ and $g : Y \to Z$ be given. Then for all $A \in \mathscr{P}(X)$,*

$$\left(\overline{g \circ f}\right)(A) = \overline{g}\left(\overline{f}(A)\right) = \left(\overline{g} \circ \overline{f}\right)(A).$$

Let $C \subseteq Z$ and recall that

$$\overline{g^{-1}}(C) = \left\{ y \in Y : g(y) \in C \right\},$$

and so $\overline{g^{-1}}$ is a function from $\mathscr{P}(Z)$ to $\mathscr{P}(Y)$. (Do not jump to the sometimes false conclusion that there is necessarily a function g^{-1} from Z to Y.) Similarly, we have the function $\overline{f^{-1}} : \mathscr{P}(Y) \to \mathscr{P}(X)$, and so $\overline{f^{-1}}(\overline{g^{-1}}(C))$ belongs to $\mathscr{P}(X)$. At the same time, $\overline{(g \circ f)^{-1}}$ also maps subsets of Z to subsets of X.

Lemma 4.3.13   *Let X, Y, and Z be sets, and let the functions $f : X \to Y$ and $g : Y \to Z$ be given. Then for all $C \in \mathscr{P}(Z)$*

$$\overline{(g \circ f)^{-1}}(C) = \left(\overline{f^{-1} \circ g^{-1}}\right)(C) = \left(\overline{f^{-1}} \circ \overline{g^{-1}}\right)(C) = \overline{f^{-1}}\left(\overline{g^{-1}}(C)\right).$$

Proof. Let x be an arbitrary element of X. The argument proceeds by chasing up and down the following sequence of equivalent statements.

$$\begin{aligned}
x \in \overline{(g \circ f)^{-1}}(C) \quad &\Longleftrightarrow \quad (g \circ f)(x) \in C \\
&\Longleftrightarrow \quad g(f(x)) \in C \\
&\Longleftrightarrow \quad f(x) \in \overline{g^{-1}}(C) \\
&\Longleftrightarrow \quad x \in \overline{f^{-1}}(\overline{g^{-1}}(C)).
\end{aligned}$$

□

Compare the order in which the various functions are written in the previous two lemmas, especially the reverse order of the inverses of the set functions in Lemma 4.3.13. This makes sense intuitively. One may think of an inverse as *undoing* something. To undo a sequence of actions, the actions often must be undone in an order opposite from the order in which they were done. For example, when *un*dressing, do you ever take off your socks before taking off your shoes?

Exercise 4.3.14 Prove Lemma 4.3.12.

Exercise 4.3.15 Let $f : X \to Y$ and $A, B \in \mathscr{P}(Y)$. Prove the following.
(a) $\overline{f^{-1}}(A \cap B) = \overline{f^{-1}}(A) \cap \overline{f^{-1}}(B)$.
(b) $\overline{f^{-1}}(A \cup B) = \overline{f^{-1}}(A) \cup \overline{f^{-1}}(B)$.
(c) $\overline{f^{-1}}(A \setminus B) = \overline{f^{-1}}(A) \setminus \overline{f^{-1}}(B)$.
Compare to Theorem 4.3.4 and Proposition 4.3.6.

Exercise 4.3.16 Let $f : X \to Y$. Show that for all $S \in \mathscr{P}(X)$ and $T \in \mathscr{P}(Y)$,

$$\overline{f}\left(\overline{f^{-1}}(T)\right) \subseteq T \quad \text{and} \quad \overline{f^{-1}}\left(\overline{f}(S)\right) \supseteq S.$$

4.4 Surjections, Injections, and Bijections

Recall the definition of a *function* from X into Y and (once again) note carefully the order of the quantified variables x and y:

$$(\forall x \in X)(\exists! y \in Y)[f(x) = y]. \tag{4.4.1}$$

By Definition 4.1.1, statement (4.4.1) is true of *every* function. Functions for which this statement *also* holds with the variables (but not the quantifiers) interchanged are of special interest. They will be defined at the end of this section as *bijections*. But we first consider a weaker version, one with the usual existential quantifier $\exists$ rather than with the unique existential quantifier $\exists!$.

Definition 4.4.1   *A function $f : X \to Y$ with the property*

$$(\forall y \in Y)(\exists x \in X)[f(x) = y]$$

is a **surjection**[4] *of X onto Y.*

Saying that a given function is a surjection is equivalent to saying that *every element of the codomain has* at least *one preimage*. We can also say that *a surjection is a function whose range equals its codomain*. In symbols, this means $\overline{f}(X) = Y$.

The codomain of a function determines whether it is a surjection, because every function is a surjection onto its own range. For example, the exponential function $f(x) = e^x$ for all $x \in \mathbb{R}$ is a surjection if we regard f as a function from $\mathbb{R}$ to $(0, \infty)$, but it is not a surjection if we consider f as a function from $\mathbb{R}$ to $\mathbb{R}$. Therefore, to prove that a given function is a surjection, one picks an arbitrary element of the *codomain* and shows that it must have at least one preimage.

Example 4.4.2   Let $f(x) = x^2 - 1$ for $x \in \mathbb{R}$. To prove that f is a surjection onto $[-1, \infty)$, we note every real number $y \geq -1$ has a preimage; 0 is the (unique) preimage of -1, while both $\sqrt{y+1}$ and $-\sqrt{y+1}$ are preimages of y when $y > -1$.

Exercise 4.4.3   A **linear function** is a function $f : \mathbb{R} \to \mathbb{R}$ of the form $f(x) = ax + b$ for all $x \in \mathbb{R}$. Prove that if $a \neq 0$, then f is a surjection.

Theorem 4.4.4   *The composition of two surjections is a surjection.*

---

[4]Surjections are sometimes called *onto functions*. The prefix *sur* is the French word for *on, onto*, or *upon*.

Proof. Suppose that $f : X \to Y$ and $g : Y \to Z$ are surjections. [We must show that $g \circ f$ is a surjection. The codomain of $g \circ f$ is Z.] Let c be an arbitrary element of Z. Since g is a surjection, there exists $b \in Y$ such that $g(b) = c$. Since f is a surjection, there exists $a \in X$ such that $f(a) = b$. Thus

$$c = g(b) = g(f(a)) = (g \circ f)(a).$$

We have shown that the arbitrary element $c \in Z$ has a preimage—namely, a—with respect to the function $g \circ f$. Hence $g \circ f$ satisfies the definition of a surjection. $\square$

Using Lemma 4.3.12, we could have given a shorter proof of Theorem 4.4.4 by arguing that, since $Z = \overline{g}(Y)$ and $Y = \overline{f}(X)$, then $Z = \overline{g}(\overline{f}(X)) = \overline{(g \circ f)}(X)$.

Consider the graph in the plane of a function $f : S \to \mathbb{R}$, where $S \subseteq \mathbb{R}$. We know that equivalent to statement (4.4.1) is the condition that every vertical line meets this graph at most once. If f is a surjection, then every horizontal line meets this graph at least once. (Why is this so?)

Definition 4.4.5   *A function $f : X \to Y$ with the property*

$$(\forall x_1, x_2 \in X)[x_1 \neq x_2 \;\Rightarrow\; f(x_1) \neq f(x_2)] \tag{4.4.2}$$

is an **injection of X into Y**.

Injections are sometimes called *one-to-one functions*. This name is suggested by the contrapositive of the statement (4.4.2): if an element of the range of f is the image both of x_1 and of x_2, then x_1 and x_2 are one and the same element of X. Saying that a given function is an injection is equivalent to saying that every element of the codomain has *at most* one preimage.

Example 4.4.6   Let $f : \mathbb{R} \to \mathbb{R}$ be given by

$$f(x) = \begin{cases} 1/x & \text{if } x \neq 0; \\ 0 & \text{if } x = 0. \end{cases}$$

To prove that f is an injection, let x_1 and x_2 be arbitrary *distinct* elements of $\mathbb{R}$. We must show that $f(x_1) \neq f(x_2)$. There are several cases.

Case 1: $x_1 = 0$. Then $f(x_1) = 0$ and $f(x_2) \neq 0$.

At this point, we lose no generality in assuming that $x_1 < x_2$.

Case 2: $x_1 < 0 < x_2$. Then $f(x_1)$ is negative while $f(x_2)$ is positive, and so they cannot be equal.

Case 3: $0 < x_1 < x_2$. Then $f(x_1) = 1/x_1 > 1/x_2 = f(x_2)$. Again $f(x_1) \neq f(x_2)$.

Case 4: $x_1 < x_2 < 0$. The argument is similar to Case 3 and is left to the reader.

Exercise 4.4.7   Let $f : S \to \mathbb{R}$, where $S \subseteq \mathbb{R}$.
(a) Prove that if f is increasing on S or if f is decreasing on S, then f is an injection.
(b) Show that if f is linear and not constant on S, then f is an injection. (Compare Exercise 4.4.3.)

Exercise 4.4.8   Show that the injection of Example 4.4.6 is also a surjection.

Theorem 4.4.9   *The composition of two injections is an injection.*

Proof. Suppose that $f : X \to Y$ and $g : Y \to Z$ are injections. We must show that $g \circ f$ is an injection.

Let x_1 and x_2 be distinct elements of X. Since f is an injection, $f(x_1)$ and $f(x_2)$ are distinct elements of Y. Since g is an injection, $g(f(x_1))$ and $g(f(x_2))$ are distinct elements of Z. Thus $(g \circ f)(x_1) \neq (g \circ f)(x_2)$, as required. $\square$

The contrapositive of the implication in statement (4.4.2) offers a way to prove that a given function f is an injection. Let x_1 and x_2 be arbitrary elements of the domain of f and assume that $f(x_1) = f(x_2)$. Then deduce that $x_1 = x_2$. For example, to show that the function $f(x) = 7\sqrt[3]{x+1} + 5$ is an injection, let x_1 and x_2 be arbitrary real numbers and set

$$7\sqrt[3]{x_1 + 1} + 5 = 7\sqrt[3]{x_2 + 1} + 5.$$

A sequence of elementary algebraic operations on this equality yields $x_1 = x_2$.

Information about a function f gives information about its induced set function $\overline{f}$, as we see in the next theorem and in Exercise 4.4.14.

Theorem 4.4.10 *If the function $f : X \to Y$ is an injection, then so is its induced set function $\overline{f} : \mathscr{P}(X) \to \mathscr{P}(Y)$.*

Proof. Assume that $f : X \to Y$ is an injection. Let A and B be arbitrary, distinct subsets of X. [We must prove that $\overline{f}(A)$ and $\overline{f}(B)$ are distinct subsets of Y.]

To say that A and B are distinct means that (at least) one of these sets includes an element of X that does not belong to the other. Since these sets were chosen arbitrarily, we may assume that there exists some element $x \in A \setminus B$. Considering X as a universal set, we have $x \in A \cap B'$. Let $y = f(x)$. This implies

$$y \in \overline{f}(A \cap B') \subseteq \overline{f}(A) \cap \overline{f}(B');$$

this last inclusion follows from Theorem 4.3.4(i) (with B' in place of B). Let us note here that $y \in \overline{f}(A)$.

Suppose that $y \in \overline{f}(B)$. [This is not inconsistent (yet) with y belonging to $\overline{f}(B')$. Do you see why?] Then there exists some element $w \in B$ such that $y = f(w)$. But $y = f(x)$, and since f is assumed to be an injection, it must hold that $x = w$. This presents a contradiction: $w \in B$ while $x \notin B$. Hence $y \notin \overline{f}(B)$.

We have shown that $y \in \overline{f}(A) \setminus \overline{f}(B)$. Thus $\overline{f}(A)$ and $\overline{f}(B)$ are distinct subsets of Y. $\square$

Definition 4.4.11 *A function that is both an injection and a surjection is a **bijection**.*

Suppose that $f : X \to Y$ is a bijection. Let $y \in Y$. Since f is an injection, y is the image of *at most one* element of X. Since f is a surjection, y is the image of *at least one* element of X. Hence, each element of Y is the image of *exactly one* element of X. Thus a bijection is a function for which (in addition to statement (4.4.1) which holds for all functions anyway) we have

$$(\forall y \in Y)(\exists! \, x \in X)[f(x) = y]. \qquad (4.4.3)$$

From Theorems 4.4.4 and 4.4.9, we immediately obtain the following result.

Corollary 4.4.12   *The composition of two bijections is a bijection.*

Exercise 4.4.13   Let X be a set and consider the function

$$\alpha : \mathscr{P}(X) \to \mathscr{P}(X)$$

such that for all $S \in \mathscr{P}(X)$, $\alpha(S) = X \setminus S$. Show that α is a bijection. What is $(\alpha \circ \alpha)(S)$ for any $S \in \mathscr{P}(X)$?

The bijection α of Exercise 4.4.13 shows by example that a bijection from $\mathscr{P}(X)$ onto $\mathscr{P}(Y)$ is not necessarily equal to an induced set function $\overline{f}$ for some bijection $f : X \to Y$.

Exercise 4.4.14   Prove that if $f : X \to Y$ is a surjection (respectively, a bijection), then $\overline{f} : \mathscr{P}(X) \to \mathscr{P}(Y)$ is also a surjection (respectively, a bijection).

Exercise 4.4.15   Let $f : X \to Y$. By Theorem 4.4.10 and Exercise 4.4.14, we know that, if f is a surjection (respectively, an injection, a bijection), then so is its induced set function $\overline{f} : \mathscr{P}(X) \to \mathscr{P}(Y)$. Determine whether the converse is true.

Exercise 4.4.16   Let A, B, and C be nonempty sets. Construct a bijection
(a)   from $A \times B$ to $B \times A$;
(b)   from $A \times (B \times C)$ to $(A \times B) \times C$;
(c)   from $A \times (B \times C)$ to $B \times (C \times A)$.

Exercise 4.4.17   Let $f : X \to Y$ and $g : Y \to Z$. Prove the following.
(a) If $g \circ f$ is a surjection, then g is a surjection.
(b) If $g \circ f$ is an injection, then f is an injection.

4.5 Identity Functions, Cancellation, Inverse Functions, and Restrictions

Definition 4.5.1 *For any set X, the **identity function** on X is the function $i_X : X \to X$ given by*

$$(\forall x \in X)\big[i_X(x) = x\big].$$

Clearly, i_X is a bijection. It is also easy to see that given any function $f : X \to Y$, we have

$$f \circ i_X \;=\; f \;=\; i_Y \circ f.$$

Observe that i_X induces the identity function on $\mathscr{P}(X)$; that is, $\overline{i_X} = i_{\mathscr{P}(X)}$.

The following result is very, very useful.

Theorem 4.5.2 *If the functions $f : X \to Y$ and $g : Y \to X$ satisfy $g \circ f = i_X$, then f is an injection and g is a surjection.*

Proof. Assume that $g \circ f = i_X$. To prove that f is an injection, let $x_1, x_2 \in X$ where $f(x_1) = f(x_2)$. [We show that f satisfies the contrapositive of the conditional (4.4.2).] Then

$$x_1 = i_X(x_1) = (g \circ f)(x_1) = g(f(x_1)) = g(f(x_2)) = (g \circ f)(x_2) = i_X(x_2) = x_2.$$

Hence f is an injection.

To prove that g is a surjection, let x_0 be an arbitrary element of X, the codomain of g. Then $x_0 = i_X(x_0) = (g \circ f)(x_0) = g(f(x_0))$. This says that x_0 is the image with respect to g of $f(x_0)$, which means that x_0 is in the range of g. Hence g is a surjection. $\qquad\square$

Example 4.5.3 Suppose that $X = \{a, b\}$ and $Y = \{p, q, r\}$. Define functions $f : X \to Y$ and $g : Y \to X$ by

$$f(a) = p, \quad f(b) = q; \qquad g(p) = a, \quad g(q) = g(r) = b.$$

Then $g \circ f = i_X$. Note that f is not a surjection and g is not an injection. It follows from Theorem 4.5.2 that $f \circ g \neq i_Y$. In particular, $(f \circ g)(r) = q$. If we define $h : Y \to X$ by

$$h(p) = h(r) = a, \quad h(q) = b,$$

then $h \circ f = i_X = g \circ f$, but $h \neq g$. This shows that injections have "left inverses," but they are not necessarily unique.

Similarly, define $j : X \to Y$ by

$$j(a) = p, \quad j(b) = r.$$

Then $g \circ j = i_X = g \circ f$, but $j \neq f$. This shows that surjections have "right inverses," but they are not necessarily unique. (These notions will be formalized in Section 8.1.)

Lemma 4.5.4 *Let X and Y be nonempty sets and let $f : X \to Y$ be a function.*
(i) If f is an injection, then there exists a surjection $g : Y \to X$ such that $g \circ f = i_X$.
(ii) If f is a surjection, then there exists an injection $g : Y \to X$ such that $f \circ g = i_Y$.

Exercise 4.5.5 Prove part (i) of Lemma 4.5.4.

The proof of part (ii) of Lemma 4.5.4 requires the following historically controversial axiom.

The Axiom of Choice.[5] *Let U be any set and let $\mathscr{A}$ be any family of nonempty subsets of U; that is, $\mathscr{A} \subseteq \mathscr{P}(U) \setminus \{\varnothing\}$. Then there exists a function $c : \mathscr{A} \to U$ such that $c(A) \in A$ for all $A \in \mathscr{A}$.*

---

[5]The Axiom of Choice is one of the most controversial declarations in mathematics. It was formulated by the German mathematician Ernst Zermelo (1871–1953) in 1904 in order to prove some theorems about subsets of the real numbers. It seems innocent enough, but among other consequences of the Axiom of Choice is the Banach–Tarski paradox: there exists a decomposition of a solid sphere into a finite number of pieces that can be reassembled to produce two identical copies of the original sphere. The paradox is resolved because the notion of volume is not preserved in the reassembly of the sphere, the pieces being what are known as "unmeasurable sets." It is the Axiom of Choice that allows for the construction of unmeasurable sets. The status of the Axiom of Choice

In many cases, the existence of this function c, which is called a **choice function**, is not at all controversial. For example, when the family $\mathscr{A}$ is finite, then one can explicitly specify for each set $A \in \mathscr{A}$ the element of A chosen by the function c. Another noncontroversial example would be when $U \subseteq \mathbb{N}$. Then, by the Well Ordering Principle, each set $A \in \mathscr{A}$ has a least element, and one may specify that $c(A)$ is always the least element of A.

On the other hand, if, for example, $U = \mathbb{R}$ and $\mathscr{A} = \mathscr{P}(\mathbb{R}) \setminus \{\emptyset\}$, then there is no obvious way that one can describe an explicit choice function c. In such a situation, we need an axiom to assure us that such a choice function does in fact exist.

Proof of Lemma 4.5.4(ii). Let a surjection $f : X \to Y$ be given, and let $\mathscr{A} = \{\overline{f^{-1}}(\{y\}) : y \in Y\}$. Since f is a surjection, $\overline{f^{-1}}(\{y\}) \neq \emptyset$ for all $y \in Y$, and so $\mathscr{A} \subseteq \mathscr{P}(X) \setminus \{\emptyset\}$. By the Axiom of Choice, there exists a choice function $c : \mathscr{A} \to X$ such that for each set $\overline{f^{-1}}(\{y\}) \in \mathscr{A}$, we have $c(\overline{f^{-1}}(\{y\})) \in \overline{f^{-1}}(\{y\})$. This is equivalent to saying that for each $y \in Y$, there exists an element $x \in \overline{f^{-1}}(\{y\})$ such that $c(\overline{f^{-1}}(\{y\})) = x$. Note that $f(x) = y$ for any such $x \in \overline{f^{-1}}(\{y\})$.

We now define the function $g : Y \to X$ by the rule that, for each $y \in Y$, $g(y) = c(\overline{f^{-1}}(\{y\}))$. Thus for each $y \in Y$, $g(y) = x$ for some $x \in \overline{f^{-1}}(\{y\})$. It is now easy to see that $(f \circ g)(y) = y$ for all $y \in Y$, and so $f \circ g = i_Y$.

It remains only to show that g is an injection. Let $y_1, y_2 \in Y$ and suppose that $g(y_1) = g(y_2)$. The choice function c must then have "chosen" the same element $x \in X$ from both $\overline{f^{-1}}(\{y_1\})$ and $\overline{f^{-1}}(\{y_2\})$. But then $y_1 = f(x) = y_2$, implying that g is an injection. $\qquad\square$

---

as an *axiom* is evident in the fact that in 1938, Austrian mathematician Kurt Gödel (1906–1978) proved that assumption of the Axiom of Choice leads to no contradiction to the axioms of set theory. In 1963, American mathematician Paul Cohen (1934–2007) proved that assumption of the negation of the Axiom of Choice is also consistent with the axioms of set theory. Because of its utility in many proofs, the mathematics community generally accepts the Axiom of Choice. But because of its nonintuitive consequences, mathematicians generally agree to full disclosure when the Axiom of Choice is assumed in the course of a proof (as do we in our proof of part (ii) of Lemma 4.5.4). However, there are mathematicians, who call themselves "constructivists," who consider the Axiom to be false and any proof invalid that uses the Axiom of Choice.

The following corollary is an immediate consequence of Lemma 4.5.4.

Corollary 4.5.6 *Let X and Y be nonempty sets. There exists an injection from X into Y if and only if there exists a surjection from Y onto X.*

Proof. Suppose that $f : X \to Y$ is an injection. A surjection $g : Y \to X$ exists by Lemma 4.5.4(i).

Conversely, suppose that $g : Y \to X$ is a surjection. An injection $f : X \to Y$ exists by Lemma 4.5.4(ii). [Note that the proof in this direction depends indirectly upon the Axiom of Choice. Why is that so?]   □

An operation $\bullet$ on a set S satisfies the **left cancellation law** if, for all $a, b, c \in S$, we have: $a \bullet b = a \bullet c \Rightarrow b = c$. The **right cancellation law** is defined similarly: $a \bullet c = b \bullet c \Rightarrow a = b$. We have seen in Example 4.5.3 that if S is a set of functions and $\bullet$ represents the operation of composition of functions, then *in general*, both cancellation laws may fail.

Corollary 4.5.7 *Let X and Y be sets and let $f : X \to Y$ be a function. The following two statements are equivalent.*
(i) f is an injection.
(ii) $(\forall\ h_1, h_2 : Y \to X)[f \circ h_1 = f \circ h_2 \Rightarrow h_1 = h_2]$; that is, the left cancellation law holds.

Proof. (i)$\Rightarrow$(ii). Assume that f is an injection, and let $g : Y \to X$ be a function whose existence is assured by Lemma 4.5.4(i); that is, $g \circ f = i_X$.

Let $h_1, h_2 : Y \to X$, and assume that $f \circ h_1 = f \circ h_2$. By Exercise 4.2.9 (used twice),

$$h_1 = i_X \circ h_1 = (g \circ f) \circ h_1 = g \circ (f \circ h_1)$$
$$= g \circ (f \circ h_2) = (g \circ f) \circ h_2 = i_X \circ h_2 = h_2.$$

(ii)$\Rightarrow$(i). Assume that (ii) holds. Let $x_1, x_2 \in X$ such that $f(x_1) = f(x_2)$. Let $y_0 \in Y$. Define $h_1 : Y \to X$ to be the constant function $h_1(y) = x_1$ for all $y \in Y$, and define

$$h_2(y) = \begin{cases} x_2 & \text{if } y = y_0; \\ x_1 & \text{if } y \neq y_0. \end{cases}$$

(See Figure 4.5.1.) One straightforwardly verifies that $f \circ h_1 = f \circ h_2$. This implies by (ii) that $h_1 = h_2$. Hence $x_1 = h_1(y_0) = h_2(y_0) = x_2$, and so f is an injection. $\square$

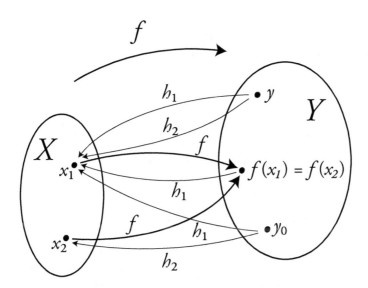

Figure 4.5.1: Corollary 4.5.7.

What the preceding corollary tells us is that, if the function being canceled is an injection, then it can be left canceled. (Example 4.5.3 shows that an injection cannot necessarily be right canceled.) The next corollary tells us that, on the other hand, surjections can be right canceled.

Corollary 4.5.8 *Let X and Y be sets, where X has at least two elements, and let $f : X \to Y$ be a function. The following two statements are equivalent.*
(i) f is a surjection.
(ii) $(\forall g_1, g_2 : Y \to X)[g_1 \circ f = g_2 \circ f \implies g_1 = g_2]$; that is, the right cancellation law holds.

Proof. (i)$\Rightarrow$(ii). Assume that f is a surjection, and let g be a function whose existence is assured by Lemma 4.5.4(ii); that is, $f \circ g = i_Y$. The argument is now similar to the proof of (i)$\Rightarrow$(ii) of Corollary 4.5.7 and is left as Exercise 4.5.9.

(ii)$\Rightarrow$(i). We prove the contrapositive. Suppose that f is not a surjection. There exists an element $y_0 \in Y \setminus \overline{f}(X)$. By hypothesis, there exist distinct elements x_1 and x_2 of X. Define g_1 to be the constant function $g_1(y) = x_1$ for all $y \in Y$, and define $g_2 : Y \to X$ by

$$g_2(y) = \begin{cases} x_1 & \text{if } y \neq y_0; \\ x_2 & \text{if } y = y_0. \end{cases}$$

Then, since $f(x) \neq y_0$ for all $x \in X$, we have for all $x \in X$,

$$(g_1 \circ f)(x) = g_1(f(x)) = x_1 = g_2(f(x)) = (g_2 \circ f)(x).$$

Hence $g_1 \circ f = g_2 \circ f$, but $g_1 \neq g_2$.   □

Exercise 4.5.9   Complete the proof of (i)$\Rightarrow$(ii) in Corollary 4.5.8.

By putting these last two corollaries together, we obtain that a function is a bijection if and only if it can be *both* left and right canceled. Bijections alone enjoy other nice properties, as we presently see.

Definition 4.5.10   *Let X and Y be sets and let $f : X \to Y$ be a function. If $g : Y \to X$ satisfies the two conditions $g \circ f = i_X$ and $f \circ g = i_Y$, then g is an* **inverse function** *of f (or, more briefly, simply an* **inverse** *of f).*

Theorem 4.5.11   *Let X and Y be sets, let $f : X \to Y$ be a function, and let g be an inverse of f. Then the following hold.*
(i) Both f and g are bijections.
(ii) f is an inverse of g.
(iii) g is the unique inverse of f.

Proof. (i) By definition of *inverse*, we have $g \circ f = i_X$ and $f \circ g = i_Y$. By Theorem 4.5.2, the first equality implies that g is a surjection and f is an injection, while the second equality implies that f is a surjection and g is an injection. Hence both functions are bijections.
(ii) That f is an inverse of g is immediate from the definition.
(iii) Uniqueness of the inverse follows from Corollary 4.5.7 or Corollary 4.5.8. [Write out the details in Exercise 4.5.12.]   □

Exercise 4.5.12 Prove in detail part (iii) of Theorem 4.5.11.

In light of Theorem 4.5.11(iii), we may now speak of *the* inverse of a function $f : X \to Y$ instead of *an* inverse, and we denote it by f^{-1}. From part (ii), we have that $(f^{-1})^{-1} = f$.

When the inverse of f exists—that is, when f^{-1} really is a function—then the function $\overline{f^{-1}} : \mathscr{P}(Y) \to \mathscr{P}(X)$, induced by the function f^{-1}, is identical to the inverse of the function $\overline{f} : \mathscr{P}(X) \to \mathscr{P}(Y)$ induced by f. That is (and only under this assumption),

$$\overline{f}^{-1} = \overline{f^{-1}}.$$

Now we know under what conditions, given f, the inverse f^{-1} exists. But how does one actually determine the function $f^{-1} : Y \to X$? Here's how. Because f must be a bijection, statement (4.4.3) applies: for each $y \in Y$, there is a unique $x \in X$ such that $f(x)$ equals that value y. Assign $f^{-1}(y)$ to be *that* x. Because f is an injection, that particular x is unique, and so f^{-1} really is a function. (Compare statement (4.4.1) with x and y interchanged.) Because f is a surjection, every $y \in Y$ is the image of *some* $x \in X$, and so the domain of f^{-1} is *all* of Y. In this case,

$$(\forall x \in X)(\forall y \in Y)[f(x) = y \iff f^{-1}(y) = x].$$

In single-variable calculus, you dealt with problems precisely of this type. In the calculus context, both X and Y are subsets of $\mathbb{R}$. The **graph** of f was defined to be the subset of $\mathbb{R} \times \mathbb{R}$ described as

$$\{(x, y) \in \mathbb{R} \times \mathbb{R} : y = f(x)\}.$$

It follows that the graph of f^{-1} must be the set

$$\{(y, x) \in \mathbb{R} \times \mathbb{R} : y = f(x)\}.$$

These two sets are mirror images of each other across the line $y = x$. (See Exercise 4.6.27.)

We finally come to the last new notion of this chapter.

Definition 4.5.13 *Given a function $f : X \to Y$ and a subset $S \subseteq X$, the* **restriction of f to S** *is the function $f|_S : S \to Y$ given by $f|_S(x) = f(x)$ for all $x \in S$.*

A restriction of a function thus amounts to no more than lopping off part of its domain. The reason for considering a restriction of a function f is that we would often like to have an inverse of f, but f is not a bijection. That f may not be a surjection is not generally a problem, since we can (and often do) ignore elements of the codomain that are not in the range. The problem arises when f is not an injection; some $y \in \overline{f}(X)$ has more than one preimage, and so it's not evident which of these preimages $f^{-1}(y)$ is supposed to be. Therefore we throw away just enough of the domain X of f so that the set S that's left is just big enough to contain exactly one preimage of each element $y \in \overline{f}(X)$.

As an example, consider how in calculus you defined the function that is denoted by $\sin^{-1}$, or sometimes by arcsin. Now, the sine function with domain $\mathbb{R}$ is a very far cry from being an injection. Its range is $[-1, 1]$, but every element of that range has infinitely many preimages. Hence there are infinitely many subsets S of $\mathbb{R}$ to which one might restrict the sine function in order to produce a bijection onto $[-1, 1]$. One wouldn't even have to choose an interval, but we do in this case. By convention (and for the sake of simplicity), the set S is chosen to be $[-\pi/2, \pi/2]$. Thus the function

$$\sin^{-1} : [-\pi/2, \pi/2] \to [-1, 1]$$

is the so-called inverse sine function, even though the (unrestricted) sine function, of course, cannot have an inverse.

Change of Notation. Up to this point, given a function $f : X \to Y$, we have indicated by $\overline{f}$ the function from $\mathscr{P}(X)$ to $\mathscr{P}(Y)$ induced by f. *This is not a conventional notation* but rather one that we have selected in order to clarify and to emphasize that f and $\overline{f}$ are, in fact, two distinct functions with two disjoint domains and disjoint codomains. Various authors have used other notational conventions to make this important distinction. One solution, for example,[6] is to write $f(x)$ if $x \in X$ but write $f[S]$ if $S \in \mathscr{P}(X)$.

---

[6]See J. E. Graver and M. E. Watkins, *Combinatorics with Emphasis on the Theory of Graphs*, (New York: Springer-Verlag, 1977).

However, in the majority of mathematical literature, no symbolic distinction is made between f and $\overline{f}$; the same symbol f is used for both functions, and the reader is expected to discern from the context which of the two functions the one symbol f is denoting.

The use of the same symbol doing double or even multiple duty is not new to you. In Section 4.2, for example, you saw how the plus sign may be used within the very same mathematical expression to mean both addition of real numbers and addition of functions. The prime symbol has multiple meanings: f' denotes the derivative a function f; A' denotes the complement of a set A; x and x' may denote two real numbers in the course of a proof or definition. Here is still another example: if you write 3 as a superscript to a real number x, then x^3 means the cube of x, but $\mathbb{R}^3$ denotes the Cartesian product of $\mathbb{R}$ with itself three times—that is, 3-dimensional space.

As stated in the footnote to Definition 4.3.1, separate symbols for a function and its induced set function have been used for the purpose of clarity of presentation. However, we henceforth dispense with this notational distinction (except in some of the earlier exercises in the next section) and rejoin the rest of the mathematical community by using just one functional symbol.

4.6 Further Exercises

Exercise 4.6.1 Let $S \subseteq \mathbb{R}$ and let $f, g : S \to \mathbb{R}$.
(a) Prove or disprove that if both f and g are differentiable, positive, and increasing on S, then fg is increasing on S. What if exactly one of the functions is positive on S? What if both functions are negative on S? [Hint: Use the product rule for differentiation.]
(b) Assume that f is positive on S or that f is negative on S. Prove that f is nondecreasing on S if and only if $1/f$ is nonincreasing on S. Give two proofs, one assuming that f is differentiable on S and one without that assumption.
(c) Prove that if f is a twice differentiable function that is increasing on S, and if the graph of f is concave upward, then $f + f'$ is increasing on S.

Exercise 4.6.2   Prove that the composition of two increasing (respectively, nondecreasing, nonincreasing, decreasing) functions is increasing (respectively, nondecreasing, nonincreasing, increasing).

Exercise 4.6.3   Let $S \subseteq \mathbb{R}$ and let f and g be functions from S into S. Suppose that f is increasing on S and g is decreasing on S. Is $g \circ f$ necessarily increasing on S, or decreasing on S, or neither? Prove your claim.

Exercise 4.6.4   Let $f : \mathbb{R} \to \mathbb{R}$ be given by $f(x) = |x|$ for all $x \in \mathbb{R}$. Determine each of the following sets.

$\quad$ (a) $\overline{f}((-2, 1])$ $\quad$ (b) $\overline{f^{-1}}((-2, 1])$ $\quad$ (c) $\overline{f^{-1}}(\{-5\})$
$\quad$ (d) $\overline{f}(\mathbb{Z})$ $\qquad$ (e) $\overline{f^{-1}}(\mathbb{Z})$ $\qquad$ (f) $\overline{f}(\mathbb{R})$

Exercise 4.6.5   Let X and Y be sets and let $f : X \to Y$. Let A and B be subsets of X.
(a) Prove that if $\overline{f}(A) \cap \overline{f}(B) = \varnothing$, then $A \cap B = \varnothing$.
(b) Construct a counterexample to the converse of the statement in (a).

Exercise 4.6.6   Let $f(x) = x^2 - 2$ and $g(x) = 1/x$ for all real numbers x for which these functions make sense. Determine $\overline{(g \circ f)}(A)$, $\overline{(f \circ g)}(A)$, $\overline{(g \circ f)^{-1}}(A)$, and $\overline{(f \circ g)^{-1}}(A)$ for each of the following definitions of the set A.

$\quad$ (a) $\quad A = [-2, 1)$ $\quad$ (b) $\quad A = \mathbb{N}$ $\quad$ (c) $\quad A = (-\infty, 0]$

Exercise 4.6.7   Let $f : X \to Y$, $g : Y \to Z$, and $h : Z \to U$. Prove that for all $T \in \mathscr{P}(U)$,

$$\overline{(h \circ g \circ f)^{-1}}(T) = \overline{f^{-1}}(\overline{g^{-1}}(\overline{h^{-1}}(T))).$$

[Hint: Use Lemmas 4.3.12 and 4.3.13.]

Exercise 4.6.8   (This exercise requires Exercise 3.6.12.) Let X and Y be sets and let $f : X \to Y$. Let $A, B \in \mathscr{P}(X)$ and $C, D \in \mathscr{P}(Y)$. Recall that $+$ for sets is the symmetric difference operation. Prove the following.
(a) $\overline{f}(A) + \overline{f}(B) \subseteq \overline{f}(A + B)$.
(b) $\overline{f^{-1}}(C) + \overline{f^{-1}}(D) = \overline{f^{-1}}(C + D)$.

Exercise 4.6.9 Suppose that $f : \mathbb{R} \setminus \{0\} \to \mathbb{R} \setminus \{0\}$ is given by $f(x) = 1/x$ for all $x \in \mathbb{R} \setminus \{0\}$. Find some functions g such that $f \circ g = g \circ f$.

Exercise 4.6.10 Let $f : \mathbb{Z} \to \mathbb{Z}$ and $g : \mathbb{Z} \to \mathbb{Z}$ be defined as follows.

$$f(n) = \begin{cases} n + 5 & \text{if } n \geq 1; \\ n - 1 & \text{if } n \leq 0. \end{cases}$$

And

$$g(n) = \begin{cases} n - 5 & \text{if } n \geq 1; \\ n + 1 & \text{if } n \leq 0. \end{cases}$$

(a) Determine the rule for the function $g \circ f$.
(b) By a theorem from this chapter, what does your answer to part (a) tell you about whether f or g is an injection or a surjection?
(c) Determine from the definition of f whether f is a surjection.
(d) Determine from the definition of g whether g is an injection.

Exercise 4.6.11 For each of the following descriptions, give an example of a function $f : \mathbb{Z} \to \mathbb{Z}$ that matches the description.
(a) f is a bijection.
(b) f is an injection but not a surjection.
(c) f is a surjection but not an injection.
(d) f is neither an injection nor a surjection.

Exercise 4.6.12 (a) Suppose that $f : \mathbb{R} \to \mathbb{R}$ is continuous, $\lim\limits_{x \to \infty} f(x) = \infty$, and $\lim\limits_{x \to -\infty} f(x) = -\infty$. Prove that f is a surjection. [Hint: Use the Intermediate Value Theorem from your calculus course in conjunction with the definitions of these infinite limits.]
(b) Use part (a) to prove that the function $g(x) = 1 - x - x^3$ is a bijection.
(c) Use a variation of your proof of (a) to prove that the restricted tangent function $\tan : \left(-\frac{\pi}{2}, \frac{\pi}{2}\right) \to \mathbb{R}$ is a surjection and, in fact, a bijection.

Exercise 4.6.13 Let A be any set, and let B be a nonempty subset of A. Show that there always exists a surjection from A onto B.

Exercise 4.6.14 Define $f : \mathbb{Z} \to \mathbb{N}$ by

$$f(n) = \begin{cases} 10n + 5 & \text{if } n \geq 0; \\ -10n & \text{if } n < 0. \end{cases}$$

And let $g : \mathbb{N} \to \mathbb{Z}$ satisfy $g(n) = n^2$ for all $n \in \mathbb{N}$.
(a) Prove that f is an injection.
(b) Prove that g is an injection.
(c) What do parts (a) and (b) tell you about $g \circ f$ and $f \circ g$?

Exercise 4.6.15 Let $\mathscr{P}_0(\mathbb{N})$ denote the family of all finite subsets of $\mathbb{N}$. For each set $S \in \mathscr{P}_0(\mathbb{N})$, let $\alpha(S)$ denote the number of elements in S. Show that $\alpha : \mathscr{P}_0(\mathbb{N}) \to \mathbb{N} \cup \{0\}$ is a surjection but not an injection.

Exercise 4.6.16 Prove that $f : X \to Y$ is an injection if and only if the equation $\overline{f^{-1}}\big(\overline{f}(A)\big) = A$ holds for all $A \in \mathscr{P}(X)$. Use this to prove that $f : X \to Y$ is an injection if and only if $\overline{f^{-1}} : \mathscr{P}(Y) \to \mathscr{P}(X)$ is a surjection.

Exercise 4.6.17 Let $g : A \to C$ and $h : B \to D$ be bijections. Let $x \in A \cup B$. Define

$$g \cup h : A \cup B \to C \cup D$$

by

$$(g \cup h)(x) = \begin{cases} g(x) \text{ if } x \in A; \\ h(x) \text{ if } x \in B. \end{cases}$$

(a) Prove that if $A \cap B = \varnothing$ and $C \cap D = \varnothing$, then $g \cup h$ is a bijection.
(b) Show that if $A \cap B \neq \varnothing$, then $g \cup h$ need not even be a function.

Exercise 4.6.18 Let $\mathscr{C}$ denote the set of all circles in the plane. Construct a bijection from the set $\mathbb{R} \times \mathbb{R} \times (0, \infty)$ onto the set $\mathscr{C}$ and verify that it is indeed a bijection.

Exercise 4.6.19 Let $A, B, C,$ and D be nonempty sets. Suppose that there exist injections (respectively, surjections, bijections) $f : A \to C$ and $g : B \to D$. Prove that there exists an injection (respectively, a surjection, a bijection) from $A \times B$ to $C \times D$.

Exercise 4.6.20 Let $\alpha : \mathscr{P}(\mathbb{Z}) \to \mathscr{P}(\mathbb{Z})$ be defined by

$$\alpha(S) = \begin{cases} S \cup \{0\} & \text{if } 0 \notin S; \\ S \setminus \{0\} & \text{if } 0 \in S. \end{cases}$$

Prove that α is a bijection.

Exercise 4.6.21 Define $f : \mathbb{N} \to \mathbb{Z}$ by

$$f(n) = \begin{cases} (1-n)/2 & \text{if } n \text{ is odd}; \\ n/2 & \text{if } n \text{ is even.} \end{cases}$$

Prove that f is a bijection and determine the inverse function f^{-1}.

Exercise 4.6.22 Let X, Y, f, and g be as in Example 4.5.3. Construct a function $s : Y \to Y$ such that $s \circ f = f$ and $g \circ s = g$, but $s \neq i_Y$.

Exercise 4.6.23 Here are three more situations where the Axiom of Choice is not needed. In each case, describe explicitly a choice function $c : \mathscr{A} \to \mathbb{R}$; that is, for each set $A \in \mathscr{A}$, state how you might define $c(A)$.
(a) $\mathscr{A}$ is the family of all finite nonempty subsets of $\mathbb{R}$.
(b) $\mathscr{A}$ is the family of all closed intervals $[a, b]$ on the real line.
(c) $\mathscr{A}$ is the family of all bounded, open intervals (a, b) on the real line.

Exercise 4.6.24 Bertrand Russell once spoke of the Axiom of Choice in the following context. Consider an infinite number of pairs of shoes and an infinite number of pairs of socks. To choose one of each pair of shoes does not require the Axiom of Choice, but to choose one of each pair of socks does. Explain.

Exercise 4.6.25 What goes wrong in Corollary 4.5.8 if X has only one element?

Exercise 4.6.26 Let $f : X \to Y$, and let $g, h : Y \to X$. Prove that if $g \circ f = i_X$ and $f \circ h = i_Y$, then $g = h$ and f, g, and h are bijections. [Hint: Start with Theorem 4.5.2.]

Exercise 4.6.27   Let $f : X \to Y$ be a bijection, where $X, Y \subseteq \mathbb{R}$. Prove that the graphs of f and f^{-1} are reflections of each other across the line $y = x$. [Hint: For each point (a, b) on the graph of f, show that the line with equation $y = x$ is the perpendicular bisector of the segment joining the two points (a, b) and (b, a).]

Exercise 4.6.28   For each of the following descriptions of a function f, find a subset S of the domain of f such that the restriction $f|_S$ is a bijection onto the range of f.
(a) $f : \mathbb{N} \to \mathbb{N}$, where $f(n) = n + 1$ if n is odd and $f(n) = n/2$ if n is even.
(b) $f : \mathbb{R} \to \mathbb{Z}$, where $f(x) = \lfloor x \rfloor$. Here $\lfloor x \rfloor$ denotes the floor[7] of x.
(c) $f : \mathbb{R} \to \mathbb{R}$, where $f(x) = x^3 - 3x^2$.
(d) $f : \mathbb{R} \to \mathbb{R}$, where $f(x) = x^4 - 4x^2$.
(e) $f : \mathbb{R} \to \mathbb{R}$, where $f(x) = xe^{-x}$.
(f) $f : \mathbb{R} \to \mathbb{R} \times \mathbb{R}$, where $f(x) = (\cos x, \sin x)$.
(g) $f : \mathbb{R} \setminus \mathbb{Z} \to \mathbb{R}$, where $f(x) = \csc(\pi x)$.
(h) $f : \mathscr{P}(X) \to \mathscr{P}(X)$, where A is a fixed nonempty subset of X and $f(B) = A \cap B$ for all $B \in \mathscr{P}(X)$.
(i) Same as (h) except that $f(B) = A \cup B$ for all $B \in \mathscr{P}(X)$.
(j) Same as (h) except that $f(B) = B \setminus A$ for all $B \in \mathscr{P}(X)$.

---

[7]The **floor function** from $\mathbb{R}$ to $\mathbb{Z}$ assigns to each $x \in \mathbb{R}$ the greatest integer less than or equal to x. It is denoted by $\lfloor x \rfloor$. For example, $\lfloor \pi \rfloor = 3$ and $\lfloor -\pi \rfloor = -4$.

Chapter 5

Induction

5.1 An Inductive Example

THE PLANE consists of one big region. Draw a line in the plane. Your line divides the plane into two regions. Draw a second line, not parallel to the first. Together, the two lines divide the plane into four regions. Now draw a third line so that it crosses each of the two old lines at distinct points. Maybe you're tempted to double again the previous number and guess that there now are eight regions. But if you count them, you find only seven regions. What if you were required to determine the number of regions when 100 lines are drawn in this fashion? Happily, there is a more efficient way to get the answer than to draw 100 lines and count the regions.

First, let's define a set of lines in the plane to be in **general position** when

1. no two of the lines are parallel, and

2. no three lines meet at a common point.

In Figure 5.1.1, you see five lines drawn in general position.

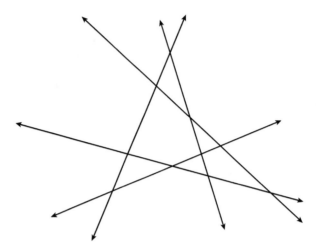

Figure 5.1.1: Five lines in general position.

In these terms, your quest is now *to find the number of regions created by 100 lines in the plane in general position.*

You could begin your quest by seeking guidance from the Oracle at Delphi.[1] While the Oracle dispensed a great deal of advice and wisdom, she was notorious for never giving a direct answer, and this time is no exception. The voice of the Oracle is heard:

"Consider the formula

$$\delta(n) = \frac{1}{2}(n^2 + n) + 1."$$

(5.1.1)

This formula yields the answers you found for $n = 0, 1, 2$, and 3. It even yields $\delta(5) = 16$, which concurs with Figure 5.1.1. However, we have no reason to believe that this formula doesn't break down somewhere between 5 and 100,

---

[1]The Oracle at Delphi dates back to 1400 BCE. People came from all over Greece to have their questions about the future answered by the priestess at the Oracle. Her answers, usually cryptic, could determine the course of everything from when a farmer would plant crops to when an empire would go to war. See http://en.wikipedia.org/wiki/Delphi#Oracle.

just as the doubling assumption broke down at $n = 3$. What we want to do is to prove that the formula is correct for *all* the infinitely many integers $n \geq 0$. If we succeed, then we'll know in particular that $\delta(100) = 5051$ is the correct number of regions (*without* having drawn 100 lines in general position). Here is how our proof proceeds.

First, note that we've verified the formula for some small values of n. We also make the following very important observation: every time we draw a new line,

(i) it meets all of the old lines (by condition 1), and
(ii) it meets no two old lines at the same point (by condition 2).

So if there are n old lines, then the new $(n+1)^{\text{st}}$ line contains exactly n points of intersection with the old lines. Therefore it cuts across exactly $n + 1$ old regions, dividing each one into two regions, thereby creating exactly $n + 1$ new regions.

What this tells us is that, **if** $\delta(n)$ gives the correct number of regions for some value of n, **then** $\delta(n) + (n+1)$ should be the correct number of regions when $n + 1$ lines are drawn. In other words, if equation (5.1.1) holds for this value of n, then $\delta(n + 1)$ *should* be equal to $\delta(n) + (n + 1)$. Well, is it?

$$\delta(n) + (n + 1) = \left[\frac{1}{2}(n^2 + n) + 1\right] + (n + 1)$$

$$= \frac{1}{2}(n^2 + 3n + 2) + 1$$

$$= \frac{1}{2}\left[(n + 1)^2 + (n + 1)\right] + 1$$

$$= \delta(n + 1).$$

It is indeed correct. So, in conclusion, if

(i) the Delphic Oracle starts out with the correct answer (that is, for $n = 0$), and
(ii) *whenever* the Oracle is correct for some value of $n \geq 0$, she is *then* also correct for the next value $n + 1$,

then the Oracle must have it right for *all* values of $n \geq 0$, as far as we can go.

We have figured out the Oracle's message and independently verified *with a proof* that her formula is correct for all nonnegative integers. This proof is an example of "proof by mathematical induction."

5.2   The Principle of Mathematical Induction

For any integer n, the propositional function $\mathbf{P}(n)$ is a statement about the integer n. For example, if $\mathbf{P}(n)$ means, "n is a multiple of 7," then $\mathbf{P}(35)$ has truth value $\mathbf{T}$ and $\mathbf{P}(36)$ has truth value $\mathbf{F}$. We emphasize that $\mathbf{P}(n)$ must be a *statement* about n. Recall that an algebraic expression containing n is *not* a statement about n. Thus it makes no sense to write $\mathbf{P}(n) = \frac{1}{2}(n^2 + n) + 1$, because a statement cannot be equal to an algebraic expression. But it is perfectly legitimate (for any given n) to let $\mathbf{P}(n)$ mean $\delta(n) = \frac{1}{2}(n^2 + n) + 1$ because *an equation is a statement*; it is either true or false. It is also legitimate to let $\mathbf{P}(n)$ denote the statement, "n lines in general position in the plane separate the plane into 2^n regions," even though this statement is false for all $n \geq 3$. (*Falseness* and *nonsense* are not the same thing!) In effect, $\mathbf{P} : \mathbb{N} \to \{\mathbf{T}, \mathbf{F}\}$; see Example 4.1.7.

In this language, let us review what we accomplished in the previous section. With the value of $\delta(n)$ defined by equation (5.1.1), we let $\mathbf{P}(n)$ for each $n \in \mathbb{N} \cup \{0\}$ mean $\delta(n)$ *equals the number of regions created when n lines are drawn in the plane in general position.* We established that $\mathbf{P}(0)$ is true; when no lines were drawn, there was $\delta(0) = 1$ single region. (We also established the truth of $\mathbf{P}(1)$ and $\mathbf{P}(2)$ and $\mathbf{P}(3)$, but we don't need that information.) We then established that the statement

$$\big(\forall n \in \mathbb{N} \cup \{0\}\big)\, [\mathbf{P}(n) \Rightarrow \mathbf{P}(n+1)] \tag{5.2.1}$$

is true. From these two pieces, we deduced

$$\big(\forall n \in \mathbb{N} \cup \{0\}\big)\mathbf{P}(n). \tag{5.2.2}$$

Statements (5.2.1) and (5.2.2) are not logically equivalent. Under the assumption that (5.2.1) is true, (5.2.2) may be true or may be false. Please *do not* forget this fact as we now state formally one of the main theorems of this book.

Theorem 5.2.1 (The Principle of Mathematical Induction)
Let $n_0 \in \mathbb{Z}$. For each integer $n \geq n_0$, let $\mathbf{P}(n)$ be a statement about n. Suppose that the following two statements are true:

(i) $\mathbf{P}(n_0)$;

(ii) $(\forall n \geq n_0)\ [\mathbf{P}(n) \Rightarrow \mathbf{P}(n+1)]$.

Then, for all integers $n \geq n_0$, the statement $\mathbf{P}(n)$ is true.

The proof of this significant theorem uses the Well Ordering Principle, first presented in Section 2.3, which we now restate in greater generality.

The Well Ordering Principle. *Let $n_0 \in \mathbb{Z}$. Every nonempty subset of the set $\{n \in \mathbb{Z} : n \geq n_0\}$ includes a least element.*

This principle says that the set of integers is very special. For example, it is easy to find subsets of $\{x \in \mathbb{Q} : x \geq 0\}$ that have no least element, even though this set is similar in appearance to the set in the statement of the Well Ordering Principle. The more standard formulation of the Well Ordering Principle, as stated in Section 2.3, is that any nonempty subset of $\mathbb{N}$ has a least element.

Proof of the Principle of Mathematical Induction. This is a proof by contradiction; we assume that conditions (i) and (ii) hold but that $\mathbf{P}(n)$ fails for some integer $m \geq n_0$. That is, the set

$$F = \{m \in \mathbb{Z} : m \geq n_0 \ \wedge \ \neg \mathbf{P}(m)\}$$

is not empty. By the Well Ordering Principle, F has a least element m_0, and so $m_0 \geq n_0$. In fact, $m_0 > n_0$ since $\mathbf{P}(m_0)$ is false while $\mathbf{P}(n_0)$ is true. Therefore $m_0 - 1 \geq n_0$.

Consider the truth value of $\mathbf{P}(m_0 - 1)$. On the one hand, if $\mathbf{P}(m_0 - 1)$ is true, then by condition (ii), $\mathbf{P}\big((m_0 - 1) + 1\big) = \mathbf{P}(m_0)$ would be true. But $\mathbf{P}(m_0)$ is false. On the other hand, if $\mathbf{P}(m_0 - 1)$ is false, then $m_0 - 1 \in F$, which contradicts that m_0 is the least element of F. These two contradictions imply that F must be empty. That is, $\mathbf{P}(n)$ is true for $n \geq n_0$. $\square$

Our first application of the Principle of Mathematical Induction is to verify a formula for the sum of the first n positive integers.[2]

Proposition 5.2.2   *For all $n \in \mathbb{N}$, $\displaystyle\sum_{k=1}^{n} k = \frac{n(n+1)}{2}$.*

Proof. Here $n_0 = 1$. For each $n \in \mathbb{N}$ (or equivalently, for each $n \geq n_0$), we let $\mathbf{P}(n)$ denote the equation $\sum_{k=1}^{n} k = n(n+1)/2$. With $n = 1$, the equation becomes $\sum_{k=1}^{1} k = 1(1+1)/2$, which is equivalent to $1 = 1$, a true statement. We have verified $\mathbf{P}(1)$.

Now we must prove that the universally quantified conditional

$$(\forall n \geq 1)[\mathbf{P}(n) \Rightarrow \mathbf{P}(n+1)]$$

is true. Let n be an arbitrary positive integer. For that n, assume $\mathbf{P}(n)$. This assumption is called **the induction hypothesis**. [No, we are not assuming what we're trying to prove. What we're trying to prove is quantified by $\forall n \in \mathbb{N}$. Our assumption is only that $\mathbf{P}(n)$ holds for *this* particular *arbitrarily* chosen n.] From the induction hypothesis, we will deduce $\mathbf{P}(n+1)$.

$$\sum_{k=1}^{n+1} k = \left(\sum_{k=1}^{n} k\right) + (n+1)$$

$$= \frac{n(n+1)}{2} + (n+1) \qquad \text{[Here's where the}$$

$$\text{induction hypothesis is used.]}$$

$$= (n+1)\left(\frac{n}{2} + 1\right)$$

$$= \frac{(n+1)(n+2)}{2}$$

---

[2]Legend has it that, as a child in elementary school, the German mathematician Carl Friedrich Gauss (1777–1855) computed the sum $1 + 2 + \cdots + 99 + 100$ in seconds. His teacher had given the class this problem in an attempt to keep the children busy for a while. Gauss recognized that the sum of each pair of numbers taken from opposite ends of the list is 101 and that there are 50 such pairs, so that the sum must be $50 \times 101 = 5050$. Gauss was an extraordinarily brilliant and prolific mathematician. His influence is evident in almost all branches of modern mathematics. It is often said that Gauss was the last mathematician who knew all of the mathematics of his time. He is revered in Germany; his likeness appeared on the 10 Deutsche mark banknote from 1989 until Germany's currency was converted to the euro in 2001.

Now $\sum_{k=1}^{n+1} k = (n+1)(n+2)/2$ is precisely the statement $\mathbf{P}(n+1)$. Thus we have shown for an arbitrary $n \in \mathbb{N}$, *if* $\mathbf{P}(n)$, *then* $\mathbf{P}(n+1)$. By the Principle of Mathematical Induction, we may now conclude that the statement $\mathbf{P}(n)$ is true *for all $n \geq 1$*. $\square$

We use this proof to emphasize once more that the two statements (5.2.1) and (5.2.2) are not logically equivalent. Let $\mathbf{Q}(n)$ denote the statement: $\sum_{k=1}^{n} k = \frac{n(n+1)}{2} + 100$, which is clearly false for all $n \in \mathbb{N}$. By inserting "+100" at the ends of the last three lines in the proof of Proposition 5.2.2, we obtain an entirely valid proof that $(\forall n \in \mathbb{N})[\mathbf{Q}(n) \Rightarrow \mathbf{Q}(n+1)]$ is true. However, since there is no $n_0 \in \mathbb{N}$ for which $\mathbf{Q}(n_0)$ is true, we cannot conclude that $\mathbf{Q}(n)$ holds for all $n \geq n_0$.

Let us make one more remark about the proof of Proposition 5.2.2. We see that $1 + 2 + 3 + 4 + 5 + 6 = 21 = 6(6+1)/2$, thereby proving $\mathbf{P}(6)$. Had we substituted this computation for the observation that $\mathbf{P}(1)$ is true, then all that we could have concluded would be that $\sum_{k=1}^{n} k = n(n+1)/2$ is true for all integers $n \geq 6$.

Example 5.2.3 We can use Proposition 5.2.2 to find a general formula for the sum

$$\sum_{k=1}^{n} (ak + b).$$

By properties of Σ-notation and the proposition, we conclude

$$\sum_{k=1}^{n} (ak + b) = \sum_{k=1}^{n} ak + \sum_{k=1}^{n} b$$
$$= a \sum_{k=1}^{n} k + b \sum_{k=1}^{n} 1$$
$$= a \frac{n(n+1)}{2} + bn.$$

We have proved

$$\sum_{k=1}^{n}(ak+b) = \frac{a}{2}n^2 + \left(\frac{a}{2}+b\right)n. \tag{5.2.3}$$

Exercise 5.2.4　Apply the formula in equation (5.2.3) to evaluate each of the following sums.[3]

(a) $\displaystyle\sum_{k=1}^{n}(2k-1) = 1+3+5+\cdots+(2n-1).$

(b) $\displaystyle\sum_{k=1}^{n}(3k-2) = 1+4+7+\cdots+(3n-2).$

Exercise 5.2.5　Using the proof of Proposition 5.2.2 as a model, prove the following formulas.

(a) $(\forall n \in \mathbb{N}),\ \displaystyle\sum_{k=1}^{n}k^2 = \frac{n(n+1)(2n+1)}{6}.$

(b) $(\forall n \in \mathbb{N}),\ \displaystyle\sum_{k=1}^{n}k^3 = \left[\frac{n(n+1)}{2}\right]^2.$

Exercise 5.2.6　Apply equation (5.2.3) and Exercise 5.2.5 to evaluate each of the following sums. [Hint: First expand the polynomials.]

(a) $\displaystyle\sum_{k=1}^{n}(2k-1)^2 = 1^2+3^2+5^2+\cdots+(2n-1)^2.$

(b) $\displaystyle\sum_{k=1}^{n}(3k-2)^3 = 1^3+4^3+7^3+\cdots+(3n-2)^3.$

Next, we tackle an algebraically more complicated application.

Example 5.2.7　We prove that, for all integers $n \geq 5$, it holds that $4^n > n^4$.

Let $\mathbf{P}(n)$ be the statement: $4^n > n^4$. Since $1024 > 625$, it is clear that $\mathbf{P}(5)$ is true. Now let n be an arbitrary integer at least 5, and for that n, assume

---

[3]The sums in (a) and (b) are the so-called *square number* and *pentagonal number formulas*, respectively.

$\mathbf{P}(n)$. We want to deduce $\mathbf{P}(n+1)$; that is, $4^{n+1} > (n+1)^4$. This time, we start from the right-hand end. We compute, since $n > 4$,

$$(n+1)^4 = n^4 + 4n^3 + 6n^2 + 4n + 1 < n^4 + n^4 + n^4 + n^4 + 1 = 4n^4 + 1.$$

By Exercise 2.7.17 and the induction hypothesis,

$$(n+1)^4 \leq 4n^4 < 4 \cdot 4^n = 4^{n+1},$$

proving $(\forall n \geq 5)[\mathbf{P}(n) \Rightarrow \mathbf{P}(n+1)]$. By the Principle of Mathematical Induction, we conclude, for all $n \geq 5$, that $\mathbf{P}(n)$ is true—that is, $4^n > n^4$.

Exercise 5.2.8 Prove the following by induction.
(a) For all $n \geq 4$, $3^n > n^3$.
(b) For all $n \geq 5$, $5^n \geq n^5$.
(c) For all $n \geq 4$, $\sqrt[n]{3} < \sqrt[3]{n}$.

Suppose that a sum of M dollars is invested in a government bond that pays interest at a fixed annual rate of r percent compounded at the end of each year. That means that, at the end of each year, r percent of the balance is added to the balance, and interest is computed on the new balance at the end of the following year. Thus at the end of the first year, the new balance is $(1 + r/100)M$, and at the end of the second year, the balance is $(1 + r/100)[(1 + r/100)M]$. We claim that for all $n \in \mathbb{N}$, the balance $B(n)$ at the end of n years is $(1 + r/100)^n M$. Let $\mathbf{P}(n)$ denote this claim, which has already been verified when $n = 1$. If we assume $\mathbf{P}(n)$ for some n, we have

$$
\begin{aligned}
B(n+1) &= (1 + r/100)B(n) \\
&= (1 + r/100)[(1 + r/100)^n M] = (1 + r/100)^{n+1} M.
\end{aligned}
$$

Thus $\mathbf{P}(n) \Rightarrow \mathbf{P}(n+1)$ is true, and hence, by the Principle of Mathematical Induction, $B(n) = (1 + r/100)^n M$ *for all* $n \in \mathbb{N}$.

Exercise 5.2.9 Determine the value after n years on an initial investment of M dollars if the interest is compounded every six months. Repeat for every three months, every month, and semimonthly. Assume that the *annual* interest rate is r percent.

The Principle of Mathematical Induction can be applied to define a very useful notion—namely, the **factorial function**. For all nonnegative integers n, "n factorial" is written as $n!$ and is defined formally as follows:

- $0! = 1$;

- $\big(\forall n \in \mathbb{N} \cup \{0\}\big)\big[(n+1)! = (n+1)n!\big]$.

Thus $1! = 1 \cdot 0! = 1 \cdot 1 = 1$, and $2! = 2 \cdot 1! = 2 \cdot 1$, and $3! = 3 \cdot 2! = 3 \cdot 2 \cdot 1$. In general, if we know the value of $n!$, then we can easily compute $(n+1)!$. By the Principle of Mathematical Induction, we can thus compute $n!$ for all nonnegative integers n.

If $a \in \mathbb{N}$, read $an!$ as $a \cdot (n!)$ and never as $(an)!$. If $a \geq 2$, then $(an)! \neq an!$. (Which one is larger?)

Exercise 5.2.10   Prove formally by induction that for every nonnegative integer n,
$$n! = n \cdot (n-1) \cdot (n-2) \cdots 3 \cdot 2 \cdot 1.$$

Exercise 5.2.11   Use induction to prove that, for all $n \in \mathbb{N}$,
$$\sum_{k=1}^{n} k(k!) = (n+1)! - 1.$$

Exercise 5.2.12   (a) Use induction to prove that $(\forall n \geq 4)[n! > 2^n]$.
(b) Use induction to prove that $(\forall n \geq 5)[(n+1)! > 2^{n+3}]$.
(c) Determine for what values of n the inequality $n! > 2^{2n}$ holds, and prove the inequality for all such n by induction.

In Section 3.1, you saw that the set $A = \{a, b, c, d\}$ with 4 elements has a power set with $2^4 = 16$ elements. This was not an isolated coincidence, and thanks to the Principle of Mathematical Induction, we can now prove the general case.

Theorem 5.2.13   *If A is a set with exactly n elements, then its power set $\mathscr{P}(A)$ has exactly 2^n elements.*

Proof. For each integer $n \geq 0$, let $\mathbf{P}(n)$ denote the statement that the power set of a set with n elements has 2^n elements. Since $\mathscr{P}(\emptyset) = \{\emptyset\}$, which has $1 = 2^0$ elements, we see that $\mathbf{P}(0)$ is true.

As the induction hypothesis, assume for some arbitrary $n \geq 0$ that the power set of every set with n elements has 2^n elements. [That is $\mathbf{P}(n)$, and we proceed to deduce $\mathbf{P}(n+1)$—namely, that the power set of any set with $n+1$ elements must have 2^{n+1} elements.]

Let A be a set with $n+1$ elements. Since $A \neq \emptyset$, there exists an element $x \in A$. There are two kinds of subsets of A: those that do not include x and those that do. Let

$$\mathscr{S}_1 = \{S \in \mathscr{P}(A) : x \notin S\}$$
$$\text{and} \quad \mathscr{S}_2 = \{S \in \mathscr{P}(A) : x \in S\}.$$

Clearly, every subset of A belongs to exactly one of $\mathscr{S}_1$ and $\mathscr{S}_2$. So all that we need to do is to count the number of sets in each of these two families and add these two numbers. Since $A \setminus \{x\}$ has only n elements and $\mathscr{S}_1 = \mathscr{P}(A \setminus \{x\})$, the induction hypothesis implies that $\mathscr{S}_1$ has 2^n elements.

For each $S \in \mathscr{S}_1$, $S \cup \{x\} \in \mathscr{S}_2$. In other words, each element of $\mathscr{S}_1$ yields an element of $\mathscr{S}_2$. Thus the number of elements in $\mathscr{S}_1$ is at most the number of elements in $\mathscr{S}_2$. Conversely, if $T \in \mathscr{S}_2$, then $T \setminus \{x\} \in \mathscr{S}_1$. So the number of elements of $\mathscr{S}_2$ is at most the number of elements of $\mathscr{S}_1$. We conclude that $\mathscr{S}_1$ and $\mathscr{S}_2$ must each include 2^n elements. Thus $\mathscr{P}(A)$ includes $2^n + 2^n = 2 \cdot 2^n = 2^{n+1}$ elements. We've shown the truth of the statement $\mathbf{P}(n) \Rightarrow \mathbf{P}(n+1)$. By the Principle of Mathematical Induction, we have that $\mathbf{P}(n)$ is true for all $n \geq 0$. $\square$

By the time that you've come this far in this chapter, you have seen enough applications of the Principle of Mathematical Induction that you pretty much know the routine. The following application will, therefore, be written in a more streamlined style, omitting the notation $\mathbf{P}(n)$ as well as recitation of the two conditions that make the Principle of Mathematical Induction work.

Example 5.2.14 We prove that, for every integer $n \in \mathbb{N}$, the integer $7^n - 4^n$ is divisible by 3.

Since 3 divides $3 = 7 - 4 = 7^1 - 4^1$, the statement is clearly true when $n = 1$. Now suppose, as the induction hypothesis, that for some $n \in \mathbb{N}$, 3 divides $7^n - 4^n$. The proof will be complete when we deduce that $7^{n+1} - 4^{n+1}$ is a multiple of 3. The induction hypothesis implies that $7^n - 4^n = 3m$ for some $m \in \mathbb{Z}$. Hence

$$
\begin{aligned}
7^{n+1} - 4^{n+1} &= 7 \cdot 7^n - 4 \cdot 4^n \\
&= 7(3m + 4^n) - 4 \cdot 4^n \quad \text{[by the induction hypothesis]} \\
&= 3 \cdot 7m + (7 - 4)4^n \\
&= 3(7m + 4^n)
\end{aligned}
$$

as required.

Inductive proofs can be used in calculus to obtain formulas for higher derivatives of any order. Consider the following. (Recall that $(-1)^n = 1$ if n is even and $(-1)^n = -1$ if n is odd.)

Proposition 5.2.15 *For all $n \geq 0$, $\dfrac{d^n}{dx^n}\left(\dfrac{1}{x}\right) = \dfrac{(-1)^n\, n!}{x^{n+1}}$.*

Proof. It is generally understood that the 0th derivative of a differentiable function is the function itself. With that understanding, we see that the formula holds when $n = 0$.

As the induction hypothesis, we assume, for some $n \geq 0$, that the formula holds for that n. We obtain

$$
\begin{aligned}
\frac{d^{n+1}}{dx^{n+1}}\left(\frac{1}{x}\right) &= \frac{d}{dx}\left(\frac{d^n}{dx^n}\left(\frac{1}{x}\right)\right) \\
&= \frac{d}{dx}\left(\frac{(-1)^n\, n!}{x^{n+1}}\right) \quad \text{[by the induction hypothesis]} \\
&= (-1)^n n! \frac{-(n+1)}{x^{n+2}} \quad \text{[by the power rule of differentiation]} \\
&= \frac{(-1)^{n+1}(n+1)!}{x^{n+2}},
\end{aligned}
$$

which is precisely the given formula with $n + 1$ in place of n. Thus the assumption that the formula holds for some n implies that it must also hold for $n + 1$. The Principle of Mathematical Induction yields that the formula holds for all $n \geq 0$. $\qquad\square$

Exercise 5.2.16 Prove the following formulas.

(a) $\dfrac{d^n}{dx^n}\left(e^{2x}\right) = 2^n e^{2x}$, for $n \geq 0$.

(b) $\dfrac{d^n}{dx^n}\left(\sqrt{x}\right) = \dfrac{(-1)^{n-1}\cdot 1\cdot 3\cdot 5\cdots(2n-3)}{2^n}x^{-(2n-1)/2}$

$\qquad\qquad = \dfrac{(-1)^{n-1}(2n-2)!}{2^{2n-1}(n-1)!}x^{-(2n-1)/2}, \quad$ for $n \geq 1$.

5.3   The Principle of Strong Induction

In this section, we do three things. We state the Principle of Strong Induction; we apply it to prove an important theorem in number theory; we show that it is not "stronger" at all but, in reality, is equivalent to the Principle of Mathematical Induction.

Theorem 5.3.1 (The Principle of Strong Induction)   *Let $n_0 \in \mathbb{Z}$. For each integer $n \geq n_0$, let $\mathbf{P}(n)$ be a statement about n. Suppose that the following two statements are true:*

$\quad$ *(i) $\mathbf{P}(n_0)$;*

$\quad$ *(ii) $(\forall n \geq n_0)\ [(\bigwedge_{k=n_0}^{n} \mathbf{P}(k)) \Rightarrow \mathbf{P}(n+1)]$.*

Then, for all integers $n \geq n_0$, the statement $\mathbf{P}(n)$ is true.

Let's compare the two principles of induction, Theorems 5.2.1 and 5.3.1. The only apparent difference is in the induction hypothesis. In Theorem 5.2.1, all that is required to deduce $\mathbf{P}(n+1)$ is $\mathbf{P}(n)$. In Theorem 5.3.1, we assume, not only $\mathbf{P}(n)$ but also $\mathbf{P}(n-1)$ and $\mathbf{P}(n-2)$ and $\mathbf{P}(n-3)\ldots$ all the way back to $\mathbf{P}(n_0+1)$ and even $\mathbf{P}(n_0)$. The part that is stronger in the Principle of Strong Induction is only the induction hypothesis. As you know from

Chapter 1, making a hypothesis *stronger* makes a conditional *weaker* because more conditions have to be assumed in order to infer the same conclusion. In this instance, that same conclusion is $\mathbf{P}(n+1)$. Ironically, on the surface, it would appear that so-called "Strong" Induction should be weaker than the now familiar Principle of Mathematical Induction. More about this after the following two applications of Theorem 5.3.1.

Example 5.3.2 We have a rectangular piece of some material, such as plywood, whose area is n square units for some positive integer n. Its length is ℓ units and its width is w units, where ℓ and w are positive integers, and so $n = \ell w$. Using a table saw,[4] we want to saw this board into n squares, each one unit by one unit. The Principle of Strong Induction is used to show that no matter how we make the (edge-to-edge) saw cuts, exactly $n-1$ cuts are needed to do the job.

Obviously, all cuts must be parallel to one pair of opposite sides and hence perpendicular to the other pair. If $n = 1$, then the dimensions of our board must be 1×1; zero cuts are needed, and since $0 = 1 - 1$, our claim holds for $n = 1$.

Suppose that $n \geq 1$. As the induction hypothesis, assume that, whenever $1 \leq k \leq n$, if the area of the board is k, then exactly $k - 1$ cuts are required. (Note that this is the induction hypothesis for strong induction.) Now suppose that the area of the board is $n + 1 = \ell w$. If the first cut is lengthwise, then the board is separated into two pieces whose respective dimensions are $\ell \times w_1$ and $\ell \times w_2$, where $w_1 + w_2 = w$. (See Figure 5.3.1.) Each of these pieces has area $\leq n$, and so by the induction hypothesis, they can be reduced to (1×1)-squares using $\ell w_1 - 1$ and $\ell w_2 - 1$ cuts, respectively. Hence, including the initial cut, the total number of cuts required to reduce our board to exactly $n + 1$ little (1×1)-squares is

$$(\ell w_1 - 1) + (\ell w_2 - 1) + 1 = \ell w - 1 = (n + 1) - 1,$$

---

[4]A table saw consists of a platform, or table, and a circular saw blade that protrudes upward through a slit in the middle of the table. The blade rotates rapidly about its center, which is just below the table. The height of the blade is adjustable so that enough of the blade protrudes in order to cut through a piece of wood. The important thing about a table saw is that it can make only a straight cut from one side of the piece to the opposite side.

as claimed. (The argument is similar if the initial cut had been width-wise.) Note that had we assumed merely that the claim held for boards of area n, we would not have had a strong enough assumption to deduce that it holds for boards of area $n + 1$. The mere Principle of Mathematical Induction would have been an ineffective tool.

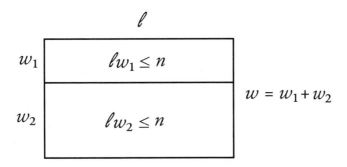

Figure 5.3.1: The consequence of the first cut.

Our second application, which we present more formally, is the following important result.

Theorem 5.3.3 (The Fundamental Theorem of Arithmetic)
(i) Every integer at least 2 is either a prime number or a product of prime numbers.
(ii) Prime factorizations are unique up to the order in which the prime factors occur.

Proof. To prove part (i), let $\mathbf{P}(n)$ denote the statement: n is a prime number or a product of prime numbers. [Here $n_0 = 2$.] Since 2 is prime, $\mathbf{P}(2)$ is true.

Let n be any integer at least 2, and assume the induction hypothesis $\bigwedge_{k=2}^{n} \mathbf{P}(k)$. If $n+1$ is prime, then clearly $\mathbf{P}(n+1)$ is true. If $n+1$ is composite, then there exist integers a and b such that $n + 1 = ab$ and $2 \leq a \leq n$ and $2 \leq b \leq n$.

By assuming the induction hypothesis, we have automatically assumed $\mathbf{P}(a)$ and $\mathbf{P}(b)$; that is, each of a and b is either prime or a product of primes.

Since $n+1 = ab$, it follows that $n+1$ is a product of primes, and, again, we deduce $\mathbf{P}(n+1)$. Symbolically, we've shown

$$\bigwedge_{k=2}^{n} \mathbf{P}(k) \;\Rightarrow\; \mathbf{P}(a) \wedge \mathbf{P}(b) \;\Rightarrow\; \mathbf{P}(n+1).$$

By the Principle of Strong Induction, we have $(\forall n \geq 2)\mathbf{P}(n)$. This proves part (i).

Remark. We really needed the Principle of Strong Induction in this last proof. The Principle of Mathematical Induction would not have been up to this job. The weaker assumption, merely that n is a prime number or a product of prime numbers, would have been no help in concluding that the same holds for $n+1$. Since $\gcd(n, n+1) = 1$, the prime factors of n have nothing whatsoever to do with the prime factors of $n+1$. We absolutely needed the statements $\mathbf{P}(a)$ and $\mathbf{P}(b)$ for *all* integers a and b from 2 to n.

To prove part (ii), we again require the Principle of Strong Induction. Since 2 is prime, there is only one prime factorization of 2. The statement of uniqueness holds for $n = 2$.

Let $n \geq 2$. The induction hypothesis is that every natural number less than $n+1$ has a unique prime factorization. Suppose that $n+1$ has (at least) two prime factorizations:

$$p_1 p_2 p_3 \cdots p_k = n+1 = q_1 q_2 q_3 \cdots q_\ell, \tag{5.3.1}$$

where the factors p_i and q_j are prime. We can assume that none of the prime numbers $p_1, p_2, \ldots, p_k$ occurs in the list $q_1, q_2, \ldots, q_\ell$, for if one did, then the factors could be reordered so that $p_1 = q_1$. Dividing equation (5.3.1) by p_1 yields

$$\frac{n+1}{p_1} = p_2 p_3 \cdots p_k = q_2 q_3 \cdots q_\ell. \tag{5.3.2}$$

Since $(n+1)/p_1 < n+1$, the induction hypothesis implies that $(n+1)/p_1$ has a unique prime factorization. That is, the two products of prime numbers in line (5.3.2) are really the same, except perhaps for the orders of the factors. Hence $n+1 = p_1 \left(\dfrac{n+1}{p_1} \right)$ would also have a unique prime factorization.

Therefore we may assume that none of the prime numbers $p_1, p_2, p_3, \ldots, p_k$ occurs in the list $q_1, q_2, q_3, \ldots, q_\ell$. In particular, $p_1 \neq q_1$, and, without loss of generality, $p_1 < q_1$.

Set $N = (q_1 - p_1)q_2q_3 \cdots q_\ell$. Then

$$N = (q_1 - p_1)q_2q_3 \cdots q_\ell \tag{5.3.3}$$
$$= q_1(q_2q_3 \cdots q_\ell) - p_1(q_2q_3 \cdots q_\ell)$$
$$= (n+1) - p_1q_2q_3 \cdots q_\ell \tag{5.3.4}$$
$$= p_1p_2p_3 \cdots p_k - p_1q_2q_3 \cdots q_\ell$$
$$= p_1(p_2p_3 \cdots p_k - q_2q_3 \cdots q_\ell). \tag{5.3.5}$$

From line (5.3.4), we have $N < n+1$. By the induction hypothesis, the prime factorization of N is unique. However, equating lines (5.3.3) and (5.3.5) implies

$$N = (q_1 - p_1)q_2q_3 \cdots q_\ell = p_1(p_2p_3 \cdots p_k - q_2q_3 \cdots q_\ell). \tag{5.3.6}$$

The factors $(q_1 - p_1)$ and $(p_2p_3 \cdots p_k - q_2q_3 \cdots q_\ell)$ are not necessarily prime, but they are each less than $N < n+1$. By the induction hypothesis, each of their prime factorizations is unique. Since $p_1 \nmid (q_1 - p_1)$ [why?], we now have two distinct factorizations of N: the factorization expressed in the right member of equation (5.3.6) in which the prime number p_1 is a factor, and the other factorization expressed in the middle member of (5.3.6) in which p_1 is a not a factor. This contradicts the induction hypothesis. Thus the factorization of $n+1$ is unique, and part (ii) of the theorem now follows from the Principle of Strong Induction. $\qquad\square$

The following corollary to Theorem 5.3.3 is needed in Section 7.3. Its proof, which does not require induction, is left as Exercise 5.5.15.

Corollary 5.3.4 *Every integer $n \in \mathbb{N}$ can be written uniquely as $n = 2^{k-1} \cdot m$, where $k \in \mathbb{N}$ and m is an odd natural number.*

To conclude this section, we prove that the Principle of Mathematical Induction (PMI) and the Principle of Strong Induction (PSI) are equivalent, that is, if either one of them is valid, then so is the other. In fact, we show that both of these principles are equivalent to the Well Ordering Principle (WOP).

Lemma 5.3.5 *If the PMI is valid, then the PSI is valid.*

Proof. We continue the notation of the statements of these two principles. Since the statement $\left(\bigwedge_{k=n_0}^{n} \mathbf{P}(k)\right) \Rightarrow \mathbf{P}(n)$ is a tautology, in Table 5.1, only the lines where this conditional is true need to be considered.

We see that whenever $\mathbf{T}$ appears in the fourth column, $\mathbf{T}$ also appears in the fifth column. Hence condition (ii) of the PMI implies condition (ii) of the PSI. Since condition (i) is the same in both principles, the proof is complete. □

$\mathbf{P}(n)$	$\bigwedge_{k=n_0}^{n} \mathbf{P}(k)$	$\mathbf{P}(n+1)$	$\mathbf{P}(n) \Rightarrow \mathbf{P}(n+1)$	$\left(\bigwedge_{k=n_0}^{n} \mathbf{P}(k)\right) \Rightarrow \mathbf{P}(n+1)$
T	T	T	T	T
T	F	T	T	T
F	F	T	T	T
T	T	F	F	F
T	F	F	F	T
F	F	F	T	T

Table 5.1: Proof of Lemma 5.3.5.

Lemma 5.3.6 *If the PSI is valid, then the WOP is valid.*

Exercise 5.3.7 The steps of a proof of Lemma 5.3.6 are outlined below. Your job in this exercise is to write a coherent proof by filling in all of the details and fully justifying all of the steps.
1. Assume the PSI.
2. Let $n_0 \in \mathbb{Z}$ and let $S \subseteq \{n \in \mathbb{Z} : n \geq n_0\}$. Assume $S \neq \varnothing$.
3. We may assume that $n_0 \notin S$. [For otherwise, ...]
4. If for all $m \in \{n \in \mathbb{Z} : n \geq n_0\} \setminus S$, it were to hold that

$$\{n_0, n_0 + 1, \ldots, m, m + 1\} \subseteq \{n \in \mathbb{Z} : n \geq n_0\} \setminus S,$$

then we could conclude that $S = \varnothing$. [This is the crucial step.]
5. Hence there exists some $m \in \{n \in \mathbb{Z} : n \geq n_0\} \setminus S$ such that this is not the case.
6. $m + 1$ is the least element of S. □

Theorem 5.3.8 *The Principle of Mathematical Induction, the Principle of Strong Induction, and the Well Ordering Principle are logically equivalent. That is, if any one of these is valid, then so are the other two.*

Proof. From the proof of Theorem 5.2.1, we see that the Well Ordering Principle implies the Principle of Mathematical Induction. Lemmas 5.3.5 and 5.3.6 complete the cycle of equivalence. $\square$

5.4   The Binomial Theorem

In this section, n and k denote integers such that $0 \leq k \leq n$.

Definition 5.4.1   *A number of the form* $\dfrac{n!}{k!(n-k)!}$ *is a* **binomial coefficient**, *denoted by*

$$\binom{n}{k} = \frac{n!}{k!(n-k)!}.$$

When reading aloud the symbol $\binom{n}{k}$, say, "n choose k." That is because, as one learns in a course in combinatorics, $\binom{n}{k}$ is the number of ways that one can choose k objects from a set of n objects. A set with n elements has exactly $\binom{n}{k}$ subsets having exactly k elements. For example,

$$\binom{5}{2} = 5!/(2! \cdot 3!) = 120/(2 \cdot 6) = 10.$$

If $A = \{a, b, c, d, e\}$, then the ten subsets of A having exactly two elements are

$$\{a,b\}, \; \{a,c\}, \; \{a,d\}, \; \{a,e\}, \; \{b,c\}, \; \{b,d\}, \; \{b,e\}, \; \{c,d\}, \; \{c,e\}, \; \{d,e\}.$$

Here are some notable properties of binomial coefficients that are easy to verify.

- $\displaystyle \binom{n}{k} = \binom{n}{n-k}$

- $\dbinom{n}{0} = \dbinom{n}{n} = 1$

- $\dbinom{n}{1} = \dbinom{n}{n-1} = n$

- $\dfrac{n+1}{k+1}\dbinom{n}{k} = \dbinom{n+1}{k+1}$

Lemma 5.4.2 (Pascal's Identity[5])   *If* $1 \leq k \leq n$, *then*

$$\binom{n+1}{k} = \binom{n}{k-1} + \binom{n}{k}.$$

Exercise 5.4.3   Use Definition 5.4.1 to prove Pascal's Identity.

In high school algebra, you learned the formula $(a+b)^2 = a^2 + 2ab + b^2$ and perhaps also the formula $(a+b)^3 = a^3 + 3a^2b + 3ab^2 + b^3$. These are special cases of a very important theorem in algebra, which we prove by induction.

Theorem 5.4.4 (The Binomial Theorem)   *For any* $a, b \in \mathbb{R}$ *and for any* $n \in \mathbb{N}$,

$$(a+b)^n = \sum_{k=0}^{n} \binom{n}{k} a^{n-k} b^k. \tag{5.4.1}$$

Proof. When $n = 1$, we have $(a+b)^1 = a+b = \binom{1}{0}a^1 b^0 + \binom{1}{1}a^0 b^1$. This verifies equation (5.4.1) when $n = 1$. As the induction hypothesis, suppose that equation (5.4.1) holds for some $n \geq 1$. It suffices to show that equation (5.4.1)

---

[5]Named for the French mathematician Blaise Pascal (1623–1662). Pascal worked in projective geometry and helped develop probability theory, especially as it applies to gambling. He was also a scientist and inventor in the field of hydraulics.

must then hold with $n+1$ in place of n.

$$(a+b)^{n+1} = (a+b)(a+b)^n$$

$$= (a+b) \sum_{k=0}^{n} \binom{n}{k} a^{n-k} b^k \quad \text{[by the induction hypothesis]}$$

$$= \sum_{k=0}^{n} \binom{n}{k} a^{n-k+1} b^k + \sum_{k=0}^{n} \binom{n}{k} a^{n-k} b^{k+1}$$

$$= a^{n+1} + \sum_{k=1}^{n} \binom{n}{k} a^{n-k+1} b^k + \sum_{k=0}^{n-1} \binom{n}{k} a^{n-k} b^{k+1} + b^{n+1}.$$

Note the new limits of the sums after we pulled the $k = 0$ term out of the first sum and the $k = n$ term out of the second sum. Next we change the indices in each of the sums. We substitute h for k in the first sum and h for $k+1$ in the second sum. This yields

$$a^{n+1} + \sum_{h=1}^{n} \binom{n}{h} a^{n-h+1} b^h + \sum_{h=1}^{n} \binom{n}{h-1} a^{n-h+1} b^h + b^{n+1}$$

$$= a^{n+1} + \sum_{h=1}^{n} \left[\binom{n}{h} + \binom{n}{h-1} \right] a^{n-h+1} b^h + b^{n+1}$$

$$= a^{n+1} + \sum_{h=1}^{n} \binom{n+1}{h} a^{n-h+1} b^h + b^{n+1} \quad \text{[by Pascal's Identity]}$$

$$= \sum_{h=0}^{n+1} \binom{n+1}{h} a^{(n+1)-h} b^h,$$

as required. $\qquad\qquad\qquad\qquad\qquad\qquad\qquad\qquad\qquad\qquad\qquad\qquad\square$

By substituting various values for a and b into equation (5.4.1), one can derive some interesting identities. For example, setting $a = b = 1$ yields

$$2^n = \sum_{k=0}^{n} \binom{n}{k}. \tag{5.4.2}$$

This equation affords an alternative proof of Theorem 5.2.13. Recall the comment earlier in this section that, if S is a set with n elements, then the binomial coefficient $\binom{n}{k}$ is the number of subsets of S having exactly k elements. The right-hand member of equation (5.4.2) thus counts up all of the subsets of S. Hence the left-hand member 2^n must be the total number of such subsets—that is, the number of elements of $\mathscr{P}(S)$.

If $n > 0$, setting $a = 1$ and $b = -1$ in equation (5.4.1) yields

$$\sum_{k=0}^{n}(-1)^k \binom{n}{k} = 0,$$

or, equivalently,

$$\binom{n}{0} + \binom{n}{2} + \binom{n}{4} + \cdots = \binom{n}{1} + \binom{n}{3} + \binom{n}{5} + \cdots \qquad (5.4.3)$$

where the final term on each side depends on whether n is even or odd. A consequence of equation (5.4.3) is that, for any given $n > 0$, the sum of the binomial coefficients $\binom{n}{k}$ with even k equals the sum with odd k. In terms of subsets, we have the following.

Corollary 5.4.5 *For any nonempty finite set, exactly half of its subsets have an even number of elements (and half have an odd number of elements).*

Proofs of other identities are exercises in the next section.

5.5   Further Exercises

Exercise 5.5.1   Prove by induction (rather than by algebraic factoring) that the following hold for all $n \in \mathbb{N}$.
(a) $(-7)^n - 9^n$ is divisible by 16.
(b) $107^n - 97^n$ is divisible by 10.
(c) If h and k are any two distinct integers, then $h^n - k^n$ is divisible by $h - k$.

Exercise 5.5.2   Prove by induction that $\mathbb{Z} = \{3x + 2y : x, y \in \mathbb{Z}\}$. [Don't forget the negative integers!]

Exercise 5.5.3 Prove that the inequality $\left(1 + \frac{1}{n}\right)^n < n$ holds for all $n \geq 3$.

Exercise 5.5.4 Let $a, b, c, d \in \mathbb{R}$. Using formulas derived in this chapter, obtain formulas (as polynomials in n) for the following sums.

(a) $\displaystyle\sum_{k=1}^{n} \left(ak^2 + bk + c\right)$

(b) $\displaystyle\sum_{k=1}^{n} \left(ak^3 + bk^2 + ck + d\right)$

Exercise 5.5.5 Let $A \subset B$. Suppose that A has m elements and B has n elements, where $0 < m < n$. Use Theorem 5.2.13 to answer the following.
(a) How many sets are there in $\mathscr{P}(B \setminus A)$?
(b) How many subsets of B include at least one element in A and at least one element in $B \setminus A$?

Exercise 5.5.6 Let A be a set consisting of two elements, say $A = \{x, y\}$. You know that $\mathscr{P}(A)$ has $2^2 = 4$ elements.
(a) List and count the elements of $\mathscr{P}(\mathscr{P}(A))$.
(b) For the purposes of this exercise, let $\mathscr{P}^{<1>}(A) = \mathscr{P}(A)$, and for $n \geq 2$, let $\mathscr{P}^{<n>}(A) = \mathscr{P}\left(\mathscr{P}^{<n-1>}(A)\right)$. State and prove a theorem about the number of elements in $\mathscr{P}^{<n>}(A)$ for $n \in \mathbb{N}$.

Exercise 5.5.7 Many married couples arrive one couple at a time at a restaurant. As each new couple arrives, they each shake hands exactly once with everybody who arrived before them (but nobody shakes hands with one's own spouse). Prove by induction that for any $n \in \mathbb{N}$, the total number of handshakes that have taken place when n couples are present is $2n^2 - 2n$. [Hint: When the $(n+1)^{\text{st}}$ couple arrives, how many additional handshakes take place?]

Exercise 5.5.8 The Tower of Hanoi game[6] consists of three identical upright pegs and n rings all of different diameters that can be stacked over any of the pegs, as seen in Figure 5.5.1. Initially, all of the rings are stacked

---

[6]The Tower of Hanoi game is not Vietnamese at all but was invented in 1883 by the French mathematician Edouard Lucas (1841–1891).

around one of the pegs in order of descending diameter with the largest ring on the bottom. The object of this game is to transfer all of the rings, one at a time, until they are stacked in the same order about another peg, but at no time may any ring be placed above a ring of smaller diameter.

(a) Prove that, for any number n of rings, the transfer can be made in exactly $2^n - 1$ moves.

(b) Can the transfer ever be made in fewer than $2^n - 1$ moves?

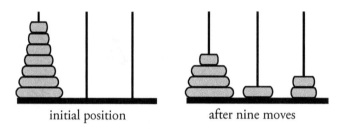

initial position   after nine moves

Figure 5.5.1: The game of the Tower of Hanoi.

Exercise 5.5.9 Prove by induction the following formula for the sum of a partial geometric series. For all $r \in \mathbb{R} \setminus \{0\}$ and for all $n \in \mathbb{N}$,

$$\sum_{k=0}^{n} r^k = \frac{1 - r^{n+1}}{1 - r}.$$

Exercise 5.5.10 Find a formula like those in Exercise 5.2.16 for each of the following. Then prove by induction that your formula is correct for all $n \in \mathbb{N}$.

(a) $\dfrac{d^n}{dx^n}\left(\log_{10} x\right)$

(b) $\dfrac{d^n}{dx^n}\left(\ln(2x + 1)\right)$

(c) $\dfrac{d^n}{dx^n}\left(\sqrt[3]{x}\right)$

(d) $\dfrac{d^{2n}}{dx^{2n}}\left(\sin(\pi x/2)\right)$

(e) $\dfrac{d^{2n}}{dx^{2n}}\big(\sin(2x) - \cos(2x)\big)$

(f) $\dfrac{d^n}{dx^n}\big(2^{2x}\big)$

Exercise 5.5.11 We define inductively a sequence $f_0, f_1, f_2, \ldots$ of functions with domain $\mathbb{R}$ as follows. Let $f_0(x) = 1$ for all $x \in \mathbb{R}$. For each $n \geq 0$, define
$f_{n+1}(x) = \displaystyle\int_0^x f_n(t)\, dt$ for all $x \in \mathbb{R}$.
(a) Guess and then verify by induction a general formula for $f_n(x)$ for all $n \geq 0$.
(b) Repeat part (a), but this time let $f_0(x) = e^{2x}$ for all $x \in \mathbb{R}$.
(c) Repeat part (a), but this time let $f_0(x) = \sqrt{x}$ for all $x \in [0, \infty)$.

Exercise 5.5.12 Generalize Exercise 5.2.12 in the following way. Prove by induction that for any integer $k \geq 2$, there exists an integer n_k such that, for all positive integers $n \geq n_k$, we have $n! > k^n$. (This proves that sooner or later, the factorial function eventually catches up to and overtakes all exponential functions.)

Exercise 5.5.13 (a) Prove by induction that, if $n \in \mathbb{N} \cup \{0\}$, then $10^{2n} - 1$ is divisible by 11.
(b) Prove by induction that, if $n \in \mathbb{N} \cup \{0\}$, then $10^{2n+1} + 1$ is divisible by 11.
(c) Deduce from parts (a) and (b) that, if $n \in \mathbb{N}$ is written with decimal digits $a_k a_{k-1} \cdots a_2 a_1 a_0$, then $11 \mid n$ if and only if $11 \mid \sum_{i=0}^{k}(-1)^i a_i$.

Exercise 5.5.14 (Bernoulli's Inequality[7]) Prove that for all $a \in \mathbb{R}$ and all $n \in \mathbb{N}$, if $1 + a > 0$, then $(1 + a)^n \geq 1 + na$.

Exercise 5.5.15 Prove Corollary 5.3.4.

---

[7]Named for the Swiss mathematician Johann Bernoulli (1667–1748), one of several notable mathematicians in the Bernoulli family. In 1705, he had planned to assume a professorship in classical Greek at Basel University in his hometown when, upon his older brother's death, he was able to assume his brother's position as a professor of mathematics.

Exercise 5.5.16 Prove that any integer $n \geq 18$ can be written in the form $n = \sum_{i=1}^{m} k_i$, where $k_i \in \{4, 7\}$ for $i = 1, 2, \ldots, m$. (This means that if the only coins of the realm are in denominations of 4 gwoks and 7 gwoks, then any transaction of at least 18 gwoks can be paid in exact change.)

Exercise 5.5.17 For $n \geq 2$, prove that

$$\left(1 - \frac{1}{4}\right)\left(1 - \frac{1}{9}\right)\left(1 - \frac{1}{16}\right)\cdots\left(1 - \frac{1}{n^2}\right) = \frac{n+1}{2n}.$$

Exercise 5.5.18 Prove by induction that, for each natural number n, the product of the first n odd natural numbers is

$$\frac{(2n)!}{2^n\, n!}.$$

[Suggestion: Designate the nth odd natural number by $2n - 1$.]

Exercise 5.5.19 For $n \in \mathbb{N}$, the nth **Fibonacci**[8] **number** f_n is defined as follows.
$$f_1 = 1, \qquad f_2 = 1, \qquad f_n = f_{n-1} + f_{n-2} \text{ for } n \geq 2.$$

Prove the following for all $n \in \mathbb{N}$.

(a) $\displaystyle\sum_{j=1}^{n} f_j = f_{n+2} - 1.$

(b) $\displaystyle\sum_{j=1}^{n} f_{2j-1} = f_{2n}.$

(c) $\displaystyle\sum_{j=1}^{n} f_{2j} = f_{2n+1} - 1.$

---

[8]The Italian mathematician Fibonacci (c. 1170–c. 1250) was born Leonardo of Pisa. As a youth, he traveled with his merchant father to the Algerian port city of Bejaia where Leonardo learned the Hindu-Arabic numeral system and the associated algorithms of arithmetic. In 1202, he wrote the book *Liber Abaci*, which introduced this system to Europe. It included an exercise involving the population increase of a colony of rabbits. The solution generates the first twelve numbers of the infinite sequence now known as *the Fibonacci sequence*.

(d) $\displaystyle\sum_{j=1}^{n} (f_j)^2 = f_n f_{n+1}$.

(e) $f_n^2 = f_{n-1} f_{n+1} + (-1)^{n+1}$.

(f) $2 | f_{3n}$.

(g) $5 | f_{5n}$.

(h) f_n and f_{n+1} are relatively prime.

Exercise 5.5.20 Use the Binomial Theorem to expand fully the following powers of binomials (i.e., write out all the terms).
(a) $(x - y)^5$
(b) $(2x + 3y)^4$
(c) $\left(2x - \frac{1}{2}y\right)^6$
(d) $(x + y + z)^3$ [Hint: Expand the *trinomial* $x + y + z$ as though it were the binomial $x + (y + z)$. Then apply the Binomial Theorem again to each power of $y + z$ in the expansion.]

Exercise 5.5.21 Prove the following identities for all $n \in \mathbb{N} \cup \{0\}$.
(a) $\displaystyle\sum_{k=0}^{n} (-1)^k \binom{n}{k} 2^{n-k} = 1$.

(b) $\displaystyle\sum_{k=0}^{n} (-1)^{n-k} \binom{n}{k} 2^k = (-1)^n$.

(c) $\displaystyle\sum_{k=0}^{n} (-1)^{n-k} \binom{n}{k} 2^{2k} = 3^n$.

Exercise 5.5.22 Evaluate each of the following.
(a) $\displaystyle\sum_{k=0}^{101} (-1)^{101-k} \binom{101}{101-k} 2^{2k}$

(b) $\displaystyle\sum_{k=0}^{50} \binom{101}{k}$

Exercise 5.5.23   Let $\{A_n : n \in \mathbb{N}\}$ be a family of subsets of some universe U. We generalize the notion of symmetric difference (see Exercise 3.6.12) in the following way. Define $\overset{1}{\underset{k=1}{+}} A_k = A_1$ and $\overset{2}{\underset{k=1}{+}} A_k = (A_1 \cup A_2) \setminus (A_1 \cap A_2)$. For each $n \geq 2$, define $\overset{n+1}{\underset{k=1}{+}} A_k = \left(\overset{n}{\underset{k=1}{+}} A_k \right) + A_{n+1}$.

(a) Prove that the definition of $\overset{n+1}{\underset{k=1}{+}} A_k$ is independent of the order of the sets A_k.

(b) Prove by induction that for all $n \in \mathbb{N}$, $\overset{n}{\underset{k=1}{+}} A_k$ is the set of elements of U that belong to exactly an odd number of the sets $A_1, \ldots, A_n$.

Exercise 5.5.24   Is there anything incorrect in the following proof by induction?

Claim. *Given any finite subset S of $\mathbb{N}$, if S includes a prime number, then all the elements of S are prime.*

Proof. We proceed by induction on the number of elements of S. Let S be a finite subset of $\mathbb{N}$ that includes a prime number, say p. If $S = \{p\}$, then the claim obviously holds for S; that is, the claim is true for sets of size 1.

As the induction hypothesis, suppose that, for some arbitrary $n \in \mathbb{N}$, if a subset of $\mathbb{N}$ contains n elements at least one of which is prime, then all of its elements are prime. Now suppose that S is a subset of $\mathbb{N}$ of size $n + 1$ and that at least one of its elements, say p, is prime. We need to show that all the elements of S are prime.

Since $n+1 > 1$, there exists some element x of S distinct from p. Then $S \setminus \{x\}$ has only n elements, and so by the induction hypothesis, all the elements of $S \setminus \{x\}$ are prime, including in particular some element $y \neq x$. Now consider the set $S \setminus \{y\}$. It, too, has only n elements, and so by another application of the induction hypothesis, all of its elements are prime. In particular, x is prime too. Therefore all the elements of S are prime as required. $\square$

Exercise 5.5.25 Consider a 3-dimensional analogue of Example 5.3.2. You have a block of wood in the shape of a rectangular parallelepiped that is ℓ units long, w units wide, and t units tall, where $\ell, w, t \in \mathbb{N}$, so that its volume is $n = \ell w t$ cubic units. Find a formula for the number of cuts required to reduce the block to n $(1 \times 1 \times 1)$-cubes.

Chapter 6

Binary Relations

A BINARY RELATION on a set S is no more than a subset of $S \times S$. With such a loose a definition, binary relations become interesting only when further conditions are imposed. The first such structure that we study in this chapter is the relation of *equivalence*, for which the ground is prepared by a study of partitions. Then we consider various types of order. Of particular usefulness is the natural order of the real numbers, and from this standpoint, we reformulate and formalize some basic theorems of first-semester calculus. Finally, we revisit functions, this time defining them rigorously as a special kind of binary relation.

6.1 Partitions

If you encountered the word *partition* in your calculus course, it was likely in the context of your introduction to the definite integral. You constructed a Riemann sum for a function f that is continuous on an interval $[a, b]$, and the first step was to "let $a = x_0 < x_1 < \cdots < x_n = b$ be a partition of $[a, b]$." Exactly what kind of an object was this so-called partition? The motivating idea was to consider a family of subintervals $[x_{i-1}, x_i]$ of the interval $[a, b]$ whose union is all of $[a, b]$. Strictly speaking, this family of subintervals

171

is not a partition; it meets only the first and third of the three conditions for a partition in the following definition. [Think about how the calculus application might be slightly modified in order to satisfy the second condition as well.]

Definition 6.1.1   *Let S be any nonempty set. A family $\mathscr{A} \subseteq \mathscr{P}(S)$ is a* **partition** *of S if the following three statements about $\mathscr{A}$ hold.*

(i) $\emptyset \notin \mathscr{A}$,

(ii) $(\forall A, B \in \mathscr{A})\big[(A = B) \vee (A \cap B = \emptyset)\big]$, and

(iii) $\bigcup\limits_{A \in \mathscr{A}} A = S$.

The elements of a partition are the **cells** *of the partition.*

We analyze this definition. A partition is a collection of subsets of a set S (called cells); in particular, the first condition tells us that cells are nonempty subsets. The second condition tells us that no element of S belongs to two distinct cells; that is, each element of S belongs to *at most one* cell. The third condition tells us, by definition of union of sets, that every element of S belongs to *at least one* cell. Thus a partition of S is a family of nonempty subsets of S such that each element of S belongs to *exactly one* of these subsets.

Like any set, a partition is finite if and only if it has finitely many elements—that is, finitely many cells. The cells themselves may be finite or infinite or some of each. Clearly, if S is a finite set, then any partition of S consists of finitely many cells, each of which is a finite set. However, if S is infinite, then there are infinitely many possibilities. Let us consider some of them.

Example 6.1.2   We consider three different partitions of the set $\mathbb{N}$.

1. For each $n \in \mathbb{N}$, let $A_n = \{k \in \mathbb{N} : 5n - 4 \leq k \leq 5n\}$. For example, we have $A_3 = \{11, 12, 13, 14, 15\}$. Then $\mathscr{A} = \{A_n : n \in \mathbb{N}\}$ is a partition of $\mathbb{N}$ consisting of infinitely many cells, each having a finite number (five) of elements.

2. For each $n \in \{1, 2, 3, 4, 5\}$, let $A_n = \{5k + n : k \in \mathbb{N} \cup \{0\}\}$. For example, $A_2 = \{2, 7, 12, 17, 22, \ldots\}$. Then $\mathscr{A} = \{A_n : n \in \{1, 2, 3, 4, 5\}\}$ is a partition of $\mathbb{N}$ consisting of finitely many (five) cells, each having infinitely many elements.

3. For each prime number p, let $A_p = \{p^k : k \in \mathbb{N}\}$. Then, for example,

$A_3 = \{3, 9, 27, 81, 243, \ldots\}$. Let B consist of all natural numbers that are divisible by two or more distinct prime numbers. Thus

$$B = \{6, 10, 12, 14, 15, 18, 20, 21, 22, \ldots\},$$

and so

$$\mathscr{A} = \{\{1\}, B, A_2, A_3, A_5, A_7, A_{11}, \ldots\}$$

is a partition of $\mathbb{N}$ consisting of infinitely many infinite cells together with one very small finite cell.

Exercise 6.1.3 Construct a partition of $\mathbb{N}$ consisting of six finite cells and six infinite cells.

Exercise 6.1.4 (a) Show that the family of lines in the plane all having the same slope m forms a partition of the set $\mathbb{R} \times \mathbb{R}$.
(b) Show that the set of circles in the plane all having the same center (x_0, y_0), together with the singleton set $\{(x_0, y_0)\}$, form a partition of the set $\mathbb{R} \times \mathbb{R}$.

An important example of a partition arises in the following situation. Let X and Y be sets, and let a function $f : X \to Y$ be given. By definition of a function (Definition 4.1.1), each element $x \in X$ has a unique image $f(x) \in Y$. That means that each element $x \in X$ belongs to *exactly one* subset of X of the form $f^{-1}(y)$, where $y \in f(X)$. Thus the family $\{f^{-1}(y) : y \in f(X)\}$ is a partition of X.

Proposition 6.1.5 *If $f : X \to Y$ is a surjection, then the family*

$$\{f^{-1}(y) : y \in Y\}$$

is a partition of X.

Exercise 6.1.6 Which of the three conditions in Definition 6.1.1 fails when f is not a surjection in Proposition 6.1.5?

Definition 6.1.7 *Let S be a nonempty set, and suppose that $\mathscr{A}$ and $\mathscr{B}$ are partitions of S. If for every cell $B \in \mathscr{B}$ there exists a cell $A \in \mathscr{A}$ such that $B \subseteq A$, then $\mathscr{B}$ is a **refinement** of $\mathscr{A}$, and $\mathscr{B}$ **refines** $\mathscr{A}$.*

Equivalently, one could say that $\mathscr{B}$ is a refinement of $\mathscr{A}$ if and only if every cell of $\mathscr{A}$ is a union of cells of $\mathscr{B}$.

To illustrate this notion, let $\mathscr{A}$ be as in Example 6.1.2(2). For each integer $n \in \{1, 2, 3, 4, 5, 6, 7, 8, 9, 10\}$, let $B_n = \{10k + n : k \in \mathbb{N} \cup \{0\}\}$, and let $\mathscr{B} = \{B_n : n = 1, 2, \ldots, 10\}$. Then $\mathscr{B}$ refines $\mathscr{A}$. For instance, $A_2 = B_2 \cup B_7$.

Obviously, every partition is a refinement of itself.

Exercise 6.1.8   Let $\mathscr{A}, \mathscr{B}$, and $\mathscr{C}$ be partitions of the same set. Prove the following.
(a) If $\mathscr{A}$ refines $\mathscr{B}$ and $\mathscr{B}$ refines $\mathscr{A}$, then $\mathscr{A} = \mathscr{B}$.
(b) If $\mathscr{A}$ refines $\mathscr{B}$ and $\mathscr{B}$ refines $\mathscr{C}$, then $\mathscr{A}$ refines $\mathscr{C}$.

In the next section, we begin a study of various kinds of *binary relations*. The first to be studied are called *equivalence relations*.

6.2   Equivalence Relations

In this section and the next section, we consider how various elements of the same set do or do not relate to each other. Let S be a set, let $x, y \in S$, and let $\mathbf{R}$ denote some possible way that x may be related to y. We will call $\mathbf{R}$ a **binary relation** or, briefly, a **relation**, and write $x\mathbf{R}y$ when x is related in this way to y. (So $x\mathbf{R}y$ is a statement; it assumes the truth value $\mathbf{T}$ or $\mathbf{F}$.)

Example 6.2.1   The following six familiar examples should suggest that with every relation come conditions determining that if a relation holds for certain ordered pairs, then it must also hold (or must not hold) for certain other ordered pairs.

1. Let $S = \mathbb{R}$ and let $x\mathbf{R}y$ mean $x < y$. It is correct to write $3\mathbf{R}\pi$, but neither $3\mathbf{R}3$ nor $\pi\mathbf{R}3$ is true.

2. Let $S = \mathscr{P}(X)$, where X is a set. For sets $A, B \in \mathscr{P}(X)$, write $A\mathbf{R}B$ when $A \subseteq B$. Thus for all $A, B, C \in \mathscr{P}(X)$, we have $A\mathbf{R}A$, $(A\mathbf{R}B \wedge B\mathbf{R}A) \Rightarrow A = B$, and $(A\mathbf{R}B \wedge B\mathbf{R}C) \Rightarrow A\mathbf{R}C$.

3. Let $S = \mathbb{R}$ and let $x\mathbf{R}y$ mean $|x-y| < 1$. Obviously, $x\mathbf{R}x$ for all $x \in \mathbb{R}$, and $x\mathbf{R}y$ holds if and only if $y\mathbf{R}x$ also holds.

4. Let S be the set of all humans who have ever been alive, and let $x\mathbf{R}y$ mean "x is an ancestor of y." The relation $\mathbf{R}$ behaves somewhat like $<$ in the first example. No one is one's own ancestor, and no two people are mutual ancestors, but your ancestor's ancestor is also your ancestor.

5. Again, let S be a set of people, but now let $x\mathbf{R}y$ mean "x is a sibling[1] of y." This situation is like none of the previous ones. The relationship is mutual, and your sibling's sibling is also your sibling—unless that person happens to be yourself.

6. Once more, let S be a set of people, and let $x\mathbf{R}y$ mean "x is a friend of y." It is fair to assume that friendship is mutual, but perhaps you don't like your friends' friends. Whether you are a friend of yourself is a psychological matter and not in the scope of this book.

Definition 6.2.2 *A **relation** on a set S is a subset of $S \times S$.*

Thus $\mathbf{R} \subseteq S \times S$, and we may write either $x\mathbf{R}y$ or $(x,y) \in \mathbf{R}$, whichever is more convenient. A relation on a set S may also be regarded as a propositional function from $S \times S$ to the set $\{\mathbf{T}, \mathbf{F}\}$. However, in the definition that we are using (Definition 6.2.2), a relation is identical to the truth set of the propositional function. Compare this remark with Example 4.1.7.

Definition 6.2.3 *Let S be a set and let $\mathbf{R}$ be a relation on S.*

$\mathbf{R}$ *is **reflexive** if*

$$(\forall x \in S)\big[(x,x) \in \mathbf{R}\big].$$

$\mathbf{R}$ *is **symmetric** if*

$$(\forall x, y \in S)\big[(x,y) \in \mathbf{R} \;\Rightarrow\; (y,x) \in \mathbf{R}\big].$$

$\mathbf{R}$ *is **transitive** if*

$$(\forall x, y, z \in S)\big[\big((x,y) \in \mathbf{R} \;\wedge\; (y,z) \in \mathbf{R}\big) \;\Rightarrow\; (x,z) \in \mathbf{R}\big].$$

---

[1]In this context, for the sake of simplicity, we understand one individual to be a sibling of another when they have the same two biological parents.

R *is an* **equivalence relation** *if* **R** *is reflexive, symmetric, and transitive, in which case, if* $(x, y) \in$ **R**, *we say* x *is* **equivalent to** y.

Note that x and y need not be distinct in the definition of *symmetric*. Similarly, x, y, and z need not be distinct in the definition of *transitive*.

We apply these definitions to the six relations in Example 6.2.1.

1. The relation $<$ on the set $\mathbb{R}$ is transitive but not reflexive and not symmetric.

2. The relation $\subseteq$ on $\mathscr{P}(S)$ is reflexive and transitive but not symmetric.

3. The relation on $\mathbb{R}$ of being distance less than 1 unit apart is reflexive and symmetric. A counterexample shows that this relation is not transitive. Although $|0 - 2/3| < 1$ and $|2/3 - 4/3| < 1$, we have $|0 - 4/3| > 1$.

4. The ancestor relation is like $<$ in the first example in that it is transitive but not reflexive and not symmetric. However, there is an important difference. Given two distinct real numbers, one of them is always less than the other, but there can be two distinct people such that neither one is an ancestor of the other.

5. The sibling relation is symmetric but not reflexive. The problem with transitivity is that, if you have a sibling, then your sibling's siblings include yourself. More about this to come shortly.

6. Friendship is presumed to be symmetric. It is not transitive. We're still not discussing whether it is reflexive.

The properties of being reflexive, symmetric, and transitive are completely independent of each other. If, in spite of these examples, you still don't believe it, try finding the flaw in the attempt to prove following false theorem.

False Theorem *If a relation* **R** *on a set* S *is symmetric and transitive, then it is reflexive.*

Flawed proof. Let $x \in S$ and suppose $(x, y) \in \mathbf{R}$. Since $\mathbf{R}$ is symmetric, we have $(y, x) \in \mathbf{R}$. Since $\mathbf{R}$ is transitive and both (x, y) and (y, x) are in $\mathbf{R}$, it follows that $(x, x) \in \mathbf{R}$. Since x was chosen arbitrarily in S, it follows that $\mathbf{R}$ is reflexive. $\qquad\square$

To find the flaw, consider again the sibling relation in Example 6.2.1. Suppose that the definition of "siblinghood" were extended to allow that people who have a sibling are also siblings of themselves. Then the sibling relation would become transitive. But even then, people without siblings would not be their own sibling. Since people without siblings exist, the "extended sibling relation" provides a counterexample. This relation is symmetric and transitive but not reflexive. [Note the universal quantifier in the definition of reflexive in Definition 6.2.3.] The first sentence of the flawed proof says "and suppose $(x, y) \in \mathbf{R}$." That may be too much to suppose! What if, for this "arbitrary" x, there exists no $y \in S$ such that $(x, y) \in \mathbf{R}$? For such an element x, we cannot deduce that $(x, x) \in S$.

Exercise 6.2.4 Define the relation $\mathbf{R}$ on the set of points in the plane, as follows. For any points (x_1, y_1) and (x_2, y_2) in $\mathbb{R} \times \mathbb{R}$, say that $(x_1, y_1)\mathbf{R}(x_2, y_2)$ if the distance between the two points is a rational number. Determine whether $\mathbf{R}$ an equivalence relation on $\mathbb{R} \times \mathbb{R}$.

The **diagonal** of the set S is the set

$$\Delta(S) = \{(x, x) : x \in S\}.$$

If you plot $\Delta(\mathbb{R})$ in the xy-plane, you can immediately see where the name "diagonal" comes from.

Exercise 6.2.5 Let S be a set and let $\mathbf{R}$ be a relation on S. Prove the following.
(a) $\mathbf{R}$ is reflexive if and only if $\Delta(S) \subseteq \mathbf{R}$.
(b) $\Delta(S)$ is an equivalence relation.

From the two parts of Exercise 6.2.5, we see that $\Delta(S)$ is the smallest possible equivalence relation on S. It is the relation of *equality*; every element of S is equivalent (that is, equal) to itself and only to itself. The diagonal is truly an uninteresting equivalence relation. For a more interesting and more important example of an equivalence relation on $\mathbb{Z}$, you need to recall the definition of divides (Definition 2.3.5) on $\mathbb{Z}$.

Definition 6.2.6 *Let $m \in \mathbb{N}$ and $a, b \in \mathbb{Z}$. Then a is **congruent to** b* **modulo** *m, written $a \equiv b \pmod{m}$, if $m \mid a - b$. The relation on $\mathbb{Z}$ of* **congruence modulo** *m is the set*

$$\{(a,b) \in \mathbb{Z} \times \mathbb{Z} : a \equiv b \pmod{m}\}.$$

Theorem 6.2.7 *Let $m \in \mathbb{N}$. The relation of congruence modulo m is an equivalence relation on $\mathbb{Z}$.*

Proof. Let $a \in \mathbb{Z}$. Since $a - a = 0 = 0 \cdot m$, we have $a \equiv a \pmod{m}$. Since a was arbitrary, the relation of congruence modulo m is reflexive on $\mathbb{Z}$.

Let $a, b \in \mathbb{Z}$, and suppose $a \equiv b \pmod{m}$. By Definition 6.2.6, for some $k \in \mathbb{Z}$, we have $a - b = km$. Hence $b - a = (-k)m$. Since $-k \in \mathbb{Z}$, we have $b \equiv a \pmod{m}$, and so congruence modulo m is symmetric.

Finally, suppose that $a \equiv b \pmod{m}$ and $b \equiv c \pmod{m}$ for some arbitrary integers a, b, and c. By definition, there exist integers $k, \ell \in \mathbb{Z}$ such that

$$a - b = km \quad \text{and} \quad b - c = \ell m.$$

Addition of these two equations gives $a - c = (k + \ell)m$. Since $k + \ell \in \mathbb{Z}$, we have $a \equiv c \pmod{m}$, and congruence modulo m is transitive.

Since congruence modulo m is reflexive, symmetric, and transitive, it is an equivalence relation on the set $\mathbb{Z}$. □

Example 6.2.8 Let $A_n = \{5k + n : k \in \mathbb{Z}\}$ for $n \in \{0, 1, 2, 3, 4\}$. It is easy to verify that $\{A_0, A_1, A_2, A_3, A_4\}$ is a partition of $\mathbb{Z}$. For any integers $a, b \in \mathbb{Z}$, we have $a \equiv b \pmod{5}$ if and only if a and b belong to the same cell A_n.

Definition 6.2.9 *Let $\mathbf{R}$ be an equivalence relation on a set S. For each element $x \in S$, the set*

$$[x] = \{y \in S : (x,y) \in \mathbf{R}\}$$

is the **equivalence class of x with respect to $\mathbf{R}$.**

The following theorem binds tightly together the notions of equivalence relation and partition.

Theorem 6.2.10   *Let S be a nonempty set.*
(i) If $\mathbf{R}$ is an equivalence relation on S, then the set of equivalence classes with respect to $\mathbf{R}$ is a partition of S.
(ii) If $\mathscr{A}$ is any partition of S, then there exists an equivalence relation $\mathbf{R}$ on S such that the cells of $\mathscr{A}$ are exactly the equivalence classes with respect to $\mathbf{R}$.

Proof. Let $\mathbf{R}$ be an equivalence relation on S, and let $\mathscr{E}$ be the set of equivalence classes with respect to $\mathbf{R}$, namely $\mathscr{E} = \{[x] : x \in S\}$. To prove part (i) we must show that $\mathscr{E}$ is a partition of S.

Because $\mathbf{R}$ is reflexive, for each $x \in S$, we have $x \in [x]$. Thus the sets in $\mathscr{E}$ are nonempty, and the union of all the sets in $\mathscr{E}$ is the whole set S. We have shown that $\mathscr{E}$ satisfies the first and third of the three conditions for a partition in Definition 6.1.1, and it remains only to show that distinct sets in $\mathscr{E}$ are disjoint. We prove the contrapositive: equivalence classes that are not disjoint are not distinct.

Let x and y be arbitrary elements of S, and suppose that $[x] \cap [y] \neq \emptyset$. Hence there exists some $z \in [x] \cap [y]$. (Note that z need not be distinct from x or y.) By definition of *equivalence class*, we have $(x, z), (y, z) \in \mathbf{R}$. By the symmetry of $\mathbf{R}$, $(z, y) \in \mathbf{R}$. Then by transitivity, $(x, y) \in \mathbf{R}$.

Let w be an arbitrary element of $[y]$; thus $(y, w) \in \mathbf{R}$. By transitivity, $(x, w) \in \mathbf{R}$, and so $w \in [x]$. This proves that $[y] \subseteq [x]$. By reversing the roles of x and y in this argument, one can prove that $[x] \subseteq [y]$. Thus $[x] = [y]$; these equivalence classes are not distinct. This completes the proof of part (i).

To prove part (ii), let $\mathscr{A}$ be an arbitrary partition of the set S, and define the relation

$$\mathbf{R} = \big\{(x, y) : x \text{ and } y \text{ belong to the same cell of } \mathscr{A}\big\}.$$

It is easy to verify that $\mathbf{R}$ is an equivalence relation. $\qquad\square$

To describe in words the relationship between $\mathbf{R}$ and $\mathscr{A}$ in the previous theorem, we say, "$\mathscr{A}$ is the partition with respect to $\mathbf{R}$," and "$\mathbf{R}$ is the equivalence relation induced by $\mathscr{A}$."

Exercise 6.2.11 Define the relation $\sim$ on $\mathbb{Z} \times (\mathbb{Z} \setminus \{0\})$ by

$$(a, b) \sim (c, d) \quad \Leftrightarrow \quad ad = bc. \tag{6.2.1}$$

Prove that $\sim$ is an equivalence relation. (Note that elements of this relation are ordered pairs of ordered pairs.)

We are now able to give a rigorous definition of a rational number. A **rational number** is an equivalence class in $\mathbb{Z} \times (\mathbb{Z} \setminus \{0\})$ with respect to the relation (6.2.1). Notationally, instead of writing, for example, $[(8, 6)]$, we suppress the brackets and write $\frac{8}{6}$. Of course, $\frac{8}{6}$ is equivalent to $\frac{-4}{-3}$ and to $\frac{4000}{3000}$, and we express this equivalence with the usual equals sign:

$$\frac{8}{6} = \frac{-4}{-3} = \frac{4000}{3000}.$$

Thus any representative of the equivalence class of $(8, 6)$ will do, but it is customary to pick one that is in lowest terms, and when possible, one where both elements of the ordered pair are positive. In this case, $\frac{4}{3}$ would be preferred.

Definition 6.2.12   *Let $\mathbf{R}_1$ and $\mathbf{R}_2$ be relations on a set S. Then $\mathbf{R}_1$ refines $\mathbf{R}_2$ if $\mathbf{R}_1 \subseteq \mathbf{R}_2$.*

Exercise 6.2.13   Let $\mathbf{R}_1$ and $\mathbf{R}_2$ be equivalence relations on a set S. Prove that $\mathbf{R}_1$ refines $\mathbf{R}_2$ if and only if the partition with respect to $\mathbf{R}_1$ is a refinement of the partition with respect to $\mathbf{R}_2$.

Exercise 6.2.14   Let $\mathbf{R}$ be an equivalence relation on A and let $\mathbf{S}$ be an equivalence relation on B. Define a relation $\mathbf{T}$ on $A \times B$ by

$$\big((a_1, b_1), (a_2, b_2)\big) \in \mathbf{T} \quad \Leftrightarrow \quad (a_1, a_2) \in \mathbf{R} \text{ and } (b_1, b_2) \in \mathbf{S}.$$

Prove that $\mathbf{T}$ is an equivalence relation.

6.3 Order Relations

Every fall, various groups of sportswriters attempt to rank the best collegiate football teams, and every winter, they attempt the same feat for the best collegiate basketball teams. This is not an easy task. How does Team A compare with Team B? While it is generally accepted that, if A beats B, then A ought to be ranked higher than B, often A and B never face each other on the field of play. But then, perhaps A narrowly beats B, while B beats C, which in turn clobbers A. Sometimes, as in basketball, A and B play each other twice, and each team decisively wins the game on its home court. When ranking soccer teams, the sportswriters have to interpret the possibility of a tie score. Nonetheless, from a mass of inconsistent scores, the sportswriters supply eager readers of the Monday sports section with a ranking from #1 to #25 of the best collegiate teams in the United States. The fact that different polls almost never come up with identical rankings suggests that either (1) different ranking criteria are used by different sportswriters or (2) a lot of subjectivity comes into the decision.

What the sportswriters are attempting to do is to produce a *linear order*. This is indeed the simplest type of order relation. It is the antithesis of an equivalence relation. An equivalence relation bunches together (into equivalence classes) elements of a set that cannot be ranked against each other, while a linear order seeks to spread the elements out.

Definition 6.3.1 *Let* $\mathbf{R}$ *be a relation on a set* S.

$\mathbf{R}$ *is* **irreflexive** *if*

$$(\forall x \in S)[(x, x) \notin \mathbf{R}].$$

Equivalently, $\mathbf{R}$ *is irreflexive if* $\mathbf{R} \cap \Delta(S) = \emptyset$.

$\mathbf{R}$ *is* **antisymmetric** *if*

$$(\forall x, y \in S)\big[((x, y) \in \mathbf{R} \ \wedge \ (y, x) \in \mathbf{R}) \ \Rightarrow \ x = y\big].$$

Elements x *and* y *of* S *are* **comparable** *(with respect to* $\mathbf{R}$*) if* $(x, y) \in \mathbf{R}$ *or* $(y, x) \in \mathbf{R}$. *Otherwise,* x *and* y *are* **incomparable**.

From these definitions, we see that, if every two elements of S are comparable with respect to the antisymmetric relation $\mathbf{R}$, then, whenever $x \neq y$, exactly one of (x, y) and (y, x) belongs to $\mathbf{R}$. Note also that "irreflexive" is not the same as "not reflexive." [Why is that? Quantifiers are important! Compare $(\forall x \in S)[(x, x) \notin \mathbf{R}]$ with $\neg(\forall x \in S)[(x, x) \in \mathbf{R}].$]

Definition 6.3.2 *A relation $\mathbf{R}$ on a set S is an **order relation** and $(S, \mathbf{R})$ is an **ordered set** if $\mathbf{R}$ is antisymmetric and transitive. An order relation $\mathbf{R}$ is a*
*(i) **partial order** if it is also reflexive;*
*(ii) **strict partial order** if it is also irreflexive;*
*(iii) **linear order** if it is a strict partial order and every two distinct elements are comparable.*

The pair $(S, \mathbf{R})$ is a **partially ordered set**, or a **poset** for short, if S is a set and $\mathbf{R}$ is a partial order on S. When it's clear that $\mathbf{R}$ is the only relation on S under consideration, then we say even more briefly that S is a **poset**. We use the term **linearly ordered set** similarly (except that no one says "loset").

A familiar example of a poset is $(S, \leq)$ where S is any set of real numbers. This example also has the feature that any two real numbers are comparable.

Strict partial orders are easily obtained from partial orders simply by removing the diagonal Δ. Thus $\mathbf{R}$ is a strict partial order if and only if $\mathbf{R} \cup \Delta$ is a partial order and $\mathbf{R} \cap \Delta = \emptyset$. Examples of strict partial orders include the following.

- $(S, <)$ and $(S, >)$, where S is any subset of $\mathbb{R}$. These are, in fact, linearly ordered sets.

- $(\mathscr{S}, \subset)$ and $(\mathscr{S}, \supset)$, where $\mathscr{S}$ is any collection of subsets of some given set.

- $\big(\mathbb{N}, \text{is a proper divisor of}\big)$.

Exercise 6.3.3 Let $\mathbf{R}$ be irreflexive and transitive on S. Show the following.

(a) **R** is a strict partial order on S if and only if, for all $x, y \in S$, at most one of the following holds: $(x, y) \in \mathbf{R}$; $(y, x) \in \mathbf{R}$; $x = y$.

(b) **R** is a linear order on S if and only if, for all $x, y \in S$, exactly one of the following holds: $(x, y) \in \mathbf{R}$; $(y, x) \in \mathbf{R}$; $x = y$. (This is the **trichotomy property** when $(S, \mathbf{R}) = (\mathbb{R}, <)$.)

Example 6.3.4   For any set X, $(\mathscr{P}(X), \subseteq)$ is a poset. By Exercise 3.1.7(a) and Proposition 3.1.4, $\subseteq$ is reflexive and transitive on $\mathscr{P}(X)$. The very definition of equality of sets (Definition 3.1.8) tells us that $\subseteq$ is antisymmetric on $\mathscr{P}(X)$. When X has at least two elements, then $\mathscr{P}(X)$ contains pairs of incomparable elements, and so $(\mathscr{P}(X), \subseteq)$ is not a linearly ordered set. Neither is $(\mathscr{P}(X), \subset)$, although $\subset$ is a strict partial order.

When the number of elements in a poset is not too large, diagrams such as the one in Figure 6.3.1 help us to understand the partial order relation. This diagram illustrates the poset $(\mathscr{P}(A), \subseteq)$, where $A = \{a, b, c\}$. Observe that two elements are comparable if and only if there is an ascending path from one to the other.

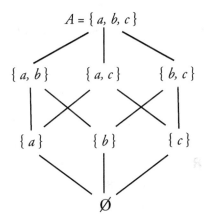

Figure 6.3.1: The poset $\big(\mathscr{P}(\{a, b, c\}), \subseteq\big)$.

Example 6.3.5   Another example of a poset is $(\mathbb{N}, \mid)$, where $\mid$ means "divides" (see Definition 2.3.5). This poset has some properties similar to those of $(\mathscr{P}(A), \subseteq)$ in the previous example. (Look ahead to Exercise 6.7.12(e).) Proofs that $(\mathbb{N}, \mid)$ is reflexive, antisymmetric, and transitive are immediate applications of results from Section 2.3. Examples of pairs of incomparable elements of $(\mathbb{N}, |)$ include (among infinitely many others) every two consecutive integers at least 2.

Definition 6.3.6 *Let $\mathbf{R}$ be any relation on a set S. The* **inverse relation** $\mathbf{R}^{-1}$ *(say, "R-inverse") of $\mathbf{R}$ is defined by the condition*

$$(x, y) \in \mathbf{R} \iff (y, x) \in \mathbf{R}^{-1}.$$

It is immediate that $\left(\mathbf{R}^{-1}\right)^{-1} = \mathbf{R}$. It is also clear that a relation is reflexive if and only if its inverse is reflexive. It is almost as immediate that a relation is transitive if and only if its inverse is transitive. Also, $\mathbf{R}$ is symmetric if and only if $\mathbf{R} = \mathbf{R}^{-1}$. Thus equivalence relations are equal to their inverses. The notion of an inverse relation adds nothing interesting to the study of equivalence relations. However, in general, $\mathbf{R} \neq \mathbf{R}^{-1}$.

Exercise 6.3.7 Prove that if $\mathbf{R}$ is reflexive and transitive, then $\mathbf{R} \cap \mathbf{R}^{-1}$ is an equivalence relation.

Exercise 6.3.8 Let $\mathbf{R}$ and $\mathbf{S}$ be relations on a set A. Prove

$$(\mathbf{R} \cup \mathbf{S})^{-1} = \mathbf{R}^{-1} \cup \mathbf{S}^{-1} \quad \text{and} \quad (\mathbf{R} \cap \mathbf{S})^{-1} = \mathbf{R}^{-1} \cap \mathbf{S}^{-1}.$$

If the relation $\mathbf{R}$ is antisymmetric, then clearly so is $\mathbf{R}^{-1}$. Thus $\mathbf{R}$ is a partial order or a strict partial order or a linear order if and only if $\mathbf{R}^{-1}$ is the same kind of order. $\mathbf{R}$ and $\mathbf{R}^{-1}$ may have different properties in the case of a *well-order*, as we will see in the next section.

We close this section by introducing an operation on the set of relations on a set.

Definition 6.3.9 *Let $\mathbf{R}_1$ and $\mathbf{R}_2$ be relations on a set S. The* **composition** *of $\mathbf{R}_2$ with $\mathbf{R}_1$ is the relation*

$$\mathbf{R}_2 \circ \mathbf{R}_1 = \left\{ (x, y) \in S \times S : (\exists v \in S)\left[(x, v) \in \mathbf{R}_1 \; \wedge \; (v, y) \in \mathbf{R}_2\right] \right\}.$$

Exercise 6.3.10   Let $S = \{a, b, c\}$.
(a) Define relations $\mathbf{R}_1$ and $\mathbf{R}_2$ on S such that $\mathbf{R}_2 \circ \mathbf{R}_1 = \mathbf{R}_1 \circ \mathbf{R}_2$.
(b) Define relations $\mathbf{R}_1$ and $\mathbf{R}_2$ on S such that $\mathbf{R}_2 \circ \mathbf{R}_1 \neq \mathbf{R}_1 \circ \mathbf{R}_2$.

Exercise 6.3.11   Let $\mathbf{R}$ be a relation on a set S. Prove the following.
(a) $\mathbf{R}$ is transitive if and only if $\mathbf{R} \circ \mathbf{R} \subseteq \mathbf{R}$.
(b) If $\mathbf{R}$ is reflexive and transitive, then $\mathbf{R} \circ \mathbf{R} = \mathbf{R}$.

6.4   Bounds and Extremal Elements

Recall the diagram of the poset $(\mathscr{P}(\{a, b, c\}), \subseteq)$ in Figure 6.3.1. Clearly there is something special about the elements $\emptyset$ and A, given their positions in the diagram.

Definition 6.4.1   *Let $(S, \mathbf{R})$ be an ordered set. Let $A \in \mathscr{P}(S)$ and let $m \in S$. Then m is a **lower bound** of A, or A is **bounded below** by m, if*

$$(\forall a \in A)\big[(m, a) \in \mathbf{R}\big].$$

*Similarly, m is an **upper bound** of A, or A is **bounded above** by m, if*

$$(\forall a \in A)\big[(a, m) \in \mathbf{R}\big].$$

*The set S is **bounded** (with respect to $\mathbf{R}$) if S has both a lower bound and an upper bound.*

Consider the ordered set $(\mathbb{R}, \leq)$. The subset $(-\infty, 0]$ has no lower bound, but every nonnegative real number is an upper bound. Meanwhile the subset $[0, \infty)$ has no upper bound, but every nonpositive number is a lower bound. Thus neither subset is bounded.

Note that in Definition 6.4.1, the element m might or might not be an element of A. For example, consider again the poset $(\mathbb{R}, \leq)$ and the half-open interval $A = [0, 1)$. Here 0 is a lower bound that happens also to be an element of A, and every negative real number is also a lower bound of A. Meanwhile, any real number at least 1 is an upper bound of A, but no upper bound of A is an element of A. Certainly, the number 0 plays a special role among all the lower bounds of A, while the number 1 plays a unique role among the upper bounds of A. These two roles motivate the following definition.

Definition 6.4.2 *Let $(S, \mathbf{R})$ be an ordered set and let $A \in \mathscr{P}(S)$. An element $m_0 \in S$ is the* **greatest lower bound** *of A, denoted* glb(A), *when both of the following hold.*

(i) m_0 *is a lower bound of A, and*

(ii) *for any lower bound $m \in S \setminus \{m_0\}$ of A, we have $(m, m_0) \in \mathbf{R}$.*

An element $m_1 \in S$ is the **least upper bound** *of A, denoted* lub(A), *when both of the following hold.*[2]

(iii) m_1 *is an upper bound of A, and*

(iv) *for any upper bound $m \in S \setminus \{m_1\}$ of A, we have $(m_1, m) \in \mathbf{R}$.*

What we're saying is that glb(A) is simply the greatest of all the lower bounds of a set A, while lub(A) is the least of all the upper bounds of A. Note the use of articles here: *a* lower bound, but *the* greatest lower bound. Is the uniqueness of glb(A) really so obvious? Well, suppose that elements m and m' of the ordered set S are greatest lower bounds of the subset A. By condition (i) of Definition 6.4.2, they are both lower bounds of A, and so by condition (ii), both $(m, m') \in \mathbf{R}$ and $(m', m) \in \mathbf{R}$. But $\mathbf{R}$ is antisymmetric, which implies that $m = m'$. We've just proved that *a greatest lower bound is unique—but only if it exists.*

Exercise 6.4.3 Let $(S, \mathbf{R})$ be an ordered set and let $A \in \mathscr{P}(S) \setminus \{\varnothing\}$. Prove that A has at most one least upper bound.

Consider, for example, the poset $(\mathbb{R}^+, \leq)$, and let $A = \{x \in \mathbb{R}^+ : x^2 < 2\}$. Then A has $\sqrt{2}$ as its (unique) least upper bound. However, if we consider instead the poset $(\mathbb{Q}^+, \leq)$ and let $B = \{x \in \mathbb{Q}^+ : x^2 < 2\}$, then B is also bounded above (for example, by 1.42), but B has no least upper bound in $(\mathbb{Q}^+, \leq)$.

Example 6.4.4 Consider the poset $(\mathbb{N}, |)$ and the subset

$$A = \{90, 120, 150, 180, 300, 360, 450, 600, 900\}$$

---

[2]An alternative terminology and accompanying notation in common use are $m_0 = \inf A$ and $m_1 = \sup A$, where inf and sup are short for *infimum* and *supremum*, respectively.

of $\mathbb{N}$. The lower bounds of A are the elements of $\mathbb{N}$ that divide every element of A—namely, 1, 2, 3, 5, 10, 15, 30. The greatest of all these lower bounds is 30, which is also the greatest common divisor of the elements of A. [Is this just a coincidence, or does it follow from Definition 2.5.3?] Clearly, A is also bounded above, and $\mathrm{lub}(A)$ is the least common multiple of its elements, which is 1800. In this particular case, neither of these bounds is an element of A.

Proposition 6.4.5 *Let $(S, \mathbf{R})$ be a poset and let $A \in \mathscr{P}(S)$. Let L be the set of all lower bounds of the set A. If A has a greatest lower bound, then L has a least upper bound and $\mathrm{glb}(A) = \mathrm{lub}(L)$.*

Proof. Let $m_0 = \mathrm{glb}(A)$. By Definition 6.4.2(i), $m_0 \in L$. By Definition 6.4.2(ii), we have $(\ell, m_0) \in \mathbf{R}$ for all $\ell \in L$. Hence m_0 is an upper bound of L. Since $m_0 \in L$, we have $(m_0, b) \in \mathbf{R}$ for every upper bound b of L. By Definition 6.4.2(iii, iv), $m_0 = \mathrm{lub}(L)$. $\qquad\square$

Exercise 6.4.6 Let $(S, \mathbf{R})$ be a poset and let $A \in \mathscr{P}(S)$. Let U be the set of all upper bounds of the set A. State and prove a proposition analogous to Proposition 6.4.5.

In the context of Example 6.4.4, consider Figure 6.4.1, which shows only the elements in A from the poset $(\mathbb{N}, |)$. As in Figure 6.3.1, two elements are comparable if and only if there is an ascending path from one to the other. We see that some of the elements of A—namely, 90, 120, and 150—are *minimal* elements of A, in the sense that no other element of A is "smaller" with respect to the order relation. In the same way, the elements 360, 600, and 900 are *maximal* elements of A. Let us formalize these terms.

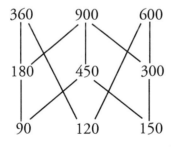

Figure 6.4.1: The poset $(A, |)$ from Example 6.4.4.

Definition 6.4.7 *Let* $(S, \mathbf{R})$ *be an ordered set and let* $A \in \mathscr{P}(S)$. *An element* $m \in A$ *is a* **minimal element** *of* A *when*

$$\big(\forall a \in A \setminus \{m\}\big) \big[(a, m) \notin \mathbf{R}\big].$$

An element $M \in A$ *is a* **maximal element** *of* A *when*

$$\big(\forall a \in A \setminus \{M\}\big) \big[(M, a) \notin \mathbf{R}\big].$$

An element of A *is an* **extremal element** *of* A *if it is a minimal element or maximal element of* A.

We make two observations about extremal elements. First, unlike upper and lower bounds of a set A, an extremal element of A must be an element of A. Second, an extremal element—for example, a maximal element—doesn't have to be "greater than" every other element of A. It merely must not be less than any element of A. This is like the sports team that hasn't necessarily beaten every other team in its conference; it simply has never lost to any team in its conference. (There may be teams in the conference against whom it has never played.)

Proposition 6.4.8 *Every finite, nonempty poset has at least one minimal element and at least one maximal element.*

Exercise 6.4.9 Prove Proposition 6.4.8. [Suggestion: Assume that $(S, \mathbf{R})$ is a finite, nonempty poset with no minimal element, and obtain a contradiction by building an infinite sequence $a_1, a_2, \ldots$ by induction such that $(a_{n+1}, a_n) \in \mathbf{R}$ for all $n \in \mathbb{N}$. Then repeat this argument for maximal elements.]

Here are three examples that show how Proposition 6.4.8 can fail for an infinite poset.

- We return to $(\mathbb{N}, |)$ and consider the set $\mathbb{N}$ itself. The unique minimal element is 1, but there is no maximal element.

- Consider the poset $(\mathbb{R}, \leq)$, and let A denote the open interval $(0, 1)$. Then A has no extremal elements.

- Consider $(\mathbb{Q}, \leq)$, and let $A = \{1/n : n \in \mathbb{N}\}$. Clearly, $1 \in A$, and 1 is its unique maximal element. However, A has no minimal element, because for any element $1/n$ of A, there exist elements of A such as $1/(n+1)$ or $1/(2n)$, which are still smaller.

Sometimes unique extremal elements are special enough to merit their own definitions.

Definition 6.4.10 *Let $(S, \mathbf{R})$ be an ordered set and let $A \in \mathscr{P}(S)$. An element $m \in A$ is the* **minimum** *of A when*

$$(\forall a \in A)[(m, a) \in \mathbf{R}].$$

An element $M \in A$ is the **maximum** *of A when*

$$(\forall a \in A)[(a, M) \in \mathbf{R}].$$

An element of A is an **extremum** *of A when it is the minimum or the maximum of A.*

As we've seen in the various examples, *extrema* (plural of *extremum*) don't necessarily exist, but when they do, they are unique. The extremum sports teams would be the ones that have played every other team in their conference and either won every game or lost every game.

Example 6.4.11 Let Π be the set of all partitions of a nonempty set S. For $\mathscr{A}, \mathscr{B} \in \Pi$, write $\mathscr{A} \preceq \mathscr{B}$ if $\mathscr{B}$ is a refinement of $\mathscr{A}$. Then $(\Pi, \preceq)$ is a poset. Clearly, $\preceq$ is reflexive. Exercise 6.1.8 gives us that $\preceq$ is antisymmetric and transitive. Although there generally exist incomparable partitions, there exists, nonetheless, a minimum element of the poset—namely, the collection $\{\{x\} : x \in S\}$—which is the *finest* partition possible. There also exists a maximum partition—namely the partition $\{S\}$ consisting of just one big cell S—which is the *coarsest* partition possible.

There remains one more kind of order relation that we postponed presenting earlier.

Definition 6.4.12 *A relation $\mathbf{R}$ on a set S is a* **well-order** *if it is reflexive, antisymmetric, and transitive (that is, a partial order) and if every nonempty subset of S has a minimum element (with respect to $\mathbf{R}$). A set with a well-order is called a* **well-ordered set**.

The posets $(\mathbb{N}, \leq)$ and $(\mathbb{Z}^-, \geq)$ are well-ordered sets. In our present terminology, we could restate the Well Ordering Principle as follows.

Every nonempty subset of $\mathbb{Z}$ having a lower bound is well-ordered.

On the other hand, the poset $(\mathbb{Z}, \leq)$ itself is not well-ordered because no subset of $\mathbb{Z}$ without a lower bound has a minimum element. The poset $(\mathbb{Q}^+, \leq)$ is also not well-ordered, even though it has a lower bound; consider the subset $\{x \in \mathbb{Q}^+ : x > 2\}$, which has no least element.

Observe that, while $(\mathbb{N}, \leq)$ is a well-order, its inverse relation $(\mathbb{N}, \geq)$ is not a well-order.

Exercise 6.4.13 Suppose that the set A has at least two elements. Prove that $\big(\mathscr{P}(A), \subset\big)$ is not well-ordered by first showing that a nonempty collection $\mathscr{S}$ of subsets of A contains a least element if and only if some (not necessarily proper) subset of $\bigcap\{A : A \in \mathscr{S}\}$ is an element of $\mathscr{S}$.

A lot of terms have been defined in this section, and we would like to establish some relationships among them. The following lemma is a step in that direction.

Lemma 6.4.14 *Let $(S, \mathbf{R})$ be a poset and let $A \in \mathscr{P}(S)$.*
(i) If $m \in A$ and m is a lower bound of A, then m is the minimum element of A.
(ii) If m is the minimum element of A, then $m = \mathrm{glb}(A)$.

Proof. (i) Assume that $m \in A$ and that m is a lower bound of A. That means that $(m, a) \in \mathbf{R}$ for all $a \in A$. Since $m \in A$, it must be the minimum element of A.

(ii) Assume that m is the minimum element of A. By Definition 6.4.10, $m \in A$ and $(m, a) \in \mathbf{R}$ for all $a \in A$. This implies that m is a lower bound of A. Since $m \in A$, we have $(\ell, m) \in \mathbf{R}$ for every lower bound ℓ of A. By Definition 6.4.2(i, ii), $m = \mathrm{glb}(A)$. $\square$

Exercise 6.4.15 State and prove a lemma analogous to Lemma 6.4.14 about maximum elements and least upper bounds.

6.5   Applications to Calculus

The words *minimum*, *maximum*, and *extremum* defined in Section 6.4 are words that you have encountered in the particular context of calculus courses, usually modified by *relative* or *absolute*. In this section, we apply these abstract definitions formally to first-year calculus. The ordered sets with which one is concerned in calculus are posets of the form $(S, \leq)$, where S is some subset of the set $\mathbb{R}$ of real numbers. One also has in hand some function $f : S \to \mathbb{R}$, which is usually (but not always) continuous at every point in S.

In most situations in calculus, the set S in question is an interval. At the risk of belaboring the obvious, let us be clear about what an interval is. A subset $I \subseteq \mathbb{R}$ is an **interval** if

$$I \neq \emptyset \quad \text{and} \quad (\forall a, b \in I)(\forall c \in \mathbb{R})[a < c < b \ \Rightarrow \ c \in I].$$

Intervals are nice, easy sets to work with. If an interval I contains its left-hand endpoint—that is, if I is of the form $\{a\}$ or $[a, b)$ or $[a, b]$ (for some $b > a$) or of the form $[a, \infty)$—then a is the minimum element of I, and $a = \mathrm{glb}(I)$ by Lemma 6.4.14. If I does not contain any left-hand endpoint, then I has no minimum element. Similarly, I contains a maximum element if and only if I contains a right-hand endpoint.

Calculus problems involving absolute and relative extrema are problems about the properties of the image $f(I)$ of a set $I \subseteq \mathbb{R}$, especially when I is an interval and particularly when the function f is continuous on I. In our current terminology, the following theorem (whose name you should recognize) states that the image of an interval via a continuous function is always an interval.

Theorem 6.5.1 (The Intermediate Value Theorem)   *Let $S \subseteq \mathbb{R}$ and let $f : S \to \mathbb{R}$ be a continuous function. Then, for any interval $I \subseteq S$, the set $f(I)$ is an interval.*

Recall that an interval is **closed** if it contains a minimum element when bounded below and contains a maximum element when bounded above. Thus a **closed interval** is precisely an interval of the form $[a, b]$ or $[a, \infty)$ or $(-\infty, b]$ or $(-\infty, \infty)$. An **open interval** is an interval that contains neither a maximum element nor a minimum element and hence is of the form (a, b) or (a, ∞) or $(-\infty, b)$ or $(-\infty, \infty)$. Intervals of the form $[a, b)$ or $(a, b]$ are neither open nor closed and are sometimes called *half-open*.[3] The entire real line $(-\infty, \infty)$ is the only interval that is both open and closed. Note that the symbols $-\infty$ and ∞ always stand, respectively, next to left and right parentheses (and), and *never* next to brackets [or]. That is because the symbols $-\infty$ and ∞ do not represent real numbers and so do not belong to any interval.

Your calculus text no doubt also included information equivalent to the following.

Proposition 6.5.2   *Let $S \subseteq \mathbb{R}$ and let $f : S \to \mathbb{R}$ be a continuous function. Then, for any closed and bounded interval $I \subseteq S$, the set $f(I)$ is also a closed and bounded interval.*

The following examples demonstrate why each word in Proposition 6.5.2 is essential.

Example 6.5.3   In each of the following cases, consider whether I and $f(I)$ are closed intervals or bounded intervals (or intervals at all) and whether f is continuous on I. What conjectures can one make about whether extrema are attained?

1. $I = [-1, 1]$ and

$$f(x) = \begin{cases} x + 1 & \text{if } -1 \le x < 0; \\ 0 & \text{if } x = 0; \\ x - 1 & \text{if } 0 < x \le 1. \end{cases}$$

2. $I = [-1, 1]$ and

$$f(x) = \begin{cases} 1/x & \text{if } x \ne 0; \\ 0 & \text{if } x = 0. \end{cases}$$

3. $I = (-\pi, \pi)$ and $f(x) = \sin x$ for all $x \in I$.

---

[3]A pessimist would likely call such an interval *half-closed*.

4. $I = [0, \pi/2)$ and $f(x) = \tan x$ for all $x \in I$.

5. $I = [0, \infty)$ and $f(x) = \arctan x$ for all $x \in I$.

Cases 1 and 2 show that, even though I may be closed and bounded, when f is not continuous, $f(I)$ may fail to be closed (as in case 1) or fail to be bounded (as in case 2). In fact, in case 2, $f(I)$ is not even an interval. In the other examples, f is continuous. Case 3 shows that $f(I)$ may still be closed and bounded even when I is not closed. However, in case 4, I is bounded but not closed, while $f(I)$ is closed but not bounded. In case 5, I is closed but not bounded, while $f(I)$ is bounded but not closed.

Since a closed and bounded interval is precisely one that contains both its minimum and maximum elements, Proposition 6.5.2 can be rephrased in a manner familiar to calculus students as follows.

Theorem 6.5.4 (The Extreme Value Theorem) *If a function is continuous on a closed and bounded interval, then it attains its extrema on that interval.*

Your calculus text either relegated the proof of this statement to an appendix or told you that the proof is beyond the scope of the text. It is indeed, and it is also outside the scope of the text you're presently holding. The proof depends on the fundamental structure of the set of real numbers (as introduced briefly in Section 8.3). You will encounter this proof in a first course in analysis, for which this course may well be a prerequisite.

With present terminology, we can easily interpret so-called absolute extrema. The **absolute minimum** (respectively, **absolute maximum**) of $f : S \to \mathbb{R}$ is nothing other than the minimum (respectively, maximum) of the range $f(S)$. Thus the absolute minimum of f on S is $\mathrm{glb}\big(f(S)\big)$ and the absolute maximum of f is $\mathrm{lub}\big(f(S)\big)$. We now know that if f is continuous and if S is a closed and bounded interval, then these absolute extrema *do exist*.

Definition 6.5.5 *Let $S \subseteq \mathbb{R}$, let $f : S \to \mathbb{R}$, and let $x_0 \in S$. Then f has a **relative minimum** (respectively, **relative maximum**) at x_0 if there exists an open interval I such that $x_0 \in I$ and $f(x_0)$ is the minimum element (respectively, maximum element) of $f(I \cap S)$.*

Exercise 6.5.6   In each of the following examples, a set S and a function $f : S \to \mathbb{R}$ are given. In each case, find the relative extrema of f on S but also, for each relative extremum, find an appropriate open interval I that fits Definition 6.5.5.

(a) $S = \mathbb{R}$ and $f(x) = x^3 - 12x$.

(b) $S = \mathbb{R}$ and $f(x) = \sin x$.

(c) $S = (0, 2\pi]$ and $f(x) = \sin x$.

(d) $S = (0, \infty)$ and $f(x) = \sin(1/x)$.

(e) $S = (0, \infty)$ and for each $n \in \mathbb{N}$, define $f(x) = n - x$ when $n - 1 < x \le n$. [This function f has infinitely many discontinuities, but you can still do this one. Start by drawing a graph, one unit interval at a time, to get an idea of what's going on here.]

6.6   Functions Revisited

Once again, your calculus experience provides the point of departure. Often, you were given some function f with domain $X \subseteq \mathbb{R}$, and you were asked to "sketch the graph of f." You drew a pair of perpendicular lines, labeled them as the x-axis and the y-axis, plotted a few points of the form $\big(x, f(x)\big)$ for a handful of values $x \in X$, and then tried to join the points with some nice, smooth curve. That curve was what you called your "graph." A point (x, y) would be on that curve if and only if its coordinates satisfy the equation $y = f(x)$.

If the graph of the equation $y = f(x)$ were drawn so accurately that we could know exactly what points are on it, there would not be any information about f that couldn't be deduced from the graph. We could then, for all practical purposes, say that the function f *is* its graph. Change the location of just one infinitesimal point on the graph and, behold, it is a different function— that is, if it's still the graph of a function at all. Conversely, change the rule for f so that for just one single element x in its domain we have a different value for $f(x)$ and, behold, a new picture!

The point of this discussion is that we could have at the outset defined a function using the definition that we used in calculus, not for a function but for its graph. We could have defined a function to be a subset f of $\mathbb{R} \times \mathbb{R}$ with the property that for each $x \in \mathbb{R}$, there is at most one value $y \in \mathbb{R}$ such that $(x, y) \in f$. Those values of x for which a corresponding value y exists comprise the *domain* X of f. For each $x \in X$, that unique y such that $(x, y) \in f$ would be denoted by $f(x)$, and we could then say, as in Definition 4.1.1,

$$(\forall x \in X)(\exists! y \in \mathbb{R})[f(x) = y].$$

A function thus becomes a set of ordered pairs; it is a particular kind of subset of a Cartesian product of its domain by its codomain.

In Chapter 4, functions were introduced more generally than in calculus; their domains and codomains could be any sets of any kinds of objects at all. Let us now bring together all of these ideas, put aside the undefined notion of a "rule," and give a truly rigorous definition of a function.

Definition 6.6.1 *A* **function** f **from a set** X **to a set** Y*, written as* $f : X \to Y$*, is a subset of* $X \times Y$ *with the following property:*

$$(\forall x \in X)(\exists! y \in Y)[(x, y) \in f].$$

The set X *is the* **domain** *of* f*, and the set* Y *is the* **codomain** *of* f*. For each* $x \in X$*, the unique value* y *such that* $(x, y) \in f$ *is denoted by* $f(x)$ *and is called the* **image** *of* x*.*

All of the other vocabulary in Chapter 4 linked to functions can likewise be adapted to this definition. However, we give some special attention to the composition of functions as a particular case of the composition of relations. A relation *on a set* was defined in Definition 6.2.2 as a subset of $X \times X$, but one could more generally define a relation *from a set* X *to a set* Y as a subset of $X \times Y$. Doing so allows to us generalize Definition 6.3.9 as follows.

Definition 6.6.2 *Let* $\mathbf{R}_1$ *be a relation from a set* X *to a set* Y *and let* $\mathbf{R}_2$ *be a relation from* Y *to a set* Z*. The* **composition** *of* $\mathbf{R}_2$ *with* $\mathbf{R}_1$ *is the relation*

$$\mathbf{R}_2 \circ \mathbf{R}_1 = \big\{(x, z) \in X \times Z : (\exists y \in Y)[(x, y) \in \mathbf{R}_1 \ \wedge \ (y, z) \in \mathbf{R}_2]\big\}.$$

Now if both $\mathbf{R}_1$ and $\mathbf{R}_2$ are functions, then we have an appropriate definition for the composition of two functions in terms of subsets of Cartesian products.

Since a function has been redefined as a special case of a relation, it is reasonable to correlate properties of functions presented in Chapter 4 with the properties of relations presented earlier in this chapter. The following exercise includes a number of such correlations.

Exercise 6.6.3   Let $f : X \to X$ be a function. As you prove the following, regard f as a relation on the set X.
(a) f is reflexive if and only if $f = i_X$.
(b) f is symmetric if and only if $f \circ f = i_X$.
(c)   If f is symmetric, then f is a bijection, but the converse is false.
(d)   If f is transitive and $X \neq \varnothing$, then there exists a nonempty subset $A \subseteq X$ such that $f\big|_A = i_A$ and $f(X \setminus A) \subseteq A$.
(e)   If $X = \mathbb{R}$ and f is irreflexive and continuous, then we have either $(\forall x \in X)[f(x) < x]$ or $(\forall x \in X)[f(x) > x]$. [Hint: Apply the appropriate theorem to the function $g = f - i_X$.]
(f)   If $X = \mathbb{R}$ and f is symmetric and continuous, then f has a **fixed point**, i.e., there exists some $p \in X$ such that $f(p) = p$.

6.7   Further Exercises

Exercise 6.7.1   (a) Construct a partition of $\mathbb{N} \times \mathbb{N}$ each of whose cells has exactly six elements.
(b) Construct a partition of $\mathbb{N} \times \mathbb{N}$ consisting of exactly six cells, all infinite.
(c) Construct a partition of $\mathbb{N} \times \mathbb{N}$ consisting of six finite cells and six infinite cells.

Exercise 6.7.2   Let $a, b \in \mathbb{N}$. For each $n \in \mathbb{N}$, let

$$A_n = \{k \in \mathbb{N} : a(n-1) + 1 \leq k \leq an\}$$

and

$$B_n = \{k \in \mathbb{N} : b(n-1) + 1 \leq k \leq bn\}.$$

Let $\mathscr{A} = \{A_n : n \in \mathbb{N}\}$ and $\mathscr{B} = \{B_n : n \in \mathbb{N}\}$. Prove that $\mathscr{B}$ refines $\mathscr{A}$ if and only if b is a divisor of a.

Exercise 6.7.3 Let $a, b \in \mathbb{N}$. For each $n \in \{0, 1, 2, \ldots, a - 1\}$, define $A_n = \{ak + n : k \in \mathbb{N}\}$, and for each $n \in \{0, 1, 2, \ldots, b - 1\}$, define $B_n = \{bk + n : k \in \mathbb{N}\}$. Let $\mathscr{A} = \{A_n : n \in \mathbb{N}\}$ and $\mathscr{B} = \{B_n : n \in \mathbb{N}\}$. Prove that $\mathscr{B}$ refines $\mathscr{A}$ if and only if a is a divisor of b.

Exercise 6.7.4 Let X and Y be sets and let $f : X \to Y$ be a function. Let $\mathscr{A} = \{f^{-1}(y) : y \in Y\}$ and let $\mathscr{B}$ be any partition of X. Prove the following.
(a) If f is a bijection, then $\mathscr{A}$ is a refinement of $\mathscr{B}$.
(b) If Y has only one element, then $\mathscr{B}$ is a refinement of $\mathscr{A}$.

Exercise 6.7.5 Let $m, n \in \mathbb{N}$. Let $\mathbf{R}_1$ and $\mathbf{R}_2$ denote the relations of congruence modulo m and congruence modulo n, respectively, on the set $\mathbb{Z}$. Prove that $\mathbf{R}_1$ refines $\mathbf{R}_2$ if and only if n divides m.

Exercise 6.7.6 Let X, Y, and Z be sets. Suppose that $f : X \to Y$ and $g : Y \to Z$ are surjections. Prove that the partition $\{f^{-1}(y) : y \in Y\}$ is a refinement of the partition $\{(g \circ f)^{-1}(z) : z \in Z\}$.

Exercise 6.7.7 Let $\mathscr{A}$ and $\mathscr{B}$ be partitions of a set X. Let

$$\mathscr{C} = \{A \cap B : A \in \mathscr{A}; B \in \mathscr{B}; A \cap B \neq \emptyset\}.$$

(a) Prove that $\mathscr{C}$ is a partition of X. ($\mathscr{C}$ is called the **common refinement** of $\mathscr{A}$ and $\mathscr{B}$.)
(b) Prove that if $\mathscr{D}$ is a partition of S that refines both $\mathscr{A}$ and $\mathscr{B}$, then $\mathscr{D}$ refines $\mathscr{C}$.
(c) Suppose that $\mathscr{A}$ and $\mathscr{B}$ are the sets of equivalence classes of equivalence relations $\mathbf{R}$ and $\mathbf{S}$, respectively. Describe in terms of $\mathbf{R}$ and $\mathbf{S}$ the equivalence relation $\mathbf{T}$ on X such that $\mathscr{C}$ is the set of equivalence classes of $\mathbf{T}$.
(d) Suppose that $\mathbf{R}$ is the relation of congruence modulo 5 on $\mathbb{Z}$ and that $\mathbf{S}$ is the relation of congruence modulo 7 on $\mathbb{Z}$. Determine $\mathscr{C}$ and $\mathbf{T}$ for these relations $\mathbf{R}$ and $\mathbf{S}$.
(e) Repeat part (d), where $\mathbf{R}$ is the relation of congruence modulo 6 and $\mathbf{S}$ is the relation of congruence modulo 10, both on the set $\mathbb{Z}$.

Exercise 6.7.8 Let X be a set and let $\mathscr{A} = \{C_1, \ldots, C_n\}$, for $n \geq 2$, be a partition of X. Let $f : X \to \mathscr{A}$ be the function such that, for each $x \in X$,

$f(x)$ is the cell in $\mathscr{A}$ to which x belongs. Let $g : \mathscr{A} \to X$ be any function such that for each cell $C_i \in \mathscr{A}$, we have $g(C_i) \in C_i$.

(a) Prove that f is a surjection and g is an injection.

(b) Prove that $f \circ g = i_\mathscr{A}$.

(c) Find a necessary and sufficient condition on $\mathscr{A}$ for $g \circ f$ to equal i_X.

(d) Define $h : X \to \mathscr{A}$ so that for each $i = 1, \ldots, n-1$, if $x \in C_i$, then $h(x) = C_{i+1}$, and if $x \in C_n$, then $h(x) = C_1$. Prove that h is a surjection but that $h \circ g \neq i_\mathscr{A}$. Explain what this example shows concerning the converse of Theorem 4.5.2.

Exercise 6.7.9 Let S be the set of all the people in a large city. For $x, y \in S$, let $(x, y) \in \mathbf{R}_1$ if the given names of x and y begin with the same letter of the alphabet and let $(x, y) \in \mathbf{R}_2$ if x and y have the same astrological sign. Clearly, $\mathbf{R}_1$ and $\mathbf{R}_2$ are equivalence relations, but for each of the relations $\mathbf{R}_1 \cup \mathbf{R}_2$, $\mathbf{R}_1 \cap \mathbf{R}_2$, $\mathbf{R}_1 \setminus \mathbf{R}_2$, $\mathbf{R}_1 + \mathbf{R}_2$, $(S \times S) \setminus (\mathbf{R}_1 \cup \mathbf{R}_2)$, and $(S \times S) \setminus (\mathbf{R}_1 \cap \mathbf{R}_2)$, either show that it is an equivalence relation or determine what part(s) of the definition of equivalence it fails to satisfy.

Exercise 6.7.10 Let Σ be a set of (logical) statements. Let

$$\mathbf{R}_1 = \left\{ (P, Q) \in \Sigma \times \Sigma : P \Rightarrow Q \text{ is true} \right\}$$

and

$$\mathbf{R}_2 = \left\{ (P, Q) \in \Sigma \times \Sigma : (P \Rightarrow Q) \wedge \neg (Q \Rightarrow P) \text{ is true} \right\}.$$

Prove that $(\Sigma, \mathbf{R}_1)$ is a poset and $(\Sigma, \mathbf{R}_2)$ is a strictly partially ordered set.

Exercise 6.7.11 Let $\preceq$ denote the relation on the set of points in the plane whereby, for any points (x_1, y_1) and (x_2, y_2) in $\mathbb{R} \times \mathbb{R}$,

$$(x_1, y_1) \preceq (x_2, y_2) \Leftrightarrow x_1^2 + y_1^2 \leq x_2^2 + y_2^2.$$

(a) Prove that $\preceq$ is reflexive and transitive but $(\mathbb{R} \times \mathbb{R}, \preceq)$ is not a poset.

(b) Let $\mathbf{R}$ be the relation on $\mathbb{R} \times \mathbb{R}$ whereby $(x_1, y_1) \mathbf{R} (x_2, y_2)$ if and only if both $(x_1, y_1) \preceq (x_2, y_2)$ and $(x_2, y_2) \preceq (x_1, y_1)$. Show that $\mathbf{R}$ is an equivalence relation, and give a geometric description of the equivalence classes with respect to $\mathbf{R}$.

Exercise 6.7.12 An **isomorphism** from a poset $(S_1, \mathbf{R}_1)$ to a poset $(S_2, \mathbf{R}_2)$ is a bijection $f : S_1 \to S_2$ such that, for all $x,\, y \in S_1$,

$$(x, y) \in \mathbf{R}_1 \;\Leftrightarrow\; \big(f(x), f(y)\big) \in \mathbf{R}_2.$$

When such an isomorphism exists, we say that $(S_1, \mathbf{R}_1)$ is **isomorphic** to $(S_2, \mathbf{R}_2)$.
(a) Show that every poset is isomorphic to itself.
(b) Prove that if f is an isomorphism, then so is f^{-1}.
(c) Prove that the composition of two isomorphisms is an isomorphism.
(d) From parts (a), (b), and (c), deduce that "is isomorphic to" is an equivalence relation on the collection of all posets.
(e) Let $A = \{a, b, c, d\}$, and let $S_1 = \mathscr{P}(A)$. Let

$$S_2 = \big\{1, 2, 3, 5, 6, 7, 10, 14, 15, 21, 30, 35, 42, 70, 105, 210\big\}.$$

Prove that $(S_1, \subseteq)$ is isomorphic to $\big(S_2, \big|\big)$ by constructing a suitable isomorphism. [Note that A could be any set with four elements.]

Exercise 6.7.13 The **dual** of a poset $(S, \preceq)$ is the poset $(S, \succeq)$, where for all $x, y \in S$, $x \preceq y$ if and only if $y \succeq x$. A poset is **self-dual** is it is isomorphic to its dual.
(a) Verify that the dual of a poset is indeed a poset.
(b) Determine whether the posets in Exercise 6.7.12(e) are self-dual.
(c) Determine whether the poset in Example 6.4.4 is self-dual.
(c) Show that for any set X, the poset $(\mathscr{P}(X), \subseteq)$ is self-dual.

Exercise 6.7.14 A poset $(S, \preceq)$ is a **lattice** if for all $x, y \in S$, the elements $x \wedge y = \mathrm{glb}(x, y)$ and $x \vee y = \mathrm{lub}(x, y)$ exist in S. These elements are called the **meet** of x and y and the **join** of x and y, respectively.
(a) Prove that the dual of a lattice is also a lattice.
(b) Show that for any set X, the poset $(\mathscr{P}(X), \subseteq)$ is a lattice.
(c) Prove that every finite lattice has a minimum and a maximum.
(d) Prove that $\big(\mathbb{N}, \big|\big)$ and its dual are lattices, but one has no maximum while the other has no minimum.
(e) Determine all four lattices $(S, \preceq)$ having at most four elements such that no two are isomorphic, and show that they are all self-dual.
(f) Determine all five nonisomorphic lattices $(S, \preceq)$ with exactly five elements. How many of them are self-dual?
(g) Determine all 15 nonisomorphic lattices $(S, \preceq)$ with exactly six elements. [Hint: Seven of them are self-dual.]

Exercise 6.7.15 Let $(S, \mathbf{R})$ be an ordered set. We define a relation $\mathbf{L}$ on $S \times S \times S$ (which we abbreviate as S^3) in the following way. For any two elements $\mathbf{v}_1 = (x_1, y_1, z_1)$ and $\mathbf{v}_2 = (x_2, y_2, z_2)$ of S^3 we have $(\mathbf{v}_1, \mathbf{v}_2) \in \mathbf{L}$ if and only if one of the following holds:
(i) $(x_1, x_2) \in \mathbf{R}$;
(ii) $x_1 = x_2$ and $(y_1, y_2) \in \mathbf{R}$;
(iii) $x_1 = x_2$ and $y_1 = y_2$ and $(z_1, z_2) \in \mathbf{R}$.
A relation of this kind is called a *lexicographic*[4] *ordering.*
(a) Prove that $(S^3, \mathbf{L})$ is an ordered set.
(b) Prove that $(S^3, \mathbf{L})$ is a linearly ordered set if and only if $(S, \mathbf{R})$ is a linearly ordered set.
(c) Describe the extremal elements of $(S^3, \mathbf{L})$ in terms of the extremal elements of $(S, \mathbf{R})$.
(d) Prove that $(S^3, \mathbf{L})$ has extrema if and only if $(S, \mathbf{R})$ has extrema.

Exercise 6.7.16 The entries in a dictionary appear in a fixed order. One could say that they are linearly ordered. State explicitly the rules for determining, given any two words, which one follows the other. [Note that, unlike Exercise 6.7.15 where all "words" have three "letters," the entries in a dictionary may have any positive number of letters. Also, some entries are hyphenated words or may contain apostrophes.]

Exercise 6.7.17 This one is more a project than an exercise. In a Chinese dictionary, if $m, n \in \mathbb{N}$ and $m < n$, then a character with m strokes (of a pen) always precedes a character with n strokes. However, for each $m \geq 1$ (up to about $m = 30$), there are many characters with m strokes. Investigate the rules for ordering the set C of Chinese characters. Let

$$\mathbf{R} = \big\{(c_1, c_2) \in C \times C : c_1 \text{ precedes } c_2\big\}.$$

Is $\mathbf{R}$ a strict partial order? Are every two Chinese characters comparable according to these rules?

Exercise 6.7.18 Let $(S, \mathbf{R})$ be a linearly ordered set. Let F be a nonempty, finite subset of S. Define $\mathbf{R}\big|_F = \mathbf{R} \cap (F \times F)$. Does it always hold that $(F, \mathbf{R}\big|_F)$ is a well-ordered set?

---

[4]A *lexicon* is a dictionary. Do you see the similarity to the alphabetical ordering of words in a dictionary?

Chapter 7

Infinite Sets and Cardinality

SUPPOSE THAT we want to count the following array of objects.

♣   ♡   ©   ¥   £

The mathematics behind what we are doing when we say "count to five" or "count to one million" is made precise and generalized in this chapter. The process includes what it means to say that a set is infinite and gives meaning to the question, "How big is infinity?"

7.1   Counting

When an English-speaking person points successively to an array of objects and says the words "one, two, three, four, five," associating each word with a distinct object, we call that action *counting to five*. If the words uttered are instead "uno, due, tre, quattro, cinque" or "yksi, kaksi, kolme, neljä, viisi," it doesn't matter that the counter is speaking Italian or Finnish, for the action is the same. Nor does it matter what the set of objects happens to be. The set in question is representable by the symbol 5, which may be pronounced verbally as "five" or "cinque" or "viisi" or any of hundreds of other human vocal sounds. There exists an obvious matching between any set of five objects and any other set of five objects and, of course, between any such set and the set {one, two, three, four, five} of words.

Let us recast this brief discussion in more formal mathematical language. Given the set

$$A = \{\clubsuit, \heartsuit, \copyright, \yen, \pounds\},$$

we used a standard reference set; namely

$$\mathbb{N}_5 = \{1, 2, 3, 4, 5\}.$$

Finally, we constructed a bijection $f : \mathbb{N}_5 \to A$ given by

$$f(1) = \clubsuit, \; f(2) = \heartsuit, \; f(3) = \copyright, \; f(4) = \yen, \; f(5) = \pounds.$$

That's what we do when we count to five.

On the other hand, suppose that we look at a structure held together by nuts and bolts. (See Figure 7.1.1.) Each bolt is secured by one nut and each nut is threaded onto one bolt. There is an obvious bijection from the set of nuts to the set of bolts in the structure. Without having to use number words to count, we would conclude without hesitation that there are exactly as many nuts as bolts in the structure. That is to say, the set of nuts and the set of bolts have the "same size," or in mathematical terminology, these two sets "have equal cardinality."

Figure 7.1.1: A matching between nuts and bolts.

Definition 7.1.1 *For $k \in \mathbb{N}$, let $\mathbb{N}_k = \{1, 2, 3, \ldots, k\}$. A set S is called* **finite** *if $S = \varnothing$ or if for some $k \in \mathbb{N}$ there exists a bijection $f : \mathbb{N}_k \to S$. Otherwise, S is* **infinite**.

A set S is called **countable** *if there exists a bijection $f : \mathbb{N} \to S$. An infinite set that is not countable is said to be* **uncountable**.[1]

If S is a finite set, then the **cardinality** *of S, denoted $|S|$, is the natural number k if there exists a bijection from $\mathbb{N}_k$ to S, and $|\varnothing| = 0$.*

The notation $|S|$ is read as "the cardinality of (the set) S." Thus the cardinality of a finite set is simply the number of elements in the set. For example,

$$\big|\{a, b, c\}\big| = 3,$$
$$\big|\{p \in \mathbb{N} : p, p+2, p+4 \text{ are all prime}\}\big| = 1,$$
$$\big|\mathbb{N}_5\big| = 5,$$
$$\big|\{p \in \mathbb{Z} : 1 \le p \le 100 \text{ and } p \text{ is prime}\}\big| = 25.$$

Suppose that for some $k \in \mathbb{N}$, there exist bijections from $\mathbb{N}_k$ to each of the sets A and B. Then clearly there exists a bijection from A to B. [Can you supply the details?] In this case, A **has the same cardinality** as B, written $|A| = |B|$. When no such bijection exists, we write $|A| \ne |B|$.

Let us for a moment digress in order to note three basic counting principles as applied to finite sets. These principles could be regarded as definitions of three arithmetic operations on cardinalities of finite sets. In Section 7.5, we extend these same principles to infinite sets.

Proposition 7.1.2 *Let A and B be arbitrary finite subsets of some universe U.*
(i) $|A| + |B| = |A \cup B| + |A \cap B|$.
(ii) $|A| \cdot |B| = |A \times B|$.
(iii) $|B|^{|A|}$ is the cardinality of the set of functions from A into B.

---

[1]Some mathematicians include finite sets when speaking of *countable sets* and use the terms *countably infinite* or *denumerable* instead of the term *countable*. They also use the term *nondenumerable* in place of *uncountable*.

Proof. (i) Each element of U is counted the same number of times on each side of this equation. Specifically, elements of $(A \cup B)'$ are counted zero times on each side. Elements of $A \setminus B$ and $B \setminus A$ are counted once on each side. Finally, elements of $A \cap B$ are counted twice on each side.

(ii) For each $a \in A$, there are $|B|$ elements $b \in B$ such that $(a, b) \in A \times B$. As there are $|A|$ elements of A, there are $|A| \cdot |B|$ elements of $A \times B$.

(iii) For the definition of a function, we have recourse to Definition 6.6.1. Suppose that $A = \{a_1, a_2, \ldots, a_m\}$. Each function $f : A \to B$ is a subset of $A \times B$ of the form $\{(a_1, b_1), (a_2, b_2), \ldots, (a_m, b_m)\}$, where each element $b_i = f(a_i)$. The function f is uniquely determined by the list $b_1, b_2, \ldots, b_m$. Conversely, each such list determines a unique function from A to B. This bijection (between lists and functions) implies that we can count the required set of functions by counting the set of lists $b_1, b_2, \ldots, b_m$. As there are exactly $|B|$ options for each term b_i, the cardinality of the set of these lists is

$$\underbrace{|B| \cdot |B| \cdot \ldots \cdot |B|}_{m \text{ factors}},$$

giving $|B|^m = |B|^{|A|}$. $\square$

Exercise 7.1.3 (a) Let $A = \{a_1, a_2, a_3\}$ and $B = \{b_1, b_2\}$. Count the number of functions from A to B and the number of functions from B to A. (b) What fraction of the subsets of $A \times B$ are functions? How about $B \times A$?

Exercise 7.1.4 Recall that the symmetric difference (see Exercise 3.6.12) of sets $A, B \in \mathscr{P}(X)$ is the set

$$A + B = (A \cup B) \setminus (A \cap B).$$

Prove that if A and B are finite, then $|A + B| = |A| + |B| - 2|A \cap B|$.

Returning from this digression, let us extend the language about cardinality to countable sets. Suppose that there exist bijections from the set $\mathbb{N}$ to each of the sets A and B. By the same argument as for finite sets, there exists a bijection from A to B. Again, A and B have the same cardinality, and we write $|A| = |B|$. However, here we cannot use an element of $\mathbb{N}$ to represent this cardinality as we did for finite sets. For this purpose, Georg Cantor[2] selected the symbol $\aleph_0$ to denote the cardinality of any (and every) countable set. (Aleph, $\aleph$, is the first letter in the Hebrew alphabet.) So it is entirely correct to write

$$|A| = \aleph_0$$

for any countable set A. The **cardinality of a countable set** is thus defined to be $\aleph_0$.

Example 7.1.5 The set $\mathbb{E} = \{2, 4, 6, 8, \ldots\}$ of positive even integers is a proper subset of $\mathbb{N}$. Although the injection $g : \mathbb{E} \to \mathbb{N}$ defined by $g(j) = j$ is not a bijection, one cannot infer that no bijection exists. On the contrary, the function $f : \mathbb{N} \to \mathbb{E}$ defined by $f(n) = 2n$ *is* such a bijection. Thus $|\mathbb{E}| = |\mathbb{N}| = \aleph_0$. So the set of even numbers has the same size as the set of natural numbers (even though $\mathbb{E}$ is a proper subset of $\mathbb{N}$).

Now consider the set $\mathbb{O}$ of positive odd numbers. The function $h : \mathbb{N} \to \mathbb{O}$ defined by $h(n) = 2n - 1$ for all $n \in \mathbb{N}$ is a bijection, and therefore $|\mathbb{O}| = \aleph_0$, as well.

Exercise 7.1.6 (a) Let $h : \mathbb{N} \to \mathbb{O}$ defined by $h(n) = 2n - 1$. Prove that h is a bijection.
(b) Let $A = \{5, 10, 15, 20, \ldots\}$ be the set of all positive multiples of 5. Prove that $|A| = \aleph_0$. [Hint: Define an appropriate function $f : \mathbb{N} \to A$ and prove that it is a bijection.]

Exercise 7.1.7 Prove that if the set S is finite, then so are $S \times S$, $\mathscr{P}(S)$, every subset of S, and the union and intersection of S with any other finite set.

Exercise 7.1.8 Let A and B be finite sets. Prove that the following statements are equivalent.
(i) $|A| \geq |B|$.
(ii)   There exists a surjection from A onto B.
(iii)   There exists an injection from B to A.

---

[2]Georg Cantor (1845–1918), son of a Danish father and Russian mother, spent his student and adult years in Germany. He pioneered the study of infinite sets and cardinality. A brilliant and prominent mathematician, despite suffering terribly from mental illness for the last third of his life, he wrote several papers that rocked the traditional thinking about logic and infinite sets.

Exercise 7.1.9 (a) Show that the interval on the real number line $(2, 4)$ has the same cardinality as the interval $(5, 10)$. [Hint: Consider a suitable linear function.]
(b) Prove the more general statement that any two open intervals of real numbers (a, b) and (c, d) have the same cardinality. The same result holds for any two closed intervals of real numbers.

7.2 Properties of Countable Sets

One way to prove that a given set A is indeed a countable set is to demonstrate a bijection $f : \mathbb{N} \to A$ by explicitly defining its rule. That was how we proved that $|\mathbb{N}| = |\mathbb{E}|$. Another way is to list the terms $f(1), f(2), f(3), \ldots$ as a sequence. Let us formalize this.

Definition 7.2.1 *Let A be a countable set and let $f : \mathbb{N} \to A$ be a bijection. Then the sequence $(f(1), f(2), \ldots)$ is the **enumeration of A with respect to f**.*

For example, the enumerations of $\mathbb{E}$ and $\mathbb{O}$ with respect to the bijections given in Example 7.1.5 are $(2, 4, 6, 8, \ldots)$ and $(1, 3, 5, 7, \ldots)$, respectively. Often, just studying the first few terms of an enumeration tells us what the implied bijection is without our having to name the bijection and state its rule. For this reason, enumerations are very convenient.

When a finite set is enlarged by the inclusion of elements not already in the set, then the cardinality of the set is increased. This is a property that, in a way, distinguishes finite sets from infinite sets. By contrast, adjoining any finite number of elements to a countable set has absolutely no effect on its cardinality; the countable set just seems to "absorb" the new elements. Let us make this precise.

Proposition 7.2.2 *The union of a countable set and a finite set is a countable set.*

Proof. Suppose that A is a countable set and B is a finite set. The set $B \setminus A$ is finite, because it is a subset of the finite set B. Say $|B \setminus A| = k$, where

$k \in \mathbb{N} \cup \{0\}$. If $k = 0$, then $B \subset A$, and so $A \cup B = A$, which is countable by assumption. If $k \geq 1$, then there is a bijection $f_1 : \mathbb{N}_k \to B \setminus A$. By assumption, there is also a bijection $f_2 : \mathbb{N} \to A$. Define $g : \mathbb{N} \to A \cup B$ by

$$g(n) = \begin{cases} f_1(n) & \text{if } n \leq k; \\ f_2(n - k) & \text{if } n \geq k + 1. \end{cases}$$

Clearly, g is a bijection, as evidenced by the enumeration with respect to g, namely

$$\big(g(1), g(2), \ldots, g(k), g(k+1), \ldots\big) = \big(f_1(1), f_1(2), \ldots, f_1(k), f_2(1), f_2(2), \ldots\big).$$

$\square$

The proof of the next result requires the Principle of Strong Induction, introduced in Section 5.3.

Lemma 7.2.3 *Every subset of $\mathbb{N}$ is either finite or countable.*

Proof. Let M be a subset of $\mathbb{N}$. If $M = \varnothing$, then it is clearly finite, so we suppose that $M \neq \varnothing$. As the initial step of our inductive argument, define $M_1 = M$. By the Well Ordering Principle, M_1 includes a least element, which we call n_1. Let $M_2 = M_1 \setminus \{n_1\}$. If $M_2 = \varnothing$, then M_1 is finite. (It has one element.) Otherwise, M_2 includes a least element, which we call n_2. Observe that $n_1 < n_2$.

Let $m \geq 1$ and suppose (as induction hypothesis) that for $k \in \{1, 2, \ldots, m\}$, $M_{k+1} = M_k \setminus \{n_k\}$, where n_k is the least element of M_k. If $M_{m+1} = \varnothing$, then $M = \{n_1, n_2, \ldots, n_m\}$; it is finite and has m elements. Otherwise, M_{m+1} has a least element n_{m+1} and $n_{m+1} > n_m$. Thus if M_m is not empty for all $m \in \mathbb{N}$, then by the Principle of Strong Induction, some subset of M admits an enumeration $(n_1, n_2, n_3, \ldots)$; that is to say, M contains a countable subset.

It remains only to prove that the enumeration $(n_1, n_2, n_3, \ldots)$ includes *all* the elements of M. Suppose by way of contradiction that some element $h \in M$ was omitted from $(n_1, n_2, n_3, \ldots)$. Since this enumeration is an increasing sequence, there exists some $k \in \mathbb{N}$ such that $n_k < h < n_{k+1}$. Thus $h \in M_k \setminus M_{k+1}$. Although n_{k+1} was supposed to be the least element of $M_k \setminus \{n_k\}$, the element h is still smaller, giving a contradiction. $\square$

The lemma that we have just proved solidifies the notion that the infinite subsets of $\mathbb{N}$, such as $\mathbb{E}$ and $\mathbb{O}$, have the same cardinality as $\mathbb{N}$.

Corollary 7.2.4 *Every subset of a countable set is either finite or countable.*

Proof. Let A be a countable set and suppose $B \subseteq A$. Then there exists a bijection $f : \mathbb{N} \to A$. Let $M = f^{-1}(B)$. Since f is a bijection, so is f^{-1} (see Theorem 4.5.11). In particular, the restriction $f^{-1}\big|_B : B \to M$ is a bijection. Hence $|B| = |M|$. By Lemma 7.2.3, B is finite or countable. $\qquad\square$

The next theorem enables us to shorten some later proofs.

Theorem 7.2.5 *Let A be any set, and suppose that there exists a surjection $f : \mathbb{N} \to A$. Then A is finite or countable.*

Proof. By Proposition 6.1.5, since $f : \mathbb{N} \to A$ is a surjection, the set

$$\{f^{-1}(x) : x \in A\}$$

is a partition of $\mathbb{N}$. That means that each cell $f^{-1}(x)$ is a nonempty subset of $\mathbb{N}$. By the Well Ordering Principle, each cell $f^{-1}(x)$ includes a least element, which we denote by n_x. Let $M = \{n_x \in \mathbb{N} : x \in A\}$.

We show that the restriction $f\big|_M : M \to A$ is a bijection. For each $x \in A$, we have $f\big|_M(n_x) = x$, and so $f\big|_M$ is a surjection. Let us suppose that $f\big|_M(n_x) = f\big|_M(n_y)$. Then $x = y$. Since the set $f^{-1}(x) = f^{-1}(y)$ has a unique least element in $\mathbb{N}$, it follows that $n_x = n_y$, and so $f\big|_M$ is also an injection.

By virtue of the bijection $f\big|_M$, we have $|M| = |A|$. By Lemma 7.2.3, M is finite or countable, and hence so is A. $\qquad\square$

With this theorem, one easily obtains for countable sets the following analogue of Exercise 7.1.8 for finite sets.

Corollary 7.2.6 *Let A be a countable set and let B be any set. If there exists a surjection from A onto B or an injection from B into A, then B is finite or countable.*

Exercise 7.2.7 Prove Corollary 7.2.6.

Proposition 7.2.2 shows that *adjoining* a finite set to a countable set has no effect on its countability. What is the effect when a finite set is deleted from a countable set? The answer is in the next exercise.

Exercise 7.2.8 If A is a countable set and B is finite, prove that $A \setminus B$ is countable. [Hint: Use Exercise 4.6.13, Corollary 7.2.6, and Proposition 7.1.2(i).]

Exercise 7.2.9 Let $k \in \mathbb{Z}$. Prove that the sets $\{n \in \mathbb{Z} : n \geq k\}$ and $\{n \in \mathbb{Z} : n \leq k\}$ are countable.

7.3 Counting Countable Sets

An immediate consequence of considering infinite sets is that a familiar property of addition no longer applies. Children learn to add 6 to 3 by taking a set of 3 things and a disjoint set of 6 things, pushing the sets together (that is, forming their union) and then counting the new set. If we take the set of even numbers (which is countable) and adjoin to it the (disjoint) set of odd numbers (also countable) to form their union and determine its cardinality, what happens? We have the countable set $\mathbb{N}$. It would appear that $2\aleph_0 = \aleph_0$. Actually, this is exactly what happens!

The set of the integers

$$\mathbb{Z} = \{\ldots, -3, -2, -1, 0, 1, 2, 3, \ldots\}$$

as displayed here is *not* an enumeration of $\mathbb{Z}$. [Why not?] But consider this enumeration of $\mathbb{Z}$:

$$(0, 1, -1, 2, -2, 3, -3, \ldots).$$

The explicit function $f : \mathbb{N} \to \mathbb{Z}$ that gives this enumeration is

$$f(n) = \begin{cases} \dfrac{1-n}{2} & \text{if } n \text{ is odd;} \\[2mm] \dfrac{n}{2} & \text{if } n \text{ is even.} \end{cases}$$

In Exercise 4.6.21, you proved that this function is bijective. In effect, you proved that the set of integers has the same cardinality as the set of natural numbers.

The following proposition holds for all sets, finite, countable, or uncountable.

Proposition 7.3.1   *Let $A, B, C,$ and D be sets and suppose that $|A| = |C|$ and $|B| = |D|$. Then the following hold.*
(i) $|A \times B| = |C \times D|$.
(ii)   If $A \cap B = \emptyset$ and $C \cap D = \emptyset$, then $|A \cup B| = |C \cup D|$.

Proof. (i) Since $|A| = |C|$ and $|B| = |D|$, there exist bijections $g : A \to C$ and $h : B \to D$. Define $f : A \times B \to C \times D$ by $f(a,b) = \big(g(a), h(b)\big)$. We leave as an exercise the proof that f is a bijection.

To prove part (ii), we note that the function

$$g \cup h : A \cup B \to C \cup D$$

is a bijection (see Exercise 4.6.17). $\square$

Exercise 7.3.2   Prove that the function $f : A \times B \to C \times D$ defined by $f(a,b) = \big(g(a), h(b)\big)$ from the proof of part (i) of Proposition 7.3.1 is a bijection.

The set $\mathbb{N} \times \mathbb{N} = \big\{(m,n) : m \in \mathbb{N} \wedge n \in \mathbb{N}\big\}$ can be visualized as the set of points with integer coordinates in the first quadrant of the plane. (See Figure 7.3.1.) Each row and each column of dots may be regarded as a copy of $\mathbb{N}$. Believe it or not, $\mathbb{N} \times \mathbb{N}$ is countable.

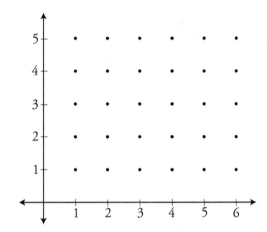

Figure 7.3.1: A representation of $\mathbb{N} \times \mathbb{N}$.

We display a bijection from $\mathbb{N}$ onto $\mathbb{N} \times \mathbb{N}$. Recall Corollary 5.3.4: for each $n \in \mathbb{N}$, there exist unique $k, m \in \mathbb{N}$ with m odd such that $n = 2^{k-1} \cdot m$. Because of the uniqueness, there exists a function $f : \mathbb{N} \to \mathbb{N} \times \mathbb{N}$ defined by $f(n) = (a, b)$, where $n = 2^{a-1} \cdot (2b - 1)$. For example, $f(72) = (4, 5)$, since $72 = 2^3 \cdot (2 \cdot 5 - 1)$. Surjectivity of f is fairly obvious; given any $(a, b) \in \mathbb{N} \times \mathbb{N}$, if $n = 2^{a-1} \cdot (2b - 1)$, then $f(n) = (a, b)$.

To show that f is injective, suppose that $f(n_1) = f(n_2)$. By Corollary 5.3.4 again, there exist unique $a_1, b_1, a_2, b_2 \in \mathbb{N}$ such that $n_1 = 2^{a_1-1}(2b_1 - 1)$ and $n_2 = 2^{a_2-1}(2b_2 - 1)$. This means $f(n_1) = (a_1, b_1)$ and $f(n_2) = (a_2, b_2)$, which translates into the equality of these two ordered pairs. Thus

$$a_1 = a_2 \quad \text{and} \quad b_1 = b_2,$$

and so $n_1 = n_2$. Therefore f is injective and hence bijective.

The enumeration of $\mathbb{N} \times \mathbb{N}$ with respect to the bijection f is

$$\big((1, 1), (2, 1), (1, 2), (3, 1), (1, 3), (2, 2), (1, 4),$$
$$(4, 1), (1, 5), (2, 3), (1, 6), (3, 2), (1, 7), (2, 4), \ldots\big).$$

We have proved the following theorem.

Theorem 7.3.3 *The set $\mathbb{N} \times \mathbb{N}$ is a countable set.*

Exercise 7.3.4   On a grid like Figure 7.3.1, write the integer $n = 2^{a-1}(2b-1)$ next to the point (a, b). Describe the sequences formed by the integers paired with the (horizontal) rows and (vertical) columns.

Corollary 7.3.5   *The Cartesian product of any two countable sets is a countable set.*

Proof. Suppose that A and B are countable sets.   From Theorem 7.3.3, $|\mathbb{N}| = |\mathbb{N} \times \mathbb{N}|$. By Proposition 7.3.1(i), $|\mathbb{N} \times \mathbb{N}| = |A \times B|$. Since the composition of two bijections is a bijection, there exists a bijection from $\mathbb{N}$ to $A \times B$. $\square$

Exercise 7.3.6   Prove that if $A \times B$ is a countable set and B is finite and not empty, then A is countable.

Corollary 7.3.7   *The Cartesian product of finitely many countable sets is a countable set.*

Proof. The proof is by induction on the number n of sets in the product. The initial step ($k = 2$) has already been done in Corollary 7.3.5. The details of the inductive step are left as Exercise 7.3.8. $\square$

Exercise 7.3.8   Write a formal proof of Corollary 7.3.7. [Note that the set $A_1 \times A_2 \times \cdots \times A_{k+1}$ may be regarded as $(A_1 \times A_2 \times \cdots \times A_k) \times A_{k+1}$.]

Once again, the rules of arithmetic for finite cardinalities appear not to apply to countable sets. The preceding corollary suggests (correctly) that $\aleph_0^k = \aleph_0$ for all $k \in \mathbb{N}$. The following corollary is a special case. It suggests that $\aleph_0 + \aleph_0 + \cdots = \aleph_0 \cdot \aleph_0 = \aleph_0$.

Corollary 7.3.9   *The union of finitely many or countably many countable sets is a countable set.*

Proof. Let $\{A_i : i \in \mathbb{N}\}$ be a family of countably many sets, each of which is countable. Then we can make a well-ordered list of all the sets A_i together with their enumerations in the following way.

$$
\begin{aligned}
A_1 : &\quad (a_{1,1},\ a_{1,2},\ a_{1,3},\ a_{1,4},\ \ldots) \\
A_2 : &\quad (a_{2,1},\ a_{2,2},\ a_{2,3},\ a_{2,4},\ \ldots) \\
A_3 : &\quad (a_{3,1},\ a_{3,2},\ a_{3,3},\ a_{3,4},\ \ldots) \\
&\qquad \vdots
\end{aligned}
$$

For each $i \in \mathbb{N}$, there exists a bijection $f_i : \mathbb{N} \to A_i$ such that, for each $j \in \mathbb{N}$, we have $f_i(j) = a_{i,j}$. Now consider the function

$$
g : \mathbb{N} \times \mathbb{N} \to \bigcup_{i=1}^{\infty} A_i
$$

given by $g(i,j) = a_{i,j}$ for each ordered pair $(i,j) \in \mathbb{N} \times \mathbb{N}$. Thus g assigns to the ordered pair (i,j) the jth term in the ith row of the above array. The function g is clearly a surjection. By Corollary 7.2.6, $\bigcup_{i=1}^{\infty} A_i$ is countable. [If the sets A_i are not pairwise disjoint, then g would not be an injection. Thanks to Corollary 7.2.6, g being a surjection is sufficient for this job, and we are spared the work of constructing a bijection.]

If the family of sets is a finite family, then the conclusion holds by the first part of this proof together with Corollary 7.2.4, since any union of finitely many sets is a subset of some union of countably many sets. $\qquad\square$

Corollary 7.3.10 *The union of countably many sets, each of which is finite or countable, is a finite or countable set.*

Exercise 7.3.11 Adapt the proof of Corollary 7.3.9 to prove Corollary 7.3.10. Under what circumstances is this union finite, and when is it countable? [The sets need not be disjoint.]

The next theorem cobbles together several ideas that we have already used. The theorem was first proved by Cantor in 1873.

By definition, every positive rational number can be written as a fraction p/q, where p, $q \in \mathbb{N}$. This immediately suggests a surjection f from $\mathbb{N} \times \mathbb{N}$ onto the set of positive rationals whereby $f(p, q) = p/q$. Notice that f is not an injection. For example, $1 = f(1, 1) = f(2, 2) = f(3, 3)$ and $\frac{1}{2} = f(1, 2) = f(2, 4) = f(3, 6)$, etc., but we don't need a bijection; by Corollary 7.2.6, just a surjection will do. Since $\mathbb{N} \times \mathbb{N}$ is countable, so is the set of positive rationals.

The pairing $p/q \leftrightarrow -p/q$ shows that the set of negative rational numbers is countable, too. Moreover, the union of two countable sets is countable, by Corollary 7.3.9. Hence the set of nonzero rational numbers is countable. By Proposition 7.2.2, we may also adjoin the finite set $\{0\}$ and still have a countable set. This proves the following theorem.

Theorem 7.3.12   *The set $\mathbb{Q}$ of rational numbers is countable.*

Exercise 7.3.13   Using the enumeration of the set $\mathbb{N} \times \mathbb{N}$ from the proof of Theorem 7.3.3, write the first 20 terms of the enumeration of the set of positive rationals suggested by the above proof. Then, using the enumeration suggested by the enumeration of $\mathbb{Z}$, write the first 20 terms of an enumeration of $\mathbb{Q}$. [Don't forget to include zero!]

Recall the notation introduce immediately before Definition 2.6.8 that $\mathbb{Z}[x]$ is the set of all polynomial functions with integer coefficients.

Lemma 7.3.14   *The set $\mathbb{Z}[x]$ of all polynomial functions with integer coefficients is countable.*

Proof. For each $n \in \mathbb{N} \cup \{0\}$, let $\mathbb{P}_n$ denote the set of all polynomial functions of degree n with integer coefficients. There is an obvious bijection onto the set $\mathbb{P}_n$ from the Cartesian product of $n + 1$ "copies" of $\mathbb{Z}$. [For example, $\mathbb{P}_0$ consists of the constant functions with integer value, so $|\mathbb{P}_0| = |\mathbb{Z}|$. The set $\mathbb{P}_1$ consists of functions of the form $a_1 x + a_0$; clearly $|\mathbb{P}_1| = |\mathbb{Z} \times \mathbb{Z}|$. The set of quadratic functions (i.e., functions of the form $a_2 x^2 + a_1 x + a_0$) corresponds bijectively in an obvious way to the set $\mathbb{Z} \times \mathbb{Z} \times \mathbb{Z}$, and so on.]

Since the set $\mathbb{Z}$ is countable, by Corollary 7.3.7, the Cartesian product of finitely many copies of $\mathbb{Z}$ is a countable set. It follows that each set $\mathbb{P}_n$ is also a countable set.

The set of all polynomial functions with integer coefficients can be expressed as $\mathbb{Z}[x] = \bigcup_{n=0}^{\infty} \mathbb{P}_n$. By Corollary 7.3.9, this set is countable. □

We want to use this lemma to prove that the set $\mathbb{A}$ of algebraic numbers is countable. In order to do so, we will need a fact about the number of *roots* of a polynomial. If p is a polynomial function, then a number x is a **root** of p if $p(x) = 0$. (For example, the roots of the polynomial function $x^3 - 3x - 2$ are -1 and 2.) All that we need for this purpose is that the number of roots of any polynomial function is finite, but we will state the needed fact in full for completeness. You will encounter its proof in a course in abstract algebra.

Proposition 7.3.15 *The number of distinct roots of a polynomial function of degree n is at most n.*

Theorem 7.3.16 *The set $\mathbb{A}$ of algebraic numbers is countable.*

Proof. Recall that an algebraic number is a root of an element of $\mathbb{Z}[x]$. For each $p \in \mathbb{Z}[x]$, let $R(p)$ denote the set of its roots. Thus

$$\mathbb{A} = \bigcup_{p \in \mathbb{Z}[x]} R(p).$$

By Proposition 7.3.15, the set $R(p)$ is finite for every $p \in \mathbb{Z}[x]$. By Lemma 7.3.14, the index set $\mathbb{Z}[x]$ is countable. By Corollary 7.3.10, $\mathbb{A}$ is finite or countable. Since $\mathbb{A} \supset \mathbb{Q}$ by Proposition 2.6.9, $\mathbb{A}$ is obviously not finite. □

We have the sequence

$$\mathbb{E} \subset \mathbb{N} \subset \mathbb{Z} \subset \mathbb{Q} \subset \mathbb{A}$$

of sets of numbers, each a proper subset of the next, and all are countable. Does this sequence of countable sets eventually embrace all the numbers that we know? That question is answered over the course of the next two sections of this chapter.

7.4   Binary Relations on Cardinal Numbers

Have you noticed that the term *cardinality* all by itself has not yet been defined? We have defined *cardinality of a finite set*, and we have defined *has the same cardinality as*. We even have the symbol $\aleph_0$ for the *cardinality of a countable set*. But just what exactly is a *cardinality*? The answer involves an equivalence relation.

Theorem 7.4.1   *The relation "has the same cardinality as" is an equivalence relation on any collection of sets.*

Proof. For any set A, the identity function $i_A : A \to A$ is a bijection. Thus $|A| = |A|$ and the relation is reflexive.

To show that the relation is symmetric, let A and B be sets and assume that $|A| = |B|$. Thus there exists a bijection $f : A \to B$. By Theorem 4.5.11, $f^{-1} : B \to A$ is a bijection, and so $|B| = |A|$.

Now assume for sets A, B, and C that $|A| = |B|$ and $|B| = |C|$. This means that there exist bijections $f : A \to B$ and $g : B \to C$. By Corollary 4.4.12, $g \circ f$ is a bijection from A to C. Thus $|A| = |C|$ and the relation is transitive. $\square$

Theorem 7.4.1 justifies the following definition of a cardinal number.

Definition 7.4.2   *A **cardinal number**, or, more briefly, a **cardinality**, is an equivalence class of sets with respect to the equivalence relation "has the same cardinality as."*

In light of this definition, every nonnegative integer may be regarded as a cardinal number. For example, 5 is the equivalence class of all sets with exactly five elements. Also, the equivalence class of all countable sets is a cardinal number; traditionally, we denote that class by the symbol $\aleph_0$. In terms of notation, if A is any set, then $|A|$ denotes the class of all sets B such that there exists a bijection from A to B, and writing $|A| = |B|$ is a way of saying that A and B belong to the same equivalence class.

Remark. We are very careful to avoid the phrase "the set of all cardinal numbers." Were we to speak of such a set, it would be natural to inquire what *its* cardinality might be. That question, however, leads to an undecidable problem deep in the foundations of all mathematics[3] and well beyond the scope of this course. If we confine our discourse to the cardinalities of sets that are already given, then we are safely away from such dangerous territory.

We next present two order relations on cardinal numbers, a partial order $\leq$ and a strict partial order $<$ (see Definition 6.3.2).

Definition 7.4.3 *For any sets A and B,*

1. $|A| \leq |B|$ *(or $|B| \geq |A|$) if there exists an injection from A into B;*

2. $|A| < |B|$ *if $|A| \leq |B|$ but $|A| \neq |B|$.*

This definition certainly conforms to our intuition and experience. We would be very uncomfortable if it were not the case that $5 < 6$. We also have that $k < \aleph_0$ holds for all $k \in \mathbb{N} \cup \{0\}$, as well it should, since there exist injections from $\mathbb{N}_k$ into $\mathbb{N}$ but no such bijection exists.

Exercise 7.4.4 Let A be any set and let $B \subseteq A$. Prove that $|B| \leq |A|$.

A direct consequence of Definition 7.4.3 and Corollary 4.5.6 is the following.

Proposition 7.4.5 *For any nonempty sets A and B, the following statements are equivalent.*

(i) $|A| \geq |B|$.

(ii) There exists an injection from B into A.

(iii) There exists a surjection from A onto B.

---

[3]To get a sense of the logical conundrum that this poses, ponder the following paradox. *The Barber of Seville is a man who shaves a man if and only if that man does not shave himself. Who shaves the Barber of Seville?* (See http://en.wikipedia.org/wiki/Barber_paradox.)

It is immediate that the relation $\leq$ is reflexive on any given set of cardinal numbers. Because the composition of two injections is also an injection, the relation $\leq$ is also transitive. The fact that $\leq$ is antisymmetric is the gist of the following deep theorem, which we present without proof.[4]

Theorem 7.4.6 (The Cantor–Schröder–Bernstein[5] Theorem) *For any sets A and B, if there exist injections from A into B and from B into A, then $|A| = |B|$.*

We have in effect proved the following corollary.

Corollary 7.4.7 *The relation $\leq$ is a partial order on any given set of cardinal numbers, and the relation $<$ is a strict partial order on that set.*

The next theorem presents another important fact about cardinality, one that we have already seen in Theorem 5.2.13 to hold for finite sets. An immediate consequence is that, yes, uncountable sets *do* exist! This theorem and its proof are both due to Cantor. The proof, though not long, is subtle; to understand it fully may require reading it patiently more than once.

Theorem 7.4.8 *For any set S,*

$$|S| < \big|\mathscr{P}(S)\big|.$$

Proof. If $S = \varnothing$, then

$$|\varnothing| = 0 < 1 = \big|\{\varnothing\}\big| = \big|\mathscr{P}(\varnothing)\big|.$$

If $S \neq \varnothing$, then the function $j : S \to \mathscr{P}(S)$ defined for all $x \in S$ by $j(x) = \{x\}$ is an injection. Thus $|S| \leq \big|\mathscr{P}(S)\big|$.

---

[4]The proof contains no mathematics beyond what is found in this book, but it is rather long and rather subtle. For a lucid and careful presentation of the proof, see Steven G. Krantz, *The Elements of Advanced Mathematics*, 2nd Ed. (Boca Raton; CRC Press, 2002).

[5]For Georg Cantor, see the footnote in Section 7.1. Cantor, together with the German mathematician Ernst Schröder (1841–1902), best known for his work in mathematical logic, wrote the first proof of this theorem, but their proof was flawed. Felix Bernstein (1878–1956), also German, studied under Cantor and, in his doctoral dissertation, corrected the flaw in 1897.

Assume, by way of contradiction, that $|S| = |\mathscr{P}(S)|$. We will obtain a contradiction by showing that no function f from S into $\mathscr{P}(S)$ can be surjective.

Let $f : S \to \mathscr{P}(S)$ be given. The argument depends on the subset

$$A = \{s \in S : s \notin f(s)\}$$

of S.

We restate the definition of A in words: the subset A of S is the set of all the elements of S that do *not* belong to the subset of S to which they are matched by the function f.

If the function f were a surjection, then the set $A \in \mathscr{P}(S)$ would have a preimage $s_0 \in S$. That is, $f(s_0) = A$. Either $s_0 \in A$ or $s_0 \notin A$.

If $s_0 \in A$, then $s_0 \notin f(s_0)$ by the definition of the set A. But $f(s_0) = A$, and so $s_0 \notin A$, a contradiction.

If $s_0 \notin A$, then, since $f(s_0) = A$, clearly $s_0 \notin f(s_0)$. But by the definition of A, this means $s_0 \in A$, again a contradiction.

Since both cases are impossible, we are forced to conclude that the set A has no preimage for any function from S to $\mathscr{P}(S)$. Thus there exists no surjection from S to $\mathscr{P}(S)$. Hence $|S| \neq |\mathscr{P}(S)|$, and so $|S| < |\mathscr{P}(S)|$. $\square$

If we apply this theorem to the set $\mathbb{N}$, we have

$$\aleph_0 = |\mathbb{N}| < |\mathscr{P}(\mathbb{N})|.$$

This proves the following corollary.

Corollary 7.4.9 *There exists a set with cardinality larger than $\aleph_0$.*

Combining Theorem 7.4.8 with the Principle of Mathematical Induction yields the following countable sequence of distinct cardinal numbers.

$$|\mathbb{N}|, \ |\mathscr{P}(\mathbb{N})|, \ |\mathscr{P}(\mathscr{P}(\mathbb{N}))|, \ \left|\mathscr{P}\left(\mathscr{P}\left(\mathscr{P}(\mathbb{N})\right)\right)\right|, \ \ldots$$

7.5   Uncountable Sets

By Corollary 7.4.9, uncountable sets exist. The understanding of the existence of uncountable sets is relatively new. Cantor first proved in 1874 that the set $\mathbb{R}$ of real numbers is uncountable. His second proof (from 1891) is the proof we show here. We start with the following lemma.

Lemma 7.5.1   *The set $\mathbb{R}$ of real numbers has the same cardinality as the interval $(0, 1)$.*

Proof. Let $f : (0, 1) \to \mathbb{R}$ be defined by $f(x) = \tan\left(\pi(x - \frac{1}{2})\right)$. The graph in Figure 7.5.1 suggests that this is a bijection.

A formal proof uses tools from calculus. Here is a sketch of the proof (compare Exercise 4.6.12(c)).

Since f is increasing on $(0, 1)$, f is an injection. (Recall Exercise 4.4.7.)

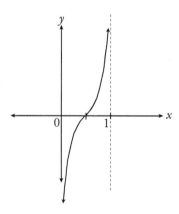

Figure 7.5.1: The graph of $y = \tan\left(\pi\left(x - \frac{1}{2}\right)\right)$, for $0 < x < 1$.

To prove that f is surjective, we note first that f is continuous on $(0, 1)$. This allows us to apply the Intermediate Value Theorem (Theorem 6.5.1): for any two values $y_1 < y_2$ in the range of f, the entire interval $[y_1, y_2]$ must be contained in the range of f. Finally, since $\lim_{x \to 1^-} f(x) = \infty$ and $\lim_{x \to 0^+} f(x) = -\infty$, no real number is too large or too small (i.e., too negative) to be beyond the range of f. Thus the range of f is $(-\infty, \infty) = \mathbb{R}$. $\square$

Theorem 7.5.2 *The open interval of real numbers $\{x \in \mathbb{R} : 0 < x < 1\}$ is uncountable.*

Proof. The proof proceeds by contradiction. Suppose that the set of real numbers in the interval $(0, 1)$ is countable and hence admits an enumeration $(r_1, r_2, r_3, r_4, r_5, \ldots)$. Each of these numbers has a unique decimal representation with no infinite block of consecutive 0's in its list of digits:[6]

$$r_1 = 0.a_{1,1}\, a_{1,2}\, a_{1,3}\, a_{1,4}\, a_{1,5}\, a_{1,6} \cdots$$
$$r_2 = 0.a_{2,1}\, a_{2,2}\, a_{2,3}\, a_{2,4}\, a_{2,5}\, a_{2,6} \cdots$$
$$r_3 = 0.a_{3,1}\, a_{3,2}\, a_{3,3}\, a_{3,4}\, a_{3,5}\, a_{3,6} \cdots$$
$$r_4 = 0.a_{4,1}\, a_{4,2}\, a_{4,3}\, a_{4,4}\, a_{4,5}\, a_{4,6} \cdots$$
$$r_5 = 0.a_{5,1}\, a_{5,2}\, a_{5,3}\, a_{5,4}\, a_{5,5}\, a_{5,6} \cdots$$
$$\vdots \qquad\qquad \ddots$$

Let

$$s_j = \begin{cases} 3 & \text{if } a_{j,j} \neq 3; \\ 7 & \text{if } a_{j,j} = 3, \end{cases}$$

and consider the number

$$s = 0.s_1\, s_2\, s_3\, s_4\, s_5\, s_6 \cdots.$$

For each $i \in \mathbb{N}$, the number s differs from r_i in at least one decimal place—namely, the ith place. Therefore s is not listed in the enumeration of the set $\{x \in \mathbb{R} : 0 < x < 1\}$. Yet $s \in \mathbb{R}$, and because of its decimal expansion, we have $0 < s < 1$. This contradiction leads to the conclusion that no enumeration of the set $\{x \in \mathbb{R} : 0 < x < 1\}$ exists. That is, it is uncountable.

$\square$

By putting together Lemma 7.5.1 and Theorem 7.5.2, we easily obtain a proof of the following result.

---

[6]If the decimal representation of a number $0.a_1 a_2 \cdots a_k$ terminates with $a_k \neq 0$, then we note that

$$0.a_1 a_2 \cdots a_k = 0.a_1 a_2 \cdots a_{k-1}(a_k - 1)999 \cdots;$$

that is, the 9s repeat indefinitely. This assures that each real number is written as exactly one sequence of digits.

Corollary 7.5.3   *The set $\mathbb{R}$ of real numbers is uncountable.*

Exercise 7.5.4   Prove that the set $\mathbb{I}$ of irrational numbers is uncountable. [Hint: Use Corollary 7.3.9.]

Since $\mathbb{R} \subset \mathbb{C}$, we have the following.

Corollary 7.5.5   *The set $\mathbb{C}$ of complex numbers is uncountable.*

The cardinality of the set $\mathbb{R}$ is conventionally denoted by the boldface, lowercase letter **c**, standing for (the cardinality of) the continuum. Thus $\big|(0,1)\big| = \mathbf{c}$. By Exercise 7.1.9 and the method of proof of Lemma 7.5.1, for any open interval $I \subseteq \mathbb{R}$, we have $\big|I\big| = \mathbf{c}$.

Lemma 7.5.6   *Let $\mathscr{F} = \big\{f : f$ is a function from $\mathbb{N}$ to $\{0,1\}\big\}$. Then*

$$\big|\mathscr{F}\big| = \big|\mathscr{P}(\mathbb{N})\big|.$$

Proof. Define the function $F : \mathscr{P}(\mathbb{N}) \to \mathscr{F}$ for all $A \subseteq \mathbb{N}$ by $F(A) = f_A$ where

$$f_A(n) = \begin{cases} 1 & \text{if } n \in A; \\ 0 & \text{if } n \notin A. \end{cases}$$

(The function f_A is the **characteristic function** of A.) To prove that F is injective, assume that $F(A_1) = F(A_2)$ for some $A_1, A_2 \in \mathscr{P}(\mathbb{N})$. So $f_{A_1} = f_{A_2}$. For any $a \in A_1$, we have $f_{A_2}(a) = f_{A_1}(a) = 1$. Thus by definition of f_{A_2}, $a \in A_2$. Hence $A_1 \subseteq A_2$. Similarly $A_2 \subseteq A_1$. So $A_1 = A_2$, and F is injective.

To prove that F is surjective, let $g \in \mathscr{F}$ be given. Set $A = \{n \in \mathbb{N} : g(n) = 1\}$. Thus for any $m \in \mathbb{N}$, $g(m) = 1$ if and only if $m \in A$. (Otherwise, $g(m) = 0$.) But the same holds for f_A. Hence $g = f_A = F(A)$, and so F is surjective.

Since F is bijective, we conclude that $\big|\mathscr{F}\big| = \big|\mathscr{P}(\mathbb{N})\big|$. $\square$

Theorem 7.5.7 $|\mathscr{P}(\mathbb{N})| = \mathbf{c}$.

Proof. Let $\mathscr{F}$ be defined as in Lemma 7.5.6. For each $r \in (0,1)$, let $r = 0.b_{1r}b_{2r}b_{3r}\ldots$ be the unique binary representation of r, with infinitely repeating 1s should the binary representation terminate.[7] Define the function $H : (0,1) \to \mathscr{F}$ by $H(r) = f_r$ where the function $f_r \in \mathscr{F}$ is given by the rule

$$f_r(n) = b_{nr}.$$

This bijection H demonstrates that $|(0,1)| = |\mathscr{F}|$. [You are asked to prove that H is a bijection as Exercise 7.5.8.] From Lemma 7.5.6 and the transitivity from Theorem 7.4.1, we conclude that $|\mathscr{P}(\mathbb{N})| = \mathbf{c}$. $\square$

The assertion that there exists no set whose cardinality is strictly greater than $\aleph_0$ but strictly less than $\mathbf{c}$ is called the **Continuum Hypothesis**. A proof of this assertion was pursued by Cantor unsuccessfully. Eventually, it was shown that the Continuum Hypothesis cannot be proved either affirmatively or negatively by using the agreed upon axioms of set theory.[8]

Exercise 7.5.8 Prove that the function H defined in in the proof of Theorem 7.5.7 is a bijection.

Corollary 7.5.9 *The set $\mathbb{T}$ of transcendental numbers is uncountable.*

Proof. We have $\mathbb{A} \cup \mathbb{T} = \mathbb{C}$. Suppose that $\mathbb{T}$ is countable. Since $\mathbb{A}$ is countable and the union of countable sets is countable, it would follow that $\mathbb{C}$ is countable, a contradiction to Corollary 7.5.5. Thus $\mathbb{T}$ is uncountable. $\square$

This chapter concludes with a brief presentation of what is referred to as cardinal arithmetic. For arbitrary cardinal numbers $\mathbf{a}$ and $\mathbf{b}$, we want to

---

[7]The binary analogue to the footnote in the proof of Theorem 7.5.2 is that

$$0.b_1\, b_2 \cdots b_{k-1}\, 1 = 0.b_1\, b_2 \cdots b_{k-1} 0\, 1\, 1\, 1 \cdots$$

with 1s repeating indefinitely,

[8]As with the Axiom of Choice, Kurt Gödel proved (1938) that assuming the Continuum Hypothesis leads to no contradiction to the axioms of set theory. Paul Cohen proved (1963) that assuming the negation of the Continuum Hypothesis is also consistent with these axioms, for which he received the Fields Medal. Therefore, the Continuum Hypothesis is not *decidable* within the axioms of set theory.

give some meaning to expressions such as $\mathbf{a} + \mathbf{b}$, $\mathbf{a} \cdot \mathbf{b}$, and $\mathbf{b^a}$. When $\mathbf{a}$ and $\mathbf{b}$ are finite cardinal numbers, we know from Proposition 7.1.2 what these resulting cardinal numbers must be. But look back at the proof of that proposition. It should be clear that the proof just makes no sense when the set A or the set B is infinite. What mathematicians do in such a situation is to *define* these operations for arbitrary cardinal numbers in such a way that the new definition embraces all results already obtained, in particular, those in Proposition 7.1.2.

Definition 7.5.10   *Let* $\mathbf{a}$ *and* $\mathbf{b}$ *be cardinal numbers.*
(i) $\mathbf{a} + \mathbf{b}$ *is the cardinal number of the union of any two disjoint sets whose cardinalities are* $\mathbf{a}$ *and* $\mathbf{b}$, *respectively.*
(ii) $\mathbf{a} \cdot \mathbf{b}$ *is the cardinal number of the Cartesian product of a set of cardinality* $\mathbf{a}$ *by a set of cardinality* $\mathbf{b}$.
(iii) $\mathbf{b^a}$ *is the cardinality of the set of functions from a set of cardinality* $\mathbf{a}$ *to a set of cardinality* $\mathbf{b}$.

Here's a subtle point. Just stating a definition is not necessarily a solution to a problem. One must also justify that the object being defined is what is called *well-defined*; that is, does the definition really make sense? In this case, are the three cardinal numbers just defined really independent of the particular sets of cardinalities $\mathbf{a}$ and $\mathbf{b}$, respectively, used to define them? If not, then these so-called cardinal numbers are not cardinal numbers at all; they would be represent nothing! Let us show that $\mathbf{b^a}$ is well-defined. The other two are easier and are left as Exercise 7.5.12.

Proposition 7.5.11   *The cardinal number* $\mathbf{b^a}$ *is well-defined.*

Proof. Suppose that A_1 and A_2 are arbitrary sets of cardinality $\mathbf{a}$ and that B_1 and B_2 are arbitrary sets of cardinality $\mathbf{b}$. For $i = 1, 2$, let F_i denote the set of all functions from A_i to B_i. It will suffice to show that $|F_1| = |F_2|$.

By our assumptions, there exist bijections $g : A_1 \to A_2$ and $h : B_1 \to B_2$. We define functions

$$\Phi : F_1 \to F_2 \quad \text{and} \quad \Psi : F_2 \to F_1$$

as follows. For each function $s \in F_1$ and each function $t \in F_2$, let

$$\Phi(s) = h \circ s \circ g^{-1} \quad \text{and} \quad \Psi(t) = h^{-1} \circ t \circ g.$$

(See Figure 7.5.2.) For any $s \in F_1$, we have

$$(\Psi \circ \Phi)(s) = \Psi(\Phi(s)) = h^{-1} \circ (h \circ s \circ g^{-1}) \circ g = s$$

by the properties of bijections and their inverses (see Section 4.5). Thus $\Psi \circ \Phi = i_{F_1}$. Similarly, $\Phi \circ \Psi = i_{F_2}$. By Theorem 4.5.2, Φ is both an injection and a surjection and hence a bijection from F_1 to F_2 (and Ψ is a bijection from F_2 to F_1). We conclude that $|F_1| = |F_2|$. $\qquad\square$

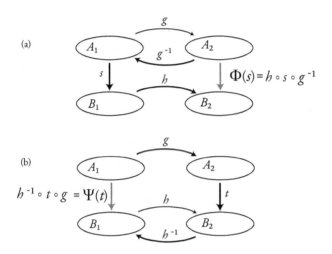

Figure 7.5.2: Proof of Proposition 7.5.11.

Exercise 7.5.12 Prove that the cardinal numbers $\mathbf{a} + \mathbf{b}$ and $\mathbf{a} \cdot \mathbf{b}$ are well-defined. [Hint: Use Proposition 7.3.1.]

In terms of Definition 7.5.10, some earlier results of this chapter about countable sets can be restated succinctly in terms of cardinal arithmetic as follows.

- Proposition 7.2.2: $\aleph_0 + n = \aleph_0$, for all $n \in \mathbb{N} \cup \{0\}$.

- Corollary 7.3.7: $\aleph_0^n = \aleph_0$, for all $n \in \mathbb{N}$.

- Corollary 7.3.9: $\displaystyle\sum_{k=1}^{n} \aleph_0 = \sum_{k=1}^{\infty} \aleph_0 = \aleph_0 \cdot \aleph_0 = \aleph_0$, for all $n \in \mathbb{N}$.

- Lemma 7.5.6 and Theorem 7.5.7: $2^{\aleph_0} = \mathbf{c}$.

Summary Remark. The following string of equalities and inequalities summarizes many of the results in this entire chapters. For all $n \in \mathbb{N}$,

$$0 < n < |\mathbb{N}| = |\mathbb{Z}| = |\mathbb{Q}| = |\mathbb{A}| = \aleph_0 = n\aleph_0 = \aleph_0^n < n^{\aleph_0} =$$
$$|\mathscr{P}(\mathbb{N})| = |\mathbb{R}| = |\mathbb{C}| = \mathbf{c} < |\mathscr{P}(\mathscr{P}(\mathbb{N}))| < \cdots .$$

7.6   Further Exercises

Exercise 7.6.1   A proposed alternative definition of an infinite set is the following. *A set S is* infinite *if and only if there exists a bijection from S onto some proper subset of S.* Prove or disprove that this definition is equivalent to the one given in Definition 7.1.1.

Exercise 7.6.2   Prove that $|\mathbb{R} \times \mathbb{R}| = \mathbf{c}$, and so $|\mathbb{C}| = \mathbf{c}$.

Exercise 7.6.3   Let A be a countable set. Let n be any integer such that $n \geq 2$, and let B be a set such that $|B| = n$.
(a) Prove that the set of surjections from A onto B is uncountable. [Suggestion: Use induction on n, starting with $n = 2$ both here and in part (b).]
(b) Prove that the set of injections from B to A is countable.
(c) Prove that the set of partitions of A with exactly n cells is uncountable.
(d) Prove that the set of finite partitions of A is uncountable.

Exercise 7.6.4   The symbol $\mathbb{R}^n$ is generally used to denote n-dimensional space. For example, $\mathbb{R}^2 = \mathbb{R} \times \mathbb{R}$ denotes the plane. Prove that $|\mathbb{R}^n| = |\mathbb{R}|$ for all $n \in \mathbb{N}$. [Suggestion: Use induction and Exercise 7.6.2.]

Exercise 7.6.5   Find the flaw in the following "proof" that $\mathbb{R}$ is countable.

Flawed proof. For each real number $x \in [0, 1)$, let $S_x = \{n + x : n \in \mathbb{Z}\}$. Then $\mathbb{R} = \bigcup\{S_x : x \in [0, 1)\}$. Since each set S_x is countable and the union of infinitely many countable sets is countable, it follows that $\mathbb{R}$ is countable. $\square$

Exercise 7.6.6 Given a set A, let $\mathrm{Sym}(A)$ denote the **set of permutations of** A—that is, the set of all bijections from A to itself. Determine whether the set of permutations of a countable set is countable.

Exercise 7.6.7 Let $\mathscr{P}_0(\mathbb{R})$ denote the family of finite subsets of $\mathbb{R}$. Prove that $|\mathscr{P}_0(\mathbb{R})| = |\mathbb{R}|$, and so $|\mathscr{P}_0(\mathbb{R})| < |\mathscr{P}(\mathbb{R})|$.

Exercise 7.6.8 Adapt the proof of Lemma 7.5.6 to prove the following generalization of Theorem 5.2.13. *For any set A of cardinality* $\mathbf{a}$,

$$|\mathscr{P}(A)| = 2^{\mathbf{a}}.$$

Exercise 7.6.9 A subset is **cofinite** if its complement is finite. Let A be a countable set. Show that the collection of finite subsets of A and the collection of cofinite subsets of A are each countable collections, but the collection of infinite subsets of A that are not cofinite is uncountable. [Hint: Consider, for each $n \in \mathbb{N}$, the collection of subsets of $\mathbb{N}$ whose largest element is n.]

Exercise 7.6.10 To apply the Cantor–Schröder–Bernstein Theorem (Theorem 7.4.6) to finite or countable sets is like using a cannon to kill a mosquito. Let A, B, and C be sets and prove directly—that is, without resorting to such heavy artillery—that if A and C are countable and $A \subset B \subset C$, then B is countable.

Exercise 7.6.11 Prove the following. [Heavy artillery is recommended.]
(a) Let $a, b \in \mathbb{R}$ with $a < b$. Then the intervals (a, b), $(a, b]$, $[a, b)$, and $[a, b]$ all have cardinality $\mathbf{c}$.
(b) The set of points in any line segment in the plane has cardinality $\mathbf{c}$.
(c) The set of points enclosed by any rectangle in the plane has cardinality $\mathbf{c}$. [First, prove this for any rectangle whose sides are parallel to the major axes, and then consider a rotation.]
(d) For arbitrary sets $A \subset B \subset C$, if $|A| = |C|$, then $|A| = |B|$.

Exercise 7.6.12 Prove that in an infinite binary tree, the cardinality of the set of paths of infinite length starting from a fixed root x_0 is uncountable. See Figure 7.6.1.

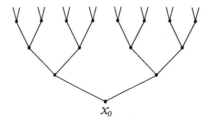

Figure 7.6.1: An infinite binary tree with root x_0.

Exercise 7.6.13 Let C_1 denote the closed interval $[0, 1]$. Form the set C_2 by deleting the open middle third of C_1; thus $C_2 = \left[0, \frac{1}{3}\right] \cup \left[\frac{2}{3}, 1\right]$. Form C_3 by deleting the open middle third of each of the two intervals that make up C_2. Inductively, for each $n \in \mathbb{N}$, the set C_{n+1} is formed by deleting the open middle third of each of the 2^n intervals whose union is C_n. The set

$$C_\infty = \bigcap_{n \in \mathbb{N}} C_n$$

is called the **Cantor ternary set**. Prove that C_∞ is uncountable. [Hint: Use ternary representation of the real numbers in $[0, 1]$. Thus $0.a_1a_2a_3\cdots$, where $a_i \in \{0, 1, 2\}$, is the real number $\sum_{n=1}^{\infty} a_n \cdot 3^{-n}$. Note, for example, that $\frac{1}{3}$ is the only element $0.a_1a_2a_3\cdots \in C_2$ for which $a_1 = 1$.]

Figure Credit

Chapter 8

Algebraic Systems

THIS FINAL CHAPTER begins by bringing together many ideas from the earlier chapters. You have studied the properties of the ways in which such differently appearing objects as statements, sets, numbers, and functions are combined. Some of these properties are shared, and some are not. These properties themselves are of special interest to mathematicians. In Section 8.2, sets of equivalence classes introduced in Section 6.2 form finite systems that satisfy most of the arithmetic properties presented in Section 8.1. In Section 8.3, starting with the set $\mathbb{N}$, we make an express tour of number systems by adjoining to $\mathbb{N}$ more and more kinds of numbers as we demand that more and more properties of binary operations be satisfied. This augmentation of the number system culminates with the complex numbers in Section 8.4.

8.1   Binary Operations

Much of the content of the early chapters in this book involves binary operations. Here is a tabulation of some of the more important operations that you have encountered.

Chapter	Objects Operated On	Operation Symbols			
1	Statements	$\wedge$	$\vee$	$\Rightarrow$	$\Leftrightarrow$
2	Numbers	$+$ $-$	$\cdot$	$/$	x^y
3	Sets	$\cup$	$\cap$	$\setminus$	$+$
4	Functions	$+$ $-$	$\cdot$	$/$	$\circ$

Our main interest in this section does not lie in the particular operations themselves, nor does it lie in the kinds of objects involved in the operations. Rather, we are concerned with more universal properties that may or may not hold for operations in general. Instead of indicating an operation by $+$ or $\cup$ or $\circ$ or any other context-related symbol, we use the bullet symbol $\bullet$ to indicate a generic operation.

Definition 8.1.1 *Given a set S, a **binary operation** (briefly, an **operation**) $\bullet$ on S is a function from $S \times S$ into S. The image under $\bullet$ of an element $(s_1, s_2) \in S \times S$ is denoted by $s_1 \bullet s_2$; that is, $s_1 \bullet s_2 \in S$. The element $s_1 \bullet s_2$ is the **product** of s_1 by s_2.*

We often suppress the word *binary* in this presentation because binary operations are the only kind of operation that we study here. But for your information, a *unary operation* on S is just a function from S to S. For example, if S is a set of statements and their negations, then $\neg$ is a unary operation on S. A *ternary operation* is a function from $S \times S \times S$ into S. For example, suppose that $S = \mathbb{Q}$ and that the image of $(x, y, z) \in \mathbb{Q} \times \mathbb{Q} \times \mathbb{Q}$ is the average $(x + y + z)/3$ of the three (not necessarily distinct) rational numbers x, y, and z. As for a *quaternary operation*, well, ... you get the idea. [How would one define an *n-ary operation*?]

Example 8.1.2

1. The operation of addition on the set $\mathbb{N}$ is a binary operation. To say that $2 + 3 = 5$ means that we have an operation $+$ on the set $\mathbb{N}$ that determines a function such that the image $2 + 3 \in \mathbb{N}$ of the element $(2, 3) \in \mathbb{N} \times \mathbb{N}$ is the element $5 \in \mathbb{N}$.

2. Let X be any set. For any subsets $A, B \in \mathscr{P}(X)$, $A \cup B$ is a well-defined element of $\mathscr{P}(X)$. That is, the set $A \cup B$ is the image (under the operation $\cup$) of the ordered pair $(A, B) \in \mathscr{P}(X) \times \mathscr{P}(X)$. Thus $\cup$ is an operation on the set $\mathscr{P}(X)$.

3. Let X be any set, and let S be the set of all functions from X to X. Then composition of functions, denoted by $\circ$, is an operation on the set S. Specifically, the image of the ordered pair (f, g) is the composition of f by g and is denoted by $g \circ f$, which is also a function from X to X.

The definition of an operation is so general and the cases of Example 8.1.2 are so basic that you might wonder why operations are of any interest at all. It seems that just about anything could be an operation. The situation becomes more interesting when we consider an operation when it is restricted to a particular subset of a given set.

Definition 8.1.3 *Let $\bullet$ be an operation on the set S, and let $A \subseteq S$. Then A is **closed** under $\bullet$ if*

$$(\forall s_1, s_2 \in A)[s_1 \bullet s_2 \in A].$$

Note that S itself is closed under any binary operation on S.

Example 8.1.4

1. The set $\mathbb{E}$ of positive even integers is a subset of $\mathbb{N}$. It is closed under both addition and multiplication. The subset $\mathbb{O}$ of positive odd integers is closed under multiplication but not under addition.

2. The subset $\mathbb{R}^+$ of $\mathbb{R}$ is closed under the operations of addition, multiplication, and division, but $\mathbb{R}^+$ is not closed under subtraction. The subset $\mathbb{R}^-$ is closed only under addition.

3. Let X be a subset of $\mathbb{R}$, let S be the set of all functions from X to X, and let D be the set of differentiable functions in S. Since the composition of two differentiable functions is differentiable (by the chain rule), the set D is closed under composition.

4. Let X be an uncountable set. Consider the subset $\mathscr{C}$ of $\mathscr{P}(X)$ consisting of all the countable subsets of X. Since the union of two countable sets is countable (by Corollary 7.3.9), the set $\mathscr{C}$ is closed under the operation of union. However, $\mathscr{C}$ is not closed under intersection. [Why not?]

Exercise 8.1.5 Let X be any set. A finite subset A of X is **even** (respectively, **odd**) if $|A|$ is an even integer (respectively, an odd integer). In particular, $\varnothing$ is an even set. Recall that the symmetric difference (see Exercise 3.6.12) of sets $A, B \in \mathscr{P}(X)$ is the set

$$A + B = (A \cup B) \setminus (A \cap B).$$

Prove that the set of even subsets of X is closed under the operation of symmetric difference, but the set of odd subsets is not closed under symmetric difference. [Hint: Use Exercise 7.1.4.]

Exercise 8.1.6 A subset A of the plane is **convex** if, for any two points in A, the segment joining them is wholly contained in A. (Thus $\varnothing$ is convex as are all the singleton sets, but if a convex set has at least two points, then it is uncountable.) Prove that the family of convex subsets of the plane is closed under intersection but is not closed under union, relative complement, or symmetric difference.

The term *algebraic system* has been given various definitions by various mathematicians. Some want to impose further conditions on the term, but there is no general agreement as to which further conditions might be imposed. Since the term is a useful one, we agree to use the following definition.

Definition 8.1.7 *An **algebraic system** (with one operation) is a pair $(S, \bullet)$ where S is a set and $\bullet$ is a binary operation on S.*

With that definition established, we turn to various conditions that one might like to impose upon an algebraic system. The most commonly accepted condition is *associativity*.

Definition 8.1.8 *An operation $\bullet$ on a set S is **associative** when*

$$(\forall a, b, c \in S)[\, a \bullet (b \bullet c) \;=\; (a \bullet b) \bullet c \,]. \tag{8.1.1}$$

When you look at $a \bullet (b \bullet c)$, don't presume that $\bullet$ is a ternary operation acting on $S \times S \times S$. It is not. The term $b \bullet c$ is an element of S, and so $\bullet$ is acting on $S \times S$ in both sides of equation (8.1.1). What is nice about associativity is that one may safely ignore the parentheses and write simply $a \bullet b \bullet c$ because the grouping that led us to this term doesn't matter. An algebraic system in which the operation is associative is called an **associative system**.

All of the operations listed in the table at the beginning of this section are associative except for $\Rightarrow$, relative complement of sets, and subtraction, division, and exponentiation of numbers. The binary operation of **exponentiation** on $\mathbb{R}$ takes the ordered pair (a, b) to the number a^b. For $a, b, c \in \mathbb{R}$, it is generally the case that $a^{(b^c)} \neq \left(a^b\right)^c$.

Definition 8.1.9 *Let $(S, \bullet)$ be an algebraic system. An element $\ell \in S$ is a* **left identity** *if*

$$(\forall s \in S)[\ell \bullet s = s].$$

Similarly, an element $r \in S$ is a **right identity** *if*

$$(\forall s \in S)[s \bullet r = s].$$

An element that is a left identity but not a right identity, or vice versa, is a **one-sided identity***. An element that is both a left identity and a right identity is a* **two-sided identity***.*

An algebraic system need not have any left identity at all, or it may have any number of left identities. The same holds for right identities. For example, $(\mathbb{N}, +)$ has no identity, left or right. However, if an algebraic system has *both* a left identity and a right identity, then watch what happens!

Proposition 8.1.10 *If an algebraic system has both a left identity ℓ and a right identity r, then $\ell = r$, and there exists but one unique, two-sided identity.*

Proof. Suppose that the algebraic system $(S, \bullet)$ has a left identity ℓ and a right identity r. Then $\ell \bullet r = r$ (because ℓ is a left identity), and $\ell \bullet r = \ell$ (because r is a right identity). Thus $\ell = r$. $\square$

When we speak of a **system with identity**, it is understood that the algebraic system has a unique two-sided identity, which is generally denoted by e.

Example 8.1.11   Here is an example of an associative system that has a right identity but no left identity. Let S be the set of all functions $f : \mathbb{N} \to \mathbb{N}$ having the property that $f(1) = f(2) = 1$, and consider the system $(S, \circ)$. The operation $\circ$ here is composition of functions, which you proved to be associative in Exercise 4.2.9. We first must justify that S is closed under $\circ$. For arbitrary elements $f, g \in S$,

$$(g \circ f)(1) = g\big(f(1)\big) = g(1) = 1 \quad \text{and} \quad (g \circ f)(2) = g\big(f(2)\big) = g(1) = 1.$$

Thus $g \circ f \in S$, and S is closed under $\circ$.

There exists a function $r \in S$ such that

$$r(n) = \begin{cases} 1 & \text{if } n = 1 \text{ or } n = 2; \\ n & \text{if } n \geq 3. \end{cases}$$

We show that r is a right identity. For any arbitrary $f \in S$, since $f \circ r \in S$ (by closure), if $n = 1$ or 2, we must have $(f \circ r)(n) = 1 = f(n)$. If $n \geq 3$, then

$$(f \circ r)(n) = f\big(r(n)\big) = f(n).$$

We've shown that $f \circ r = f$ for all $f \in S$, and so r is indeed a right identity.

It remains to show that r is not also a left identity. There exists some function $h \in S$ such that $h(3) = 2$. For any such function h,

$$(r \circ h)(3) = r(h(3)) = r(2) = 1 \neq h(3),$$

and so $r \circ h \neq h$ for some $h \in S$. This proves that r is not a left identity. By Proposition 8.1.10, no other function can be a left identity, and hence S contains no two-sided identity. (Note that the identity function $i_{\mathbb{N}}$ is not an element of S.)

One-sided identities sometimes are and sometimes are not unique. (See Exercise 8.5.6.)

The system in Example 8.1.11 is not typical of the algebraic systems that are most frequently studied. The more frequently studied systems have a (unique) two-sided identity.

Example 8.1.12 The following are examples of associative systems with identity:

1. $(\mathbb{Z}, +)$ or $(\mathbb{Q}, +)$ or $(\mathbb{R}, +)$ or $(\mathbb{C}, +)$, all with identity 0;

2. $(\mathbb{Z}, \cdot)$ or $(\mathbb{Q}, \cdot)$ or $(\mathbb{R}, \cdot)$ or $(\mathbb{C}, \cdot)$, all with identity 1;

3. $(\mathscr{P}(X), \cup)$ for any set X, with identity $\varnothing$ (see Proposition 3.2.3(ii));

4. $(\mathscr{P}(X), \cap)$ for any set X, with identity the set X (see Proposition 3.2.3(i));

5. $(\Sigma, \vee)$, for a set Σ of statements that is closed under $\vee$, where the identity is a contradiction[1];

6. $(\Sigma, \wedge)$, for a set Σ of statements that is closed under $\wedge$, where the identity is a tautology;

7. $\left(\mathbb{R}^{\mathbb{R}}, +\right)$, where $\mathbb{R}^{\mathbb{R}}$ denotes the set of all functions from $\mathbb{R}$ into $\mathbb{R}$, and the identity is the constant function with range $\{0\}$;

8. $\left(\mathbb{R}^{\mathbb{R}}, \cdot\right)$, where $\mathbb{R}^{\mathbb{R}}$ denotes the set of all functions from $\mathbb{R}$ into $\mathbb{R}$, and the identity is the constant function with range $\{1\}$;

9. $\left(X^{X}, \circ\right)$, where X^{X} denotes the set of all functions from a set X into itself, and the identity is the identity function i_X;

10. $(\mathbb{M}_n, \cdot)$, where $\mathbb{M}_n$ denotes the set of all $n \times n$ matrices with entries in $\mathbb{Z}$ (or in $\mathbb{Q}$ or in $\mathbb{R}$, your choice) with the operation of matrix multiplication and the identity being the $n \times n$ identity matrix.

In your high school algebra class, if you were to see an equation like $3x = 18$, you probably would have read it as a call to action: "Solve for x." You would have interpreted the equation as $3 \cdot x = 3 \cdot 6$ and concluded that it is quite all right to cross out the 3s and write $x = 6$. Of course, an equation is not a call to action at all; it is a statement of equality. But the questions that we want to raise here are "What does it mean to cancel?" and "Is cancellation like this always permissible?" Let us first be precise about what cancellation means.

---

[1]Equivalent statements are regarded as identical. Hence all contradictions are mutually equivalent, and the same holds for tautologies. So the identity is unique.

Definition 8.1.13 *An algebraic system* $(S, \bullet)$ *satisfies the* **left cancellation law** *when*

$$(\forall a, b, c \in S)[\ a \bullet b = a \bullet c \quad \Rightarrow \quad b = c\ ].$$

An algebraic system $(S, \bullet)$ *satisfies the* **right cancellation law** *when*

$$(\forall a, b, c \in S)[\ b \bullet a = c \bullet a \quad \Rightarrow \quad b = c\ ].$$

We pose the question again. Is left or right cancellation in this more general setting always permissible?

Example 8.1.14 Consider the following functions from $\mathbb{N}$ to $\mathbb{N}$.

$$f(n) = \begin{cases} 1 & \text{if } n = 1; \\ n - 1 & \text{if } n \geq 2. \end{cases}$$

$$h_1(n) = \begin{cases} 2 & \text{if } n = 1; \\ 1 & \text{if } n = 2; \\ n + 1 & \text{if } n \geq 3. \end{cases}$$

$$h_2(n) = \begin{cases} 1 & \text{if } n = 1 \text{ or } n = 2; \\ n + 1 & \text{if } n \geq 3. \end{cases}$$

It's easy to check that

$$f \circ h_1 = f \circ h_2. \tag{8.1.2}$$

However, one cannot cancel the f because clearly $h_1 \neq h_2$. Compare this situation to Corollaries 4.5.7 and 4.5.8 by letting $X = Y = \mathbb{N}$. The function f is clearly a surjection, and so (by Corollary 4.5.8) we *could* have canceled f had f appeared on the right in equation (8.1.2). But with f appearing on the left, we *could* have canceled f if and only if f were an injection (by Corollary 4.5.7), which it is not. Corollaries 4.5.7 and 4.5.8 tell us that one-sided cancellation is permissible if and only if certain conditions hold.

In the context of Corollaries 4.5.7 and 4.5.8, we require that $X = Y$ so that composition is defined between all functions involved. The first corollary says that injections can be canceled when they appear on the left, and the second corollary says that surjections can be canceled when they appear on the right. If we let S be the set of *all* functions from the set X to itself, then these cancellation laws appear to hold for some functions but not for others. But note the universal quantifiers in Definition 8.1.13; if the law doesn't hold all the time, then it doesn't hold.

If we want a set S of functions for which one of the cancellation laws holds (and that means, all the time), then we need to trim back the set S. Since the set of all injections from a set to itself is closed under composition, and the same holds for the set of all surjections, we immediately have the following result.

Proposition 8.1.15 *(i) Let S be the set of all injections from a set to itself. Then $(S, \circ)$ satisfies the left cancellation law.*
(ii) Let S be the set of all surjections from a set to itself. Then $(S, \circ)$ satisfies the right cancellation law.

Definition 8.1.16 *Let $(S, \bullet)$ be an algebraic system with identity, and denote the identity element by e. Let $s \in S$.*

*An element $t \in S$ is a **left inverse** of s if $t \bullet s = e$.*

*An element $u \in S$ is a **right inverse** of s if $s \bullet u = e$.*

*An element that is a left inverse of s but not a right inverse of s, or vice versa, is a **one-sided inverse** of s.*

In Example 4.5.3, you saw that an element may have more than one one-sided inverse. In Lemma 4.5.4, you saw that, with respect to composition, injections have right inverses and surjections have left inverses. It follows that bijections must have both. In fact, Theorem 4.5.11 tells us that bijections have unique, two-sided inverses. We consider this important notion in the abstract context of associative systems, stripping away all the particulars about functions.

Theorem 8.1.17 *Let $(S, \bullet)$ be an associative system with identity e. Let $s \in S$. If s has both a left inverse t and a right inverse u, then $t = u$.*

Proof. We have

$$
\begin{array}{llll}
u & = & e \bullet u & [\text{ definition of } e\ ] \\
  & = & (t \bullet s) \bullet u & [\ t \text{ is a left inverse of } s\ ] \\
  & = & t \bullet (s \bullet u) & [\text{ associativity }] \\
  & = & t \bullet e & [\ u \text{ is a right inverse of } s\ ] \\
  & = & t. & [\text{ definition of } e\ ]
\end{array}
$$

$\square$

When an element s of an associative system $(S, \bullet)$ satisfies Theorem 8.1.17, then the two-sided inverse of s is the **inverse** of s. The article *the* is appropriate because the theorem proves that an element has at most one inverse. The inverse of s is denoted by s^{-1} but is not to be confused with the reciprocal of s. This is consistent with our notation for inverse functions. In the general case, when S is not a set of numbers, the reciprocal $1/s$ need not even make sense. In the special case where S is a subset of $\mathbb{C}$ that is closed under multiplication, s^{-1} is indeed the reciprocal $1/s$ of s, because in that special case, unless $s = 0$, then $s \cdot (1/s) = 1$, and 1 is the identity of $(S, \cdot)$.

An element that has an inverse is **invertible**. Note that, if an element s is invertible, then so is s^{-1}, and $\left(s^{-1}\right)^{-1} = s$.

Example 8.1.18   Recall the cases listed in Example 8.1.12.

1. In $(\mathbb{Z}, +)$ or $(\mathbb{Q}, +)$ or $(\mathbb{R}, +)$ or $(\mathbb{C}, +)$, all elements are invertible; the inverse of any number x is $-x$.

2. In $(\mathbb{Z}, \cdot)$, only 1 and -1 are invertible. In $(\mathbb{Q}, \cdot)$ or $(\mathbb{R}, \cdot)$ or $(\mathbb{C}, \cdot)$, all elements except 0 are invertible.

3. In $(\mathscr{P}(X), \cup)$ where X is any set, only $\varnothing$ is invertible.

4. In $(\mathscr{P}(X), \cap)$ where X is any set, only the set X is invertible.

5. In $\left(\mathbb{R}^{\mathbb{R}}, +\right)$, where $\mathbb{R}^{\mathbb{R}}$ denotes the set of all functions from $\mathbb{R}$ into $\mathbb{R}$, the inverse of every function f is $-f$.

6. In $\left(\mathbb{R}^{\mathbb{R}}, \cdot\right)$, where $\mathbb{R}^{\mathbb{R}}$ denotes the set of all functions from $\mathbb{R}$ into $\mathbb{R}$, a function f has an inverse if and only if $f(x) \neq 0$ for all $x \in \mathbb{R}$. In that case, the inverse of f is $1/f$.

7. In $\left(X^X, \circ\right)$, where X^X denotes the set of all functions from a set X into itself, a function is invertible if and only if it is a bijection (see Theorem 4.5.11).

8. In $(\mathbb{M}_n, \cdot)$, where $\mathbb{M}_n$ denotes the set of all $n \times n$ matrices with entries in $\mathbb{Z}$ with the operation of matrix multiplication, a matrix is invertible if and only if its determinant equals ± 1.

9. In $(\mathbb{M}_n, \cdot)$, where $\mathbb{M}_n$ denotes the set of all $n \times n$ matrices with entries in $\mathbb{Q}$ (or in $\mathbb{R}$ or in $\mathbb{C}$) with the operation of matrix multiplication, a matrix is invertible if and only if its determinant is not zero; equivalently, its rank equals n.

The next theorem generalizes Lemma 4.3.13.

Theorem 8.1.19 *The set of invertible elements of an associative system* $(S, \bullet)$ *is closed under* $\bullet$. *Moreover, if s and t are invertible elements, then*

$$\left(s \bullet t\right)^{-1} = t^{-1} \bullet s^{-1}.$$

Proof. Let s and t be invertible elements of S. [We show that $s \bullet t$ is invertible by demonstrating that $t^{-1} \bullet s^{-1}$ is the inverse of $s \bullet t$.] The existence of an invertible element implies the existence of an identity, so let e denote the identity of $(S, \bullet)$. We have

$$
\begin{aligned}
(s \bullet t) \bullet (t^{-1} \bullet s^{-1}) &= \left(s \bullet (t \bullet t^{-1})\right) \bullet s^{-1} && [\,\text{associativity}\,] \\
&= (s \bullet e) \bullet s^{-1} && [\,\text{definition of inverse}\,] \\
&= s \bullet s^{-1} && [\,\text{definition of } e\,] \\
&= e. && [\,\text{definition of inverse}\,]
\end{aligned}
$$

Thus $t^{-1} \bullet s^{-1}$ is a right inverse of $s \bullet t$. The proof that $t^{-1} \bullet s^{-1}$ is also a left inverse is left as Exercise 8.1.20. By Theorem 8.1.17, $t^{-1} \bullet s^{-1}$ is the inverse of $s \bullet t$. $\qquad \square$

Exercise 8.1.20 Complete the proof of Theorem 8.1.19 by showing that in an associative system, $t^{-1} \bullet s^{-1}$ is the left inverse of $s \bullet t$.

Numbers that appear to be exponents are often used to avoid bulky notation. Suppose that $(S, \bullet)$ is an associative system and that $s \in S$. Writing $s \bullet s$ or even $s \bullet s \bullet s$ isn't so bulky, but what if we want to iterate this product many times? The solution is to define the iterated product s^n inductively for all $n \in \mathbb{N}$ by

$$
\begin{aligned}
s^1 &= s, \\
s^{n+1} &= s \bullet s^n, \text{ and} \\
s^{-n} &= \left(s^{-1}\right)^n \quad \text{whenever } s \text{ is invertible.}
\end{aligned}
\tag{8.1.3}
$$

The following exercise contains some important algebraic properties of associative systems with identity. While they look just like basic facts of high school algebra when applied to multiplication of real numbers, they have broader meaning when applied to arbitrary associative systems.[2]

Exercise 8.1.21 Let $(S, \bullet)$ be an associative system with identity e, and let s be an invertible element. Prove the following.
(a) For all $n \in \mathbb{N}$, $s^{n+1} = s^n \bullet s$.
(b) For all $n \in \mathbb{N}$, s^n is invertible and s^{-n} is its inverse. Thus $\left(s^{-1}\right)^n = \left(s^n\right)^{-1}$.
(c) For all $m, n \in \mathbb{Z}$, $s^m \bullet s^n = s^{m+n} = s^n \bullet s^m$. [Hint: To get started, suppose that $m, n \in \mathbb{N}$ and let $k = m+n$. Then proceed by induction on k for $k \geq 2$.]
(d) $s^0 = e$.
(e) For all $m, n \in \mathbb{Z}$, $\left(s^m\right)^n = s^{mn} = \left(s^n\right)^m$.

In all but the last two examples in Example 8.1.12, the order in which two elements are combined in the binary operation is immaterial. This is a property of much interest.

Definition 8.1.22 *An operation $\bullet$ on a set S is* **commutative** *when*

$$
(\forall a, b \in S)[\, a \bullet b = b \bullet a \,].
$$

Associative systems whose operation is commutative have certain nice and convenient properties that are easy to verify. Among such properties are the following.

[2] An associative system with identity in which *every* element is invertible is called a **group**. Group theory is one of the important topics in a modern (or abstract) algebra course.

1. The left cancellation law holds if and only if the right cancellation law holds.

2. An element is a left identity if and only if it is a right identity, in which case it is the unique identity.

3. An element s has a left inverse if and only if it has a right inverse, in which case it has a unique inverse s^{-1}.

4. If s and t are invertible, then $(s \bullet t)^{-1} = s^{-1} \bullet t^{-1}$.

If elements a and b of a system satisfy the equation $a \bullet b = b \bullet a$, then a and b **commute**. However, just because some pairs of elements commute does not mean that the operation is commutative. Note the universal quantifier in the definition. In Exercise 8.1.21(c), you showed that all powers of any given element commute with each other.

Exercise 8.1.23 Let S be the set of all functions from $\mathbb{R}$ to $\mathbb{R}$. Define a relation **R** on S whereby $(f, g) \in \mathbf{R}$ if and only if $f \circ g = g \circ f$. Prove that, although **R** is reflexive and symmetric, it is not transitive. [Hint: Consider the functions defined by $f(x) = x + 1$, $g(x) = x$, and $h(x) = (x + 2)^2$.]

We conclude this section with a brief look at systems that have two binary operations.

Definition 8.1.24 *An* **algebraic system with two binary operations** *is a triple* $(S, +, \bullet)$ *where S is a set and $+$ and $\bullet$ are binary operations with respect to which the set S is closed. Such a system is an* **associative system** *if both operations are associative.*

Example 8.1.25 Here are some associative systems with two binary operations.

1. $\mathbb{Z}, \mathbb{Q}, \mathbb{R}$, and $\mathbb{C}$ all have addition and multiplication.

2. $\mathscr{P}(X)$ for any set X admits the operations of union and intersection.

3. The set of functions from $\mathbb{R}$ into $\mathbb{R}$ admits addition and multiplication. (We're deliberately ignoring composition here. You'll see why in Exercise 8.1.27.)

4. For each $n \in \mathbb{N}$, the set of $n \times n$ matrices with entries in $\mathbb{N}, \mathbb{Z}, \mathbb{Q}, \mathbb{R}$, or $\mathbb{C}$ supports matrix addition and matrix multiplication. The addition is commutative, but the multiplication is not.

In each of these cases, there is a rule that ties the two operations together.

Definition 8.1.26 *An algebraic system $(S, +, \bullet)$ satisfies the* **left distributive law** *when*

$$(\forall a, b, c \in S)[\ a \bullet (b + c) \ = \ (a \bullet b) + (a \bullet c) \ ].$$

An algebraic system $(S, +, \bullet)$ satisfies the **right distributive law** *if*

$$(\forall a, b, c \in S)[\ (b + c) \bullet a \ = \ (b \bullet a) + (c \bullet a)].$$

If both laws are satisfied, then $\bullet$ **distributes** *over* $+$.

Exercise 8.1.27   (a) Prove that if $\bullet$ is commutative, then an algebraic system satisfies the left distributive law if and only if it satisfies the right distributive law.
(b) In each of the cases of Example 8.1.25, determine which operation distributes over the other.
(c) Show that composition of functions distributes over neither addition of functions nor multiplication of functions.
(d) Show that neither addition of functions nor multiplication of functions distributes over composition of functions.

8.2   Modular Arithmetic

This section is a natural extension of some of the notions of Chapter 2. We define some equivalence relations on the set of integers. This develops useful finite algebraic systems whose elements are equivalence classes. These systems figure prominently in modern cryptography.

We restate Definition 6.2.6:

> Let $m \in \mathbb{N}$ and $a, b \in \mathbb{Z}$. Then a *is* **congruent to** b **modulo** m, *written* $a \equiv b \pmod{m}$, *if* $m \mid a - b$.

Theorem 8.2.1 *Let $m \in \mathbb{N}$ and $a, b, c, d \in \mathbb{Z}$. Suppose $a \equiv b \pmod{m}$ and $c \equiv d \pmod{m}$. Then the following statements hold.*
(i) $a + c \equiv b + d \pmod{m}$.
(ii) $ac \equiv bd \pmod{m}$.
(iii) For all $k \in \mathbb{N}$, $a^k \equiv b^k \pmod{m}$.

Proof. We prove (ii) and (iii) and leave the proof of (i) as Exercise 8.2.2.

Since $a \equiv b \pmod{m}$ and $c \equiv d \pmod{m}$, there exist $x, y \in \mathbb{Z}$ such that $a - b = xm$ and $c - d = ym$. Then, in the standard arithmetic of $\mathbb{Z}$,

$$
\begin{aligned}
ac - bd &= ac - bc + bc - bd \\
&= (a - b)c + b(c - d) \\
&= xmc + bym \\
&= (xc + by)m.
\end{aligned}
$$

Thus $ac \equiv bd \pmod{m}$.

We prove (iii) by induction. If $k = 1$, there is nothing to prove. Suppose, as the induction hypothesis, that $k \geq 1$ and $a^k \equiv b^k \pmod{m}$. By part (ii), since $a \equiv b \pmod{m}$, we have that

$$
a^k \cdot a \equiv b^k \cdot b \pmod{m}.
$$

Thus $a^{k+1} \equiv b^{k+1} \pmod{m}$ and the claim holds by the Principle of Mathematical Induction. $\square$

Exercise 8.2.2 Prove Theorem 8.2.1(i).

By Theorem 6.2.7, congruence modulo m is an equivalence relation. For example, the equivalence classes for the relation of congruence modulo 6 are

$$[0] = \{\ldots, -12, \; -6, \; 0, \; 6, \; 12, \ldots\},$$
$$[1] = \{\ldots, -11, \; -5, \; 1, \; 7, \; 13, \ldots\},$$
$$[2] = \{\ldots, -10, \; -4, \; 2, \; 8, \; 14, \ldots\},$$
$$[3] = \{\ldots, \; -9, \; -3, \; 3, \; 9, \; 15, \ldots\},$$
$$[4] = \{\ldots, \; -8, \; -2, \; 4, \; 10, \; 16, \ldots\},$$
$$[5] = \{\ldots, \; -7, \; -1, \; 5, \; 11, \; 17, \ldots\}.$$

Recall that $[5] = [17]$ since $5 \equiv 17 \pmod 6$; however, it is customary to label each equivalence class of the relation congruence modulo m with the least nonnegative integer in the equivalence class. Thus a set of equivalence classes modulo 6 is

$$\mathbb{Z}_6 = \big\{[0], [1], [2], [3], [4], [5]\big\}.$$

The operation $+ : \mathbb{Z}_6 \times \mathbb{Z}_6 \to \mathbb{Z}_6$ is defined by $[a] + [b] = [a+b]$ where $a, b \in \mathbb{Z}$, and the addition $a + b$ inside the brackets is the usual addition for $(\mathbb{Z}, +)$. For example,

$$[4] + [5] \quad = \quad [4 + 5] \quad = \quad [9] \quad = \quad [3]$$

$$\text{and} \quad [-7] + [3] \quad = \quad [-7 + 3] \quad = \quad [-4] \quad = \quad [2]$$

since $9 \equiv 3 \pmod 6$ and $-4 \equiv 2 \pmod 6$. The second calculation can also be performed in the following way.

$$[-7] + [3] = [5] + [3] = [5 + 3] = [8] = [2],$$

where the representative of the equivalence class is changed prior to the addition.

In a similar fashion, the operation $\cdot : \mathbb{Z}_6 \times \mathbb{Z}_6 \to \mathbb{Z}_6$ is defined by $[a] \cdot [b] = [a \cdot b]$, where $a, b \in \mathbb{Z}$ and the multiplication inside the equivalence class brackets is the usual multiplication for $(\mathbb{Z}, \cdot)$. For example,

$$[4] \cdot [5] = [4 \cdot 5] = [20] = [2]$$

since $20 \equiv 2 \pmod 6$.

Theorem 8.2.1 shows that these operations are well-defined. In other words, it does not matter which representative of the equivalence class we use in the computation.

Exercise 8.2.3 Complete the following addition and multiplication tables modulo 6, where for all $[i], [j] \in \mathbb{Z}_6$, the term in the row headed by $[i]$ and the column headed by $[j]$ is $[i] + [j]$ in the table on the left and $[i] \cdot [j]$ on the right. Such tables are sometimes called **Cayley**[3] **tables**. Use the customary labels for each equivalence class.

+	[0]	[1]	[2]	[3]	[4]	[5]
[0]						
[1]						
[2]						
[3]						
[4]						[3]
[5]				[2]		

·	[0]	[1]	[2]	[3]	[4]	[5]
[0]						
[1]						
[2]						
[3]						
[4]						[2]
[5]						

Exercise 8.2.4 Verify that $(\mathbb{Z}_6, +)$ and $(\mathbb{Z}_6, \cdot)$ are associative systems with identity. Be sure to identify the identities. How can you tell from the tables that these operations are commutative? Which elements have inverses?

In general, for any positive integer m, we denote the set of equivalence classes with respect to congruence modulo m by

$$\mathbb{Z}_m = \big\{ [0], [1], [2], \ldots, [m-1] \big\}.$$

For an arbitrary integer k, we can apply the Division Algorithm (Theorem 2.3.9) to get $k = qm + r$ where $q, r \in \mathbb{Z}$ and $0 \leq r < m - 1$. Then $[k] = [r]$. (Why?) Any procedure used to find the least nonnegative r is often called *reducing k modulo m*. Equivalent to this is the addition to k, or the subtraction from k, of multiples of m until a number r is obtained,

---

[3]Attributed to the English mathematician Arthur Cayley (1821–1895). Cayley made many contributions to the fields of group theory, geometry, and linear algebra. Some of his work subsequently played an important role in the theory of relativity. He is one of the most prolific mathematician of all time, having written over 900 mathematical papers.

where $0 \leq r < m$. The relationship established by the Division Algorithm characterizes reduction of k modulo m as the determination of the remainder when k is divided by m.

To simplify what would become cumbersome notation, we label the set

$$\mathbb{Z}_m = \{0, 1, 2, \ldots, m-1\},$$

where the equivalence class brackets are suppressed, and refine the definitions of $+$ and $\cdot$ as follows.

Definition 8.2.5 *Let $a, b \in \mathbb{Z}_m$.* **Addition modulo** m *is the operation $+ : \mathbb{Z}_m \times \mathbb{Z}_m \to \mathbb{Z}_m$ defined by $a + b = r$, where $a + b \equiv r \pmod{m}$ and $r \in \mathbb{Z}_m$.* **Multiplication modulo** m *is defined similarly; $a \cdot b = r$, where $a \cdot b \equiv r \pmod{m}$ and $r \in \mathbb{Z}_m$. When the multiplication is understood, we write $a \cdot b$ as ab.*

The set $\mathbb{Z}_m$ is closed under addition and multiplication since, by the Division Algorithm, there *always* exist some $r_1, r_2 \in \mathbb{Z}_m$ such that $a + b = r_1$ and $ab = r_2$. Thus for each $m \in \mathbb{N}$, $(\mathbb{Z}_m, +)$ and $(\mathbb{Z}_m, \cdot)$ are associative systems with identity. Note that the operations are also commutative. In case that $m = 1$, the systems $(\mathbb{Z}_m, +)$ and $(\mathbb{Z}_m, \cdot)$ are identical and have only the single element 0. The situation is more interesting when $m \geq 2$.

Exercise 8.2.6 Let $a \in \mathbb{Z}_m \setminus \{0\}$. Prove that $m - a \in \mathbb{Z}_m$ and that $m - a$ is the inverse of a with respect to addition modulo m.

Example 8.2.7 Let us reduce $5427 \cdot 3155$ modulo 7. Since $5427 \equiv 2 \pmod{7}$ and $3155 \equiv 5 \pmod{7}$, we have, by Theorem 8.2.1(ii),

$$5427 \cdot 3155 \equiv 2 \cdot 5 \equiv 10 \equiv 3 \pmod{7}.$$

Now we reduce 5427^5 modulo 7. By Theorem 8.2.1(iii),

$$(5427)^5 \equiv 2^5 \equiv 32 \equiv 4 \pmod{7}.$$

The first computation is certainly easier than determining that $5427 \cdot 3155 = 17122185$ and then reducing modulo 7. As for the second computation, $5427^5 = 4707595162486055907$.

Exercise 8.2.8 Perform the following calculations modulo 15.
(a) $5674 \cdot 2031$
(b) 2031^{10}

Exercise 8.2.6 shows that every element of $\mathbb{Z}_m$ is invertible with respect to addition. You observed in Exercise 8.2.4 that this is not necessarily true for multiplication modulo m. Therefore, in the context of modular arithmetic, to say that an element $a \in \mathbb{Z}_m$ is "invertible" presumes that a has an inverse with respect to multiplication. Consider, for example, a Cayley table for multiplication in $\mathbb{Z}_9$ (make your own, if necessary). Since the multiplicative identity 1 does not appear in the row or column headed by 6, we see that 6 has no inverse in $\mathbb{Z}_9$ with respect to multiplication. The table should reveal that $1, 2, 4, 5, 7$, and 8 are the invertible elements of $\mathbb{Z}_9$.

The next theorem characterizes the invertible elements of $\mathbb{Z}_m$.

Theorem 8.2.9 *Let $m \geq 2$ be fixed. Then $ax \equiv 1 \pmod{m}$ has a solution[4] x if and only if a and m are relatively prime.*

Proof. $[\Rightarrow]$ Suppose that $ax \equiv 1 \pmod{m}$ has a solution, say $x = b$. By definition of congruence, there is an integer ℓ such that $ab - 1 = \ell m$. Thus we have the linear combination $ab - \ell m = 1$. By Theorem 2.5.5, a and m are relatively prime.

$[\Leftarrow]$ Assume that $\gcd(a, m) = 1$. Then, by Theorem 2.5.5, there are integers u, v such that $au + mv = 1$. Thus $au - 1 = (-v)m$, and so $au \equiv 1 \pmod{m}$. Therefore $x = u$ is a solution to $ax \equiv 1 \pmod{m}$. $\qquad\square$

Another way to interpret this theorem in the context of $\mathbb{Z}_m$ is to rephrase it as follows.

> *An element $a \in \mathbb{Z}_m$ is invertible*
>
> > *if and only if a and m are relatively prime.*

---

[4]When m and a are given, the phrase "$ax \equiv 1 \pmod{m}$ has a solution" means $(\exists x \in \mathbb{Z}_m)\,[ax \equiv 1 \pmod{m}]$.

Theorem 8.2.9 implies the following.

Corollary 8.2.10   *Let $m \in \mathbb{N}$ be fixed and let $a, b \in \mathbb{Z}$. If a and m are relatively prime, then the congruence $ax \equiv b \pmod{m}$ has a solution. Furthermore, the solution is unique modulo m.*

Exercise 8.2.11   Identify the pairs $\{a, a^{-1}\}$ of invertible elements of each of the following systems.
(a) $\mathbb{Z}_{12}$
(b) $\mathbb{Z}_8$
(c) $\mathbb{Z}_{11}$
(d) $\mathbb{Z}_{22}$

Exercise 8.2.12   Let p be a prime number. Describe the set of invertible elements of each of the following systems.
(a) $\mathbb{Z}_p$
(b) $\mathbb{Z}_{2p}$
(c) $\mathbb{Z}_{p^2}$

Definition 8.2.13   *Let $m \in \mathbb{N} \backslash \{1\}$ be given. A **unit of $\mathbb{Z}_m$** is an invertible element of $\mathbb{Z}_m$.*

Thus the **set of units of $\mathbb{Z}_m$**, written U_m, is the set

$$U_m = \big\{ a \in \mathbb{Z}_m : (\exists b \in \mathbb{Z}_m)\, [a \cdot b \equiv 1 \pmod{m}] \big\}.$$

By Theorem 8.2.9, we could also define U_m by

$$U_m = \big\{ a \in \mathbb{Z}_m : \gcd(a, m) = 1 \big\}.$$

Example 8.2.14   Let $m = 15$. Then

$$\mathbb{Z}_{15} = \big\{ 0, 1, 2, 3, 4, 5, 6, 7, 8, 9, 10, 11, 12, 13, 14 \big\}$$

and $U_{15} = \big\{ 1, 2, 4, 7, 8, 11, 13, 14 \big\}$.

Exercise 8.2.15   (a) Prove that, for $m \in \mathbb{N} \backslash \{1\}$, U_m is closed under multiplication modulo m.
(b) Make a Cayley table for U_{15}, where the operation is multiplication modulo 15.

8.3 Numbers Revisited

"God created the integers; all else is the work of man." Thus wrote Leopold Kronecker[5] in the 1870s. Putting theological considerations aside, let us go back beyond Kronecker's "integers." Starting with just the set $\mathbb{N}$ of positive integers, we will reproduce some of "the work of man."

From Section 8.1, we know that $\mathbb{N}$ is an associative system with respect to the two commutative operations of addition and multiplication, that multiplication distributes over addition, and that the integer 1 is the (unique) identity with respect to multiplication. But that's just about all that $(\mathbb{N}, +, \cdot)$ has to offer. We would like to have more!

Since $\mathbb{N}$ already has the identity 1 with respect to multiplication, it would be nice to have inverses with respect to multiplication as well. So let us adjoin to $\mathbb{N}$ all the reciprocals of positive integers; we bring in

$$\frac{1}{2}, \frac{1}{3}, \frac{1}{4}, \ldots, \frac{1}{n}, \ldots$$

for all $n \in \mathbb{N}$. The set of reciprocals is closed under multiplication, which is nice, but the enlarged set—that is, the union of $\mathbb{N}$ with this set of reciprocals—is not closed under multiplication. (Consider $2 \cdot \frac{1}{3}$.) Nor is this union closed under addition. (Consider $2 + \frac{1}{3}$, or $\frac{1}{2} + \frac{1}{3}$.) If we want to retain closure under addition, we can do so no more economically than to import all the rest of the set $\mathbb{Q}^+$ of positive rational numbers, which at the same time brings closure under multiplication.

Exercise 8.3.1 Prove that any set of numbers that is closed under addition and contains the reciprocals of all the positive integers must contain $\mathbb{Q}^+$.

Now we are working with the system $(\mathbb{Q}^+, +, \cdot)$, which has everything that one might want concerning multiplication, but with respect to addition, it doesn't even have an identity. That's easily remedied; we're now dealing

---

[5]The German mathematician Leopold Kronecker (1823–1891) is noted for his contributions to algebraic number theory. In the latter part of his life, he became embroiled in controversy because of his rigid stance that transcendental numbers do not exist because a constructive proof of their existence had not been given.

with $\mathbb{Q}^+ \cup \{0\}$. Addition certainly deserves the same consideration as multiplication; our system ought to have inverses with respect to addition as well. That means that we must adjoin all of the set $\mathbb{Q}^-$. Our system under consideration has grown to $(\mathbb{Q}, +, \cdot)$.

One could quit at this point were it not that we would like to have solutions to equations of the form $f(x) = 0$, where $f \in \mathbb{Z}[x]$. That requires adjoining the rest of the set $\mathbb{A} \cap \mathbb{R}$ of real algebraic numbers. The good news is that $(\mathbb{A} \cap \mathbb{R}, +, \cdot)$ has all the properties[6] discussed in Section 8.1.

Exercise 8.3.2   Prove that every element of $\mathbb{A}$ has an additive inverse in $\mathbb{A}$ and every element of $\mathbb{A} \setminus \{0\}$ has a multiplicative inverse in $\mathbb{A} \setminus \{0\}$.

Perhaps even Herr Professor Kronecker would have been content to end this section right now, but we won't. (See footnote 5 of this chapter.) So what more could one want? What may still be lacking was hinted at in Section 6.4.

Let r be any real number and consider the set $S = \{x \in \mathbb{A} \cap \mathbb{R} : x \leq r\}$. Clearly the set S is bounded above, and r is its least upper bound. However, S *contains* its least upper bound if and only if $r \in \mathbb{A} \cap \mathbb{R}$. Let us approach this problem in a more sophisticated manner, using some terminology from calculus but also anticipating some terminology that you will encounter in a first course in real analysis.

In calculus, you learned that a **sequence** of real numbers is simply a function $a : \mathbb{N} \cup \{0\} \to \mathbb{R}$, although you wrote a_n for the image of n instead of writing $a(n)$ and abbreviated the rule for a as $\{a_n\}_{n=0}^{\infty}$. You also learned that $\lim\limits_{n \to \infty} a_n = L$ means

$$(\forall \epsilon > 0)(\exists M \in \mathbb{N})[\, n > M \;\Rightarrow\; |a_n - L| < \epsilon \,], \qquad (8.3.1)$$

and we say that the sequence *converges to L*.

---

[6]The set $\mathbb{A} \cap \mathbb{R}$ is closed with respect to addition and multiplication; however, the proof of this fact requires mathematics outside the scope of this book.

Definition 8.3.3 *A sequence $\{a_n\}_{n=0}^{\infty}$ of real numbers is a* **Cauchy**[7] *sequence if it satisfies*

$$(\forall \epsilon > 0)(\exists M \in \mathbb{N})[\,(m > M \,\wedge\, n > M) \;\Rightarrow\; |a_m - a_n| < \epsilon\,]. \qquad (8.3.2)$$

Let us compare in words these two possible attributes of sequences. To say that $\{a_n\}_{n=0}^{\infty}$ converges to L is to say that, if we pick terms far enough along in the sequence, then they are very close *to the limit L*. To say that the sequence $\{a_n\}_{n=0}^{\infty}$ is a Cauchy sequence is to say that, if we pick any two terms far enough along in the sequence, then they are very close *to each other*.

Proposition 8.3.4 *If a sequence of real numbers converges to some limit, then it is a Cauchy sequence.*

Proof. Suppose that $\lim_{n\to\infty} a_n = L$. We must prove that $\{a_n\}_{n=0}^{\infty}$ satisfies condition (8.3.2). Let some arbitrary $\epsilon > 0$ be given. Then $\epsilon/2 > 0$. By condition (8.3.1), with $\epsilon/2$ in place of ϵ, there exists some $M \in \mathbb{N}$ such that, whenever $n > M$, then $|a_n - L| < \epsilon/2$.

Now let m and n be any integers greater than M. Then, using the Triangle Inequality (Theorem 1.5.3), we have

$$\begin{aligned}
|a_m - a_n| &= \big|(a_m - L) + (L - a_n)\big| \\
&\leq \big|a_m - L\big| + \big|a_n - L\big| \\
&< \quad \epsilon/2 \quad + \quad \epsilon/2 \\
&= \quad \epsilon,
\end{aligned}$$

as required of Definition 8.3.3. $\qquad\square$

Example 8.3.5 Define the sequence $\{p_n\}_{n=0}^{\infty}$ so that p_n is the decimal expansion of the transcendental number π truncated to include only the first n digits to the right of the decimal point. Thus $p_0 = 3, p_1 = 3.1,$ $p_2 = 3.14, p_8 = 3.14159265,$ etc. We show that $\{p_n\}_{n=0}^{\infty}$ is a Cauchy sequence.

---

[7]The Frenchman Augustin Louis Cauchy (1789–1857) was one of the first mathematicians to attempt to put calculus on the same kind of axiomatic footing as Euclid's geometry.

Let ϵ be an arbitrary positive number. [We should want ϵ to be very small; otherwise, it's useless!] We may pick $M \in \mathbb{N}$ so that $10^{-M} < \epsilon$. [The smaller ϵ is, the larger is the M that we must pick.] Whenever m and n are integers larger than M, then $|p_m - p_n| < 10^{-M} < \epsilon$, as required by Definition 8.3.3.

Exercise 8.3.6 Use condition (8.3.1) to prove that $\lim\limits_{n \to \infty} p_n = \pi$, where $\{p_n\}_{n=0}^{\infty}$ is defined in Example 8.3.5.

Note that the numbers p_n are all rational since they have terminating decimal expansions. Hence they are algebraic. But by Exercise 8.3.6, $\{p_n\}_{n=0}^{\infty}$ converges to π, which is transcendental. So, if we were to restrict our number system only to the real algebraic numbers, there would exist Cauchy sequences that do not converge to a limit. That means that in the universe of the real algebraic numbers, the converse of Proposition 8.3.4 is false. The set $\mathbb{R}$ of real numbers, however, is what is called **complete**. That is to say, $\mathbb{R}$ has the property of the following theorem. (You will encounter its proof in a first course in real analysis.)

Theorem 8.3.7 *Any sequence of real numbers converges to a limit in $\mathbb{R}$ if and only if it is a Cauchy sequence.*

Now that we have the set $\mathbb{R}$ of real numbers, where do we go from here? We still would like to have all solutions to *any* equation $p(x) = 0$, where $p \in \mathbb{Z}[x]$. That includes such simple equations as $x^2 + 1 = 0$. The set $\mathbb{C}$ of complex numbers, presented in the next section, provides that capability.

8.4 Complex Numbers

In Exercise 1.7.10, and again in Section 2.2, the set $\mathbb{C}$ of complex numbers was defined as the set of all objects of the form $a + bi$, where $a, b \in \mathbb{R}$ and $i^2 = -1$. The natural question to pose is then, why should there exist some object whose square is the number -1? In other words, why must -1 even have a square root?[8] We won't impose the notion of some $\sqrt{-1}$ on your

---

[8]The very notion of the existence of this square root was once considered quite radical.

credulity right away; we adopt a different approach—one that follows more directly from Section 8.1.

We begin with the set $\mathbb{R} \times \mathbb{R}$ consisting of all ordered pairs of real numbers and define two operations $+$ and $\cdot$ on $\mathbb{R} \times \mathbb{R}$. We call them *addition* and *multiplication*, respectively, and define them as follows. Let (a_1, b_1) and (a_2, b_2) belong to $\mathbb{R} \times \mathbb{R}$. Then

$$(a_1, b_1) + (a_2, b_2) = (a_1 + a_2, b_1 + b_2) \tag{8.4.1}$$

and

$$(a_1, b_1) \cdot (a_2, b_2) = (a_1 a_2 - b_1 b_2, a_1 b_2 + a_2 b_1). \tag{8.4.2}$$

Note that the plus and minus signs in the right-hand members of these two equations indicate the usual arithmetic of $\mathbb{R}$. For example,

$$(2, -3) + (3, 1) = (2 + 3, -3 + 1) = (5, -2),$$

and

$$(2, -3) \cdot (3, 1) = \big(2 \cdot 3 - (-3) \cdot 1, \ 2 \cdot 1 + 3 \cdot (-3)\big) = (9, -7).$$

You might recognize the addition in equation (8.4.1) as nothing other than the standard component-wise addition of vectors in 2-dimensional space. This addition is clearly associative and commutative because addition in $\mathbb{R}$ is associative and commutative. Moreover, this addition has an identity, which we call *zero*—namely, the ordered pair $(0, 0)$.

There exists also an operation called **scalar multiplication**, just as for vectors, defined as follows. For all $(a, b) \in \mathbb{R} \times \mathbb{R}$ and all $s \in \mathbb{R}$,

$$s(a, b) = (sa, sb). \tag{8.4.3}$$

When the number s plays the role that it does in equation (8.4.3), then it is a **scalar**. By convention, a scalar is always written to the left of the ordered pair.

In particular, $(-1)(a, b) = (-a, -b)$ is the inverse with respect to addition of (a, b); it is denoted more briefly as $-(a, b)$.

Exercise 8.4.1 Prove that scalar multiplication distributes over addition and that scalar multiplication distributes over addition of scalars. Namely, for all $r, s \in \mathbb{R}$ and for all (a_1, b_1), $(a_2, b_2) \in \mathbb{R} \times \mathbb{R}$,

$$r\big((a_1, b_1) + (a_2, b_2)\big) = r(a_1, b_1) + r(a_2, +b_2)$$

and

$$(r + s)(a_1, b_1) = r(a_1, b_1) + s(a_1, b_1).$$

Now we turn to the multiplication defined in equation (8.4.2). Here are the basic properties of multiplication.

Proposition 8.4.2 *Let $r, s \in \mathbb{R}$ and (a, b), (c, d), $(e, f) \in \mathbb{R} \times \mathbb{R}$. Then the multiplication defined in equation (8.4.2) has the following properties.*
(i)   The operation $\cdot$ is commutative.
(ii)   The operation $\cdot$ is associative.
(iii)   The element $(1, 0)$ is the identity.
(iv) $(a, b) \cdot \big((c, d) + (e, f)\big) = (a, b) \cdot (c, d) + (a, b) \cdot (e, f)$.
(v)   If $(a, b) \neq (0, 0)$, then the multiplicative inverse of (a, b) is

$$\left(\frac{a}{a^2 + b^2}, \frac{-b}{a^2 + b^2} \right).$$

(vi) $(rs)(a, b) = r\big(s(a, b)\big)$.
(vii) $r\big((a, b) \cdot (c, d)\big) = \big(r(a, b)\big) \cdot (c, d) = (a, b) \cdot \big(r(c, d)\big)$.

Exercise 8.4.3 Prove Proposition 8.4.2.

The subset $\mathbb{R} \times \{0\}$ of the algebraic system $(\mathbb{R} \times \mathbb{R}, +, \cdot)$ is closed under both $+$ and $\cdot$ and contains the identities with respect to each operation. Moreover, the inverse of every nonzero element of $\mathbb{R} \times \{0\}$ belongs to $\mathbb{R} \times \{0\}$. (Verify these claims.) This special subset may be regarded as a copy of $\mathbb{R}$ that has been embedded in the system $(\mathbb{R} \times \mathbb{R}, +, \cdot)$. Indeed, the scalar multiplication that was defined in equation (8.4.3) may be regarded as ordinary multiplication; since we identify any $s \in \mathbb{R}$ with $(s, 0)$, we have for all $(a, b) \in \mathbb{R} \times \mathbb{R}$,

$$s(a, b) = (s, 0) \cdot (a, b) = (sa, sb).$$

On the other hand, what about the subset $\{0\} \times \mathbb{R}$? It does behave just like $\mathbb{R}$ as far as addition is concerned, but it is not even closed under multiplication. The product $(0, b) \cdot (0, d) = (-bd, 0) \notin \{0\} \times \mathbb{R}$ if both $b, d \neq 0$. An element of $\{0\} \times \mathbb{R}$ of great interest is the ordered pair $(0, 1)$ because

$$(0, 1) \cdot (0, 1) = (-1, 0) = -(1, 0);$$

that is to say, the square of $(0, 1)$ is the additive inverse of the identity.

Definition 8.4.4 *The element $(0, 1)$ of the system $(\mathbb{R} \times \mathbb{R}, +, \cdot)$ is denoted by the symbol i.*

*Elements $(a, 0) \in \mathbb{R} \times \{0\}$ are denoted simply by a and are **real numbers**.*

*Elements $(0, b) \in \{0\} \times \mathbb{R}$ are denoted by bi (or ib) and are **(pure) imaginary numbers**.*

*The elements of $(\mathbb{R} \times \mathbb{R}, +, \cdot)$, where the operations $+$ and $\cdot$ on $\mathbb{R} \times \mathbb{R}$ are given by equations (8.4.1) and (8.4.2), are **complex numbers**. In this context, the set $\mathbb{R} \times \mathbb{R}$ is denoted by $\mathbb{C}$, and the operations on $\mathbb{C}$ are understood to be these two operations.*

In the terms of this definition, we see that every complex number is a sum of a real number and an imaginary number. Thus

$$(a, b) = (a, 0) + (0, b) = (a, 0) + b(0, 1) = a + bi.$$

Let us look at multiplication with this notation:

$$(a + bi)(c + di) = ac + adi + bci + bdi^2 = (ac - bd) + (ad + bc)i. \quad (8.4.4)$$

Exercise 8.4.5 Let $m, n \in \mathbb{Z}$. Prove that $i^m = i^n$ if and only if $m \equiv n$ (mod 4). (See Definition 6.2.6.)

Definition 8.4.6 *The **complex plane**[9] is the Cartesian plane, where for*

---

[9]The first mention of a "complex plane" appeared in a paper presented to the Danish Academy of Sciences in 1797 by the Norwegian surveyor Caspar Wessel (1745–1818). Wessel was renowned in his day for having used triangulations to make the first accurate map of the Danish province of Zealand. His presentation was the first to the Danish Academy not by a member of the Academy. Because he was not a member, Wessel was not allowed to make his presentation in person. The paper remained unnoticed until a translation into French was published in 1897. This is the only mathematical paper that Wessel ever wrote.

all $(x, y) \in \mathbb{R} \times \mathbb{R}$, *the point with coordinates (x, y) is understood to represent the complex number $x + yi$. The horizontal axis is the* **real axis**, *and the vertical axis is the* **imaginary axis**.

Definition 8.4.7 *Let $z = a + bi$ be a complex number. The* **real part** *of z is a, written[10] $\mathfrak{Re}(z) = a$. The* **imaginary part** *of z is b, written $\mathfrak{Im}(z) = b$. The* **modulus** *of the complex number $z \in \mathbb{C}$, denoted $|z|$, is its distance in the complex plane from the origin. Thus if $z = a + bi$, then*

$$|z| = \sqrt{a^2 + b^2}. \tag{8.4.5}$$

The **conjugate** *of the complex number $z = a + bi$, denoted $\overline{z}$, is the complex number $a - bi$.*

Observe that the notion of *modulus* generalizes the notion of absolute value from real to complex numbers.

Exercise 8.4.8 Let $z = 4 + 3i$ and $w = 2 - 5i$. Evaluate and simplify all of the following expressions.

$$|z| \qquad\qquad |w| \qquad\qquad zw$$

$$|zw| \qquad\qquad |z + w| \qquad\qquad 2z - 3w$$

$$\overline{z} \qquad\qquad \overline{w} \qquad\qquad \overline{z + w}$$

$$\overline{z} + \overline{w} \qquad\qquad \overline{z}\,\overline{w} \qquad\qquad |z|/z$$

$$z\overline{w} \qquad\qquad z/(2i) \qquad\qquad 1 + iz + (iz)^2 + (iz)^3$$

Remark. There is no natural partial order on the set $\mathbb{C}$ as there is on $\mathbb{R}$, nor is there any way to extend to $\mathbb{C}$ the standard partial order $\leq$ that exists on $\mathbb{R}$. Thus expressions of the form $z \leq w$, where z or w is in $\mathbb{C} \setminus \mathbb{R}$, are meaningless. However, since the modulus of a complex number is a

---

[10]The font used here for *Re* and *Im* is called *Fraktur*. It is a font that had been used in German text up until the 1940s but is still used internationally in this narrow application.

real number, inequalities relating the moduli of complex numbers are both meaningful and useful.

Exercise 8.4.9 Prove that the following facts hold for all $z, w \in \mathbb{C}$.
(a) $|z| \geq 0$. Furthermore, $|z| = 0$ if and only if $z = 0$.
(b) $|z| = |\bar{z}|$.
(c) $|z||w| = |zw|$.
(d) $\bar{z}\,\bar{w} = \overline{zw}$.
(e) $z\bar{z} = |z|^2$.
(f) $\left| \dfrac{z}{|z|} \right| = 1$.

It is useful to see how some of this theory plays out in the geometry of the complex plane. Here you may apply what you may have previously learned about vectors regarded as directed line segments and about polar coordinates in the plane.

Let z be any point in the complex plane. In Figure 8.4.1(a), we see that $\bar{z}$ is the reflection of z across the real axis, while $-\bar{z}$ is the reflection of z across the imaginary axis. It follows that $-z = \overline{-\bar{z}}$ is the reflection of $-\bar{z}$ across the real axis, and so $-z$ is also the reflection of z across the origin. All four of these points have the same modulus by Exercise 8.4.9 (b) and (c). That is to say, they all lie at the same distance from the origin.

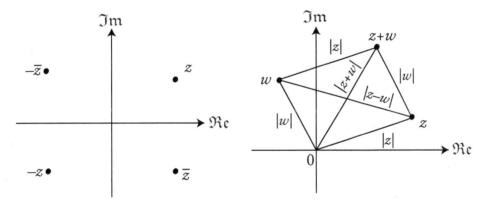

(a) Reflections of z.   (b) The Parallelogram Rule and the Triangle Inequality.

Figure 8.4.1: Points in the complex plane.

Now let z and w be any two points in the complex plane and refer to Figure 8.4.1(b). (In the figure, z and w are shown not to be scalar multiples of each other, since they are not collinear with the origin. What we are about to say would hold as well in the special case where one is a scalar multiple of the other.) In vector analysis, the vector $z + w$ is called the *resultant* of vectors z and w. The four points $0, z, z + w, w$ form a parallelogram which is a union of two triangles whose three sides have lengths $|z|$, $|w|$, and $|z+w|$. Since the length of any side of a triangle is at most the sum of the lengths of the other two sides, we have the version of the Triangle Inequality (Theorem 1.5.3) that gives it its name,

$$(\forall z, w \in \mathbb{C}) \left[|z + w| \leq |z| + |w| \right]. \tag{8.4.6}$$

Equality holds in statement (8.4.6) if and only if z and w are scalar multiples of each other. (Draw a figure and check this out. Also verify that the length of the other diagonal, the distance between z and w, is $|z - w|$.)

Example 8.4.10   We solve the equation

$$|z + i| = |z - i|. \tag{8.4.7}$$

One way to do this is by "brute force." Suppose that $z = x + iy$. Then equation (8.4.7) becomes

$$|x + (y + 1)i| = |x + (y - 1)i|.$$

Applying equation (8.4.5) and squaring both sides gives

$$x^2 + (y + 1)^2 = x^2 + (y - 1)^2.$$

After canceling, we're left with just $y = 0$. So the solution of equation (8.4.7) is just the real axis $\mathfrak{Im}(z) = 0$.

Another way to do this is geometrically. A number z is a solution of equation (8.4.7) if and only if z is equidistant from the two points i and $-i$. So the solution is the perpendicular bisector of the segment joining them. Clearly, that's the real axis.

Exercise 8.4.11   Solve the following equations and sketch their graphs in the complex plane.
(a) $|z - 1 - i| = |z + 1 + i|$.
(b) $|z - i| = 1$.

Exercise 8.4.12 What is the complex equation whose graph is the line through the points i and -1?

Let $z = a + bi \neq 0$, and let θ be the angle from the positive real axis in the counterclockwise direction to the segment joining the origin to z, as shown in Figure 8.4.2. If this were the usual Cartesian plane, then the polar coordinates of the point z would be $(|z|, \theta)$, where

$$|z| = \sqrt{a^2 + b^2} \quad \text{and,} \quad \text{if } a \neq 0, \text{ then } \tan \theta = \frac{b}{a}. \qquad (8.4.8)$$

The angle θ in radians is the **argument** of z, and we write

$$\theta = \arg(z).$$

If $a = 0$, then $\arg(z) = \dfrac{\pi}{2}$ if $b > 0$ and $\arg(z) = -\dfrac{\pi}{2}$ if $b < 0$. (One should verify that $\tan \theta = b/a$ no matter which quadrant of the plane z happens to lie in.)

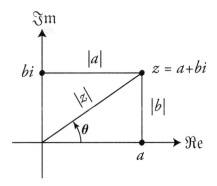

Figure 8.4.2: The polar form of a complex number.

From Figure 8.4.2, we also have

$$a = |z| \cos \theta \quad \text{and} \quad b = |z| \sin \theta,$$

which yields an important formula for any complex number $z = a + bi$ in terms of its polar coordinates. It is called the **polar form** of z:

$$z = |z|(\cos \theta + i \sin \theta). \qquad (8.4.9)$$

Equation (8.4.4) provided a rule for multiplying two complex numbers that are given in the form $z = a + bi$. It can be used as well to multiply two complex numbers given in polar form. For this computation, it is convenient to have on hand two basic trigonometric identities:

$$\sin(x + y) = \sin x \cos y + \cos x \sin y\,;$$

$$\cos(x + y) = \cos x \cos y - \sin x \sin y. \tag{8.4.10}$$

Suppose $z = |z|(\cos\alpha + i\sin\alpha)$ and $w = |w|(\cos\beta + i\sin\beta)$. Then, by equation (8.4.4) and Exercise 8.4.9(c),

$$
\begin{aligned}
zw &= |z||w|(\cos\alpha + i\sin\alpha)(\cos\beta + i\sin\beta) \\
&= |zw|\big[\cos\alpha\cos\beta - \sin\alpha\sin\beta + i(\sin\alpha\cos\beta + \cos\alpha\sin\beta)\big] \\
&= |zw|\big[\cos(\alpha + \beta) + i\sin(\alpha + \beta)\big].
\end{aligned}
$$

This computation shows, in particular, that for all $z, w \in \mathbb{C}$ and some $k \in \mathbb{Z}$,

$$\arg(zw) = \arg(z) + \arg(w) + 2\pi k,$$

as seen in Figure 8.4.3.

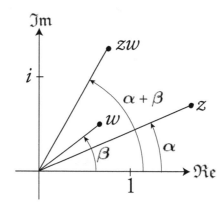

Figure 8.4.3: Multiplication in polar form.

Exercise 8.4.13 Prove that $\arg(\overline{z}) = -\arg(z)$ for all $z \in \mathbb{C}$.

Exercise 8.4.14 Plot the **unit circle** $U = \{z \in \mathbb{C} : |z| = 1\}$ in the complex plane, and prove that it has the following algebraic properties: U is closed under multiplication and contains the identity and inverses of every element (with respect to multiplication). In fact, $z^{-1} = \bar{z}$ for all $z \in U$.

From equation (8.4.9), we derive a nice formula for the integer powers of any complex number on the unit circle.

Theorem 8.4.15 (de Moivre's[11] Theorem) *Let $n \in \mathbb{N}$. Then*

$$(\cos \theta + i \sin \theta)^n = \cos(n\theta) + i \sin(n\theta).$$

Proof. We proceed by induction on n. If $n = 1$, there is nothing to prove. Let $n \geq 1$ and suppose that the formula holds for this value of n. We have

$$
\begin{aligned}
(\cos \theta + i \sin \theta)^{n+1} &= (\cos \theta + i \sin \theta)(\cos \theta + i \sin \theta)^n \\
&= (\cos \theta + i \sin \theta)\big(\cos(n\theta) + i \sin(n\theta)\big) \\
&= \cos \theta \cos(n\theta) - \sin \theta \sin(n\theta) \\
&\qquad + i\big(\sin \theta \cos(n\theta) + \cos \theta \sin(n\theta)\big) \\
&= \cos\big((n+1)\theta\big) + i \sin\big((n+1)\theta\big)
\end{aligned}
$$

by the trigonometric identities in equations (8.4.10). $\qquad\square$

It follows from de Moivre's Theorem that, if $z = |z|(\cos \theta + i \sin \theta)$, as in equation (8.4.9), then

$$z^n = |z|^n\big(\cos(n\theta) + i \sin(n\theta)\big). \tag{8.4.11}$$

Consider the complex number $u = -\frac{1}{2} + \frac{\sqrt{3}}{2}i$. Then $|u| = 1$ and $\arg(u) = \arctan(-\sqrt{3})$ by equation (8.4.8). At this point an electronic calculator would

---

[11]Abraham de Moivre (1667–1754) was a French Huguenot. He moved to England c. 1685 after the Edict of Nantes, which since 1598 had accorded some religious liberty to Protestants, was revoked under Louis XIV. De Moivre made contributions to the theory of probability applied to games of chance.

give $\arg(u) = -\pi/3$, but since u lies in the second quadrant, we have $\arg(u) = 2\pi/3$. This gives the polar form

$$u = \cos\left(\frac{2\pi}{3}\right) + i\sin\left(\frac{2\pi}{3}\right).$$

It follows from de Moivre's Theorem that $u^3 = 1$; that is, u is a cube root of 1. In fact, the number 1 has two other cube roots: 1 itself and u^2. Notice in Figure 8.4.4 that these three cube roots are evenly spaced around the unit circle.

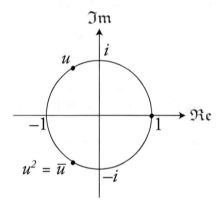

Figure 8.4.4: The three cube roots of 1.

More generally, let n be any integer at least 2. For each integer $k = 0, 1, 2, \ldots, n-1$, let

$$u_k = \cos\left(\frac{2\pi k}{n}\right) + i\sin\left(\frac{2\pi k}{n}\right).$$

Then $u_0 = 1$, and $u_1 = \cos(2\pi/n) + i\sin(2\pi/n)$ is a point on the unit circle one-n^{th} of the way around the circle from 1 in the counterclockwise direction. By de Moivre's Theorem, we have $u_1^n = 1$, and for each succeeding point $u_2, u_3, \ldots, u_{n-1}$, we have $u_k = u_1^k$. Thus u_k lies on the unit circle exactly k/n of the way around the circle from 1 in the counterclockwise direction. Moreover, for each $k = 0, 1, 2, \ldots, n-1$, we have

$$u_k^n = (u_1^k)^n = (u_1^n)^k = 1^k = 1.$$

Definition 8.4.16 *Let $n \in \mathbb{N}$. Then the n complex numbers*

$$u_k = \cos\left(\frac{2\pi k}{n}\right) + i \sin\left(\frac{2\pi k}{n}\right) \qquad \text{for } k = 0, 1, 2, \ldots, n-1$$

are the nth **roots of unity**.

Exercise 8.4.17 Without writing trigonometric functions in your answers, list all of the nth roots of unity for $n = 4$ and $n = 6$.

Exercise 8.4.18 For all $n \in \mathbb{N}$, let $I_n = \{u_k : k = 0, 1, \ldots, n-1\}$ be the set of nth roots of unity. Prove the following.
(a) I_n is closed under multiplication in $\mathbb{C}$.
(b) $I_m \subseteq I_n$ if and only if $m \mid n$.

8.5 Further Exercises

Exercise 8.5.1 Prove that the set $\mathbb{Z}[x]$ is closed under addition, multiplication, and composition of functions.

Exercise 8.5.2 Let X be any set. Show that $(\mathscr{P}(X), +)$, where $+$ denotes symmetric difference, is an associative and commutative system with identity in which every element is invertible.

Exercise 8.5.3 Let X be an infinite set. Recall that a set $A \in \mathscr{P}(X)$ is *cofinite* if its complement is finite (see Exercise 7.6.9).
(a) Prove that the family of cofinite subsets of X is closed under union and intersection but closed under neither symmetric difference[12] nor relative complement.
(b) Let $\mathscr{A}$ denote the family of infinite subsets of X that are not cofinite. Under which of the four set operations listed in part (a) is $\mathscr{A}$ closed?

---

[12]See Exercise 3.6.12 for the definition.

Exercise 8.5.4   Let $(S, \bullet)$ be an algebraic system in which $\bullet$ is associative and commutative. Using mathematical induction and Definitions 8.1.8 and 8.1.22, prove that for all $n \in \mathbb{N}$, if $s_1, s_2, \ldots, s_n \in S$, then

$$s_1 \bullet \big(s_2 \bullet (s_3 \bullet \cdots \bullet (s_{n-1} \bullet s_n) \cdots)\big) = s_n \bullet \big(s_{n-1} \bullet (s_{n-2} \bullet \cdots \bullet (s_2 \bullet s_1) \cdots)\big).$$

Exercise 8.5.5   Define $f : \mathbb{N} \to \mathbb{N}$ by the rule

$$f(n) = \begin{cases} 1 & \text{if } n = 1; \\ n - 1 & \text{if } n \geq 2. \end{cases}$$

Let $S = \big\{ f^n : n \in \mathbb{N} \cup \{0\} \big\}$. Prove that $(S, \circ)$ is an associative and commutative system with identity that has no inverses.

Exercise 8.5.6   Let S be the set of all functions $f : \mathbb{N} \to \mathbb{N}$ such that $f(1) = f(2)$. For $i \in \{1, 2\}$, define the function $r_i \in S$ by

$$r_i(n) = \begin{cases} i & \text{if } n = 1 \text{ or } n = 2; \\ n & \text{if } n \geq 3. \end{cases}$$

Show that $(S, \circ)$ is an associative system in which r_1 and r_2 are distinct right identities.

Exercise 8.5.7   Let $p_1, p_2, \ldots, p_k$ be distinct prime numbers. Let

$$S = \big\{ p_1^{m_1} p_2^{m_2} \cdots p_k^{m_k} : m_1, m_2, \ldots, m_k \in \mathbb{N} \cup \{0\} \big\}.$$

Prove that S together with the operation of multiplication is an associative, commutative system with identity.

Exercise 8.5.8   In high school algebra, you learned that for $a, b, c \in \mathbb{R}^+$, it is true that $(ab)^c = a^c b^c$, but that $a^{bc} \neq a^b a^c = a^{b+c}$. Describe these rules in terms of the one-sided distribution laws that do and do not hold. [As mentioned in Section 8.1, the binary operation of *exponentiation* takes the ordered pair (a, b) to the number a^b.]

Exercise 8.5.9   Let $m, n \in \mathbb{Z} \setminus \{0\}$. Prove that the set of linear combinations of m and n is closed under addition and multiplication (the usual operations in $\mathbb{Z}$).

Exercise 8.5.10 Let $(S, \bullet)$ be an associative system with identity e.
(a) Prove that if $(\forall a \in S)\big[a^2 = e\big]$, then $\bullet$ is commutative.
(b) Suppose that all elements of S are invertible. Prove that the operation $\bullet$ is commutative if and only if $(a \bullet b)^2 = a^2 \bullet b^2$ for all $a, b \in S$.

Exercise 8.5.11 Let $(S, \preceq)$ be a lattice with binary operations $\wedge$ and $\vee$ (see Exercise 6.7.14). Show that $\wedge$ and $\vee$ are associative and that each operation distributes over the other. Show that in a finite lattice, there exists an identity for each of these operations.

Exercise 8.5.12 Make a Cayley table (see Exercise 8.2.3) for the system $(G, *)$, where $G = \{a, b, c, d\}$ and the operation $*$ is such that all the following properties hold.
(i) $*$ is associative.
(ii) The element a is the (unique, two-sided) identity of G.
(iii) $(\forall x \in G)[x^2 = a]$.

Exercise 8.5.13 Let $G = \{0, 1, 2, 3, 4, 5, 6, 7\}$. Consider an associative system $(G, \bullet)$ with identity that satisfies both right- and left cancellation laws and for all $a, b \in G$, $\bullet$ satisfies

$$a \bullet b \leq a + b \quad \text{and} \quad a \bullet a = 0,$$

where $+$ and $\leq$ have their usual meaning as in $\mathbb{Z}$. Make a Cayley table for $(G, \bullet)$. [Hint: The solution is unique. Determine whether $\bullet$ is commutative. Whenever there are choices about which element to enter in a cell of the table, use associativity to decide.]

Exercise 8.5.14 Consider the congruence $x^2 \equiv -1 \pmod p$, where p is an odd prime number. Notice that when $p = 5$, then $x = 2$ and $x = 3$ are solutions. But when $p = 7$, there are no solutions (verify this). Investigate other prime numbers and make a conjecture about prime numbers p for which $x^2 \equiv -1 \pmod p$ has solutions.

Exercise 8.5.15 Let p be an odd prime number. Investigate prime numbers for which the congruence $x^2 \equiv 2 \pmod p$ has solutions. Make a conjecture about prime numbers for which the congruence has solutions. [Hint: Look at $p \pmod 8$.]

Exercise 8.5.16 This exercise examines one of many sequences of rational numbers that converge to a transcendental number. In particular, the alternating harmonic series $\sum_{k=1}^{\infty} \frac{(-1)^{k-1}}{k}$ converges to the transcendental number $\ln 2$. Let a_n denote the n-th partial sum of this series—that is, $a_n = \sum_{k=1}^{n} \frac{(-1)^{k-1}}{k}$—and show that $\{a_n\}_{n=1}^{\infty}$ is a Cauchy sequence of rational numbers.

Exercise 8.5.17 In the complex plane, graph the parabola with equation

$$[\mathfrak{Re}(z)]^2 + \mathfrak{Re}(z) - |z|^2 = 0.$$

Exercise 8.5.18 Prove that if $|z| < 1$, then $\lim_{n \to \infty} z^n = 0$. Prove that if $|z| \geq 1$ and $z \neq 1$, then $\lim_{n \to \infty} z^n$ does not exist (i.e., there exists no $L \in \mathbb{C}$ such that $\lim_{n \to \infty} z^n = L$).

Exercise 8.5.19 Let $n \in \mathbb{N}$ be given and let z be a complex number that is *not* an nth root of unity (as defined in Definition 8.4.16). Prove that $z^n \neq 1$, thus showing that the nth roots of unity are the *only* complex numbers whose n^{th} power equals 1.

Index of Symbols and Notation

[References are to section of first occurrence]

Specific Sets

Logical Symbols

$\wedge$	And	1.3
$\vee$	Or	1.3
$\neg$	Negation	1.3
$\Longleftrightarrow$	Logical equivalence	1.3
$\oplus$	Exclusive or	1.3
$\Rightarrow$	Conditional, implies	1.4
$\Leftrightarrow$	Biconditional, if and only if	1.4
$\forall$	Universal quantifier, for all	1.6
$\exists$	Existential quantifier, there exists	1.6
$\exists!$	Unique existential quantifier	1.6

Set Theory Symbols

$\in$	Element of	2.1
$\notin$	Not an element of	2.1
$\subseteq$	Subset of, contained in	3.1
$\supseteq$	Superset of, contains	3.1
$\nsubseteq$	Not a subset of	3.1
$\subset$	Proper subset of	3.1
$\mathscr{P}(A)$	Power set of A	3.1
$\cap$	Intersection	3.2
$\cup$	Union	3.2
$\setminus$	Relative complement	3.3
A'	Complement of A	3.3
$\times$	Cartesian Product	3.4
$+$	Symmetric difference	3.4

Miscellaneous Symbols

$n!$	Factorial function	1.1
$a \mid b$	a divides b	2.3
$\gcd(a, b)$	Greatest common divisor of a and b	2.5
$\text{lcm}(a, b)$	Least common multiple of a and b	2.5
$f : X \to Y$	Function f from X into Y	4.1
f^{-1}	Inverse of the function f	4.1
$\circ$	Composition of functions	4.2

$\overline{f}$	Set function induced by f	4.3
i_X	Identity function on X	4.5
$f\vert_S$	f restricted to S	4.5
$\binom{n}{k}$	Binomial coefficient, n choose k	5.4
$\triangle(S)$	Diagonal of S	6.2
$a \equiv b \pmod{m}$	Congruence modulo m	6.2
$[x]$	Equivalence class of x	6.2
$\mathrm{glb}(A)$	Greatest lower bound	6.4
$\mathrm{lub}(A)$	Least upper bound	6.4
$\wedge$	Meet	6.7
$\vee$	Join	6.7
$\vert A\vert$	Cardinality of A	7.1
$\aleph_0$	Cardinality of $\mathbb{N}$	7.1
$\mathbf{c}$	Cardinality of $\mathbb{R}$	7.5
i	$\sqrt{-1}$ in $\mathbb{C}$	8.4
$\mathfrak{Re}(z)$	Real part of z	8.4
$\mathfrak{Im}(z)$	Imaginary part of z	8.4
$\vert z\vert$	Modulus of z	8.4
$\overline{z}$	Complex conjugate	8.4
$\arg(z)$	Argument of z	8.4

Index of Cited Mathematicians

Index

CPSIA information can be obtained
at www.ICGtesting.com
Printed in the USA
FSHW011829170820
73047FS